THE GREAT FABLES

The Great
FABLES
OF ALL NATIONS

SELECTED BY

MANUEL KOMROFF

ILLUSTRATED BY

LOUISE THORON

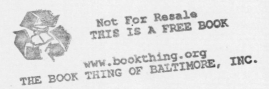

TUDOR PUBLISHING COMPANY
NEW YORK   MCMXXXIII

ACKNOWLEDGMENTS

The Editor is grateful for the various translations that have been contributed to this volume. Special thanks are due the following:—To Frances Smith and Hershel Brickell for their translations from the Spanish of Yriarte. To Albert H. Gross for his renderings from the Talmud and Albert Lippman for his German translations of Lichtwer. Also to the editor's mother, Mrs. Belle Michailovsky, for her translations from the Russian of Demyan Bedny.

The fables of Ambrose Bierce are printed here through the courtesy of Albert and Charles Boni, and those of Robert Louis Stevenson through the generosity of Charles Scribner's Sons. Thanks are also due Houghton Mifflin for permission to print the fable by Ralph Waldo Emerson. The fables of Anatole France are included by special arrangement with Dodd, Mead and Company.

The Decorations in the Text have been specially drawn for this volume by Louise Thoron (Mrs. Ewen Cameron MacVeagh)

TABLE OF CONTENTS

THE GREAT FABLES

A E S O P

*When the Delphians, in obedience to the command of the oracle,
made proclamation that if any one claimed compensation for the
murder of Aesop he should receive it, the person who at last came
forward was Iadmon, grandson of the former Iadmon, and he received the compensation. Aesop therefore must certainly have
been the former Iadmon's slave.* HERODOTUS

THE GOOSE WITH THE GOLDEN EGGS

A CERTAIN MAN HAD THE GOOD FORTUNE TO POSSESS A GOOSE
that laid him a Golden Egg every day. But dissatisfied with so
slow an income, and thinking to seize the whole treasure at once,
he killed the Goose; and cutting her open, found her—just what
any other goose would be!

THE WOLF AND THE SHEEP

A WOLF THAT HAD BEEN BITTEN BY A DOG, AND WAS IN A VERY
sad case, being unable to move, called to a Sheep, that was passing
by, and begged her to fetch him some water from the neighbouring stream. "For if you," said he, "will bring me drink, I will
find meat myself." "Yes," said the Sheep, "I make no doubt
of it; for, if I come near enough to give you the drink, you will
soon make mince-meat of me."

THE BUNDLE OF STICKS

A HUSBANDMAN WHO HAD A QUARRELSOME FAMILY, AFTER HAV-
ing tried in vain to reconcile them by words, thought he might
more readily prevail by an example. So he called his sons and

3

bade them lay a bundle of sticks before him. Then having tied them into a faggot, he told the lads, one after the other, to take it up and break it. They all tried, but tried in vain. Then untying the faggot, he gave them the sticks to break one by one. This they did with the greatest ease. Then said the father, "Thus you, my sons, as long as you remain united, are a match for all your enemies; but differ and separate, and you are undone."

THE DOG IN THE MANGER

A DOG MADE HIS BED IN A MANGER, AND LAY SNARLING AND growling to keep the horses from their feed. "See," said one of them, "what a miserable cur! who neither can eat corn himself, nor will allow those to eat it who can."

THE WOLF AND THE LION

A WOLF, ROAMING BY THE MOUNTAIN'S SIDE, SAW HIS OWN shadow, as the sun was setting, become greatly extended and magnified, and he said to himself; "Why should I, being of such an immense size, and extending nearly an acre in length, be afraid of the Lion? Ought I not to be acknowledged as King of all the collected beasts?" While he was indulging in these proud thoughts, a Lion fell upon him, and killed him. He exclaimed with a too late repentance; "Wretched me! this over-estimation of myself is the cause of my destruction."

THE WIND AND THE SUN

A DISPUTE ONCE AROSE BETWEEN THE WIND AND THE SUN, which was the stronger of the two, and they agreed to put the point upon this issue, that whichever soonest made a traveller take off his cloak, should be accounted the more powerful.

The Wind began, and blew with all his might and main a

blast, cold and fierce as a Thracian storm; but the stronger he blew the closer the traveller wrapped his cloak around him, and the tighter he grasped it with his hands. Then broke out the Sun: with his welcome beams he dispersed the vapour and the cold; the traveller felt the genial warmth, and as the Sun shone brighter and brighter, he sat down, overcome with the heat, and cast his cloak on the ground.

Thus the Sun was declared the conqueror; and it has ever been deemed that persuasion is better than force; and that the sunshine of a kind and gentle manner will sooner lay open a poor man's heart than all the threatenings and force of blustering authority.

THE SHEPHERD AND THE WOLF

A SHEPHERD ONCE FOUND THE WHELP OF A WOLF, AND BROUGHT it up, and after a while taught it to steal lambs from the neighbouring flocks. The Wolf having shown himself an apt pupil, said to the Shepherd; "Since you have taught me to steal, you must keep a sharp look-out, or you will lose some of your own flock."

THE MILLER, HIS SON, AND THEIR ASS

A MILLER AND HIS SON WERE DRIVING THEIR ASS TO A NEIGHbouring fair to sell him. They had not gone far when they met with a troop of girls returning from the town, talking and laughing. "Look there!" cried one of them, "did you ever see such fools, to be trudging along the road on foot, when they might be riding!"

The old Man, hearing this, quietly bade his Son get on the Ass, and walked along merrily by the side of him. Presently they came up to a group of old men in earnest debate. "There!" said one of them, "it proves what I was saying. What respect is shown to old age in these days? Do you see that idle young rogue riding, while his old father has to walk?—Get down, you scapegrace! and let the old Man rest his weary limbs."

Upon this the Father made his Son dismount, and got up himself. In this manner they had not proceeded far when they met a company of women and children. "Why, you lazy old fellow!" cried several tongues at once, "how can you ride upon the beast, while that poor little lad there can hardly keep pace by the side of you?"

The good-natured Miller stood corrected, and immediately took up his Son behind him. They had now almost reached the town. "Pray, honest friend," said a townsman, "is that Ass your own?" "Yes," said the old Man. "Oh! One would not have thought so," said the other, "by the way you load him. Why, you two fellows are better able to carry the poor beast than he you!" "Anything to please you," said the old Man; "we can but try."

So, alighting with his Son, they tide the Ass's legs together, and by the help of a pole endeavoured to carry him on their shoulders over a bridge that led to the town. This was so entertaining a sight that the people ran out in crowds to laugh at it; till the Ass, not liking the noise nor his situation, kicked asunder the cords that bound him, and, tumbling off the pole, fell into the river. Upon this the old Man, vexed and ashamed, made his way home, convinced that by endeavouring to please everybody he had pleased nobody, and lost his Ass into the bargain.

JUPITER AND THE MONKEY

JUPITER ISSUED A PROCLAMATION TO ALL THE BEASTS OF THE forest, and promised a royal reward to the one whose offspring should be deemed the handsomest. The Monkey came with the rest, and presented, with all a mother's tenderness, a flat-nosed, hairless, ill-featured young Monkey as a candidate for the promised reward. A general laugh saluted her on the presentation of her son. But she resolutely said; "I know not whether Jupiter will allot the prize to my son; but this I do know, that he is at least in the eyes of me, his mother, the dearest, handsomest, and most beautiful of all."

THE TWO FROGS

TWO FROGS WERE NEIGHBOURS. THE ONE LIVED IN A DEEP pond, far removed from public view; the other lived in a gully containing little water, and crossed by a country road. He that lived in the pond warned his friend, and entreated him to change his residence and to come and live with him, saying that he would enjoy greater safety from danger and more abundant food. The other refused, saying that he felt it very hard to remove from a place to which he had become so accustomed. A few days afterwards a heavy wagon passed through the gully, and crushed him to death under its wheels.

A wilful man will have his own way to his own hurt.

THE ASS AND HIS PURCHASER

A MAN WISHED TO PURCHASE AN ASS, AND AGREED WITH HIS owner that he should try him before he bought him. He took the Ass home, and put him in the straw-yard with the other Asses, upon which he left all the others, and joined himself at once to the most idle and the greatest eater of them all. The man put a halter on him, and led him back to his owner; and on his inquiring how, in so short a time, he could have made a trial of him, "I do not need," he answered, "a trial; I know that he will be just such another as the one whom of all the rest he chose for his companion."

A man is known by the company he keeps.

THE KID AND THE WOLF

A KID THAT HAD STRAYED FROM THE HERD WAS PURSUED BY A Wolf. When she saw all other hope of escape cut off, she turned round to the Wolf, and said, "I must allow indeed that I am your victim, but as my life is now but short, let it be a merry one. Do you pipe for a while, and I will dance."

While the Wolf was piping and the Kid was dancing, the Dogs

hearing the music ran up to see what was going on, and the Wolf was glad to take himself off as fast as his legs would carry him.

He who steps out of his way to play the fool, must not wonder if he misses the prize.

THE FOX AND THE LION

A FOX WHO HAD NEVER SEEN A LION, WHEN BY CHANCE HE met him for the first time, was so terrified that he almost died of fright. When he met him the second time, he was still afraid, but managed to disguise his fear. When he saw him the third time, he was so much emboldened that he went up to him and asked him how he did.

Familiarity breeds contempt.

THE HORSE AND THE GROOM

A GROOM WHO USED TO STEAL AND SELL A HORSE'S CORN, WAS yet very busy in grooming and wisping him all the day long. "If you really wish me," said the Horse, "to look well, give me less of your currying and more of your corn."

THE WOLF IN SHEEP'S CLOTHING

A WOLF, ONCE UPON A TIME, RESOLVED TO DISGUISE HIMSELF, thinking that he should thus gain an easier livelihood. Having, therefore, clothed himself in a sheep's skin, he contrived to get among a flock of Sheep, and feed along with them, so that even the Shepherd was deceived by the imposture.

When night came on and the fold was closed, the Wolf was shut up with the Sheep, and the door made fast. But the Shepherd, wanting something for his supper, and going in to fetch out a sheep, mistook the Wolf for one of them and killed him on the spot.

THE STAG AT THE POOL

A STAG ONE SUMMER'S DAY CAME TO A POOL TO QUENCH HIS thirst, and as he stood drinking he saw his form reflected in the water. "What beauty and strength," said he, "are in these horns of mine; but how unseemly are these weak and slender feet!" While he was thus criticising, after his own fancies, the form which Nature had given him, the huntsmen and hounds drew that way. The feet, with which he had found so much fault, soon carried him out of reach of his pursuers; but the horns, of which he was so vain, becoming entangled in a thicket, held him till the hunters again came up to him, and proved the cause of his death.

Look to use before ornament.

THE BIRDCATCHER, THE PARTRIDGE, AND THE COCK

A BIRDCATCHER WAS ABOUT TO SIT DOWN TO A DINNER OF HERBS, when a friend unexpectedly came in. The birdtrap was quite empty, as he had caught nothing. He proceeded to kill a Partridge, which he had tamed for a decoy. The Partridge pleaded earnestly for his life; "What would you do without me when next you spread your nets? Who would chirp you to sleep, or call for you the covey of answering birds?"

The Birdcatcher spared his life, and determined to pick out a fine young Cock just attaining to his comb. He thus cried in piteous tones from his perch; "If you kill me, who will announce to you the appearance of the dawn? Who will wake you to your daily tasks, or tell you when it is time to visit the birdtrap in the morning?" He replied; "What you say is true. You are a capital bird at telling the time of day. But I and the friend who has arrived must have our dinners."

Necessity knows no law.

THE MOON AND HER MOTHER

THE MOON ONCE ASKED HER MOTHER TO MAKE HER A LITTLE cloak that would fit her well. "How," replied she, "can I make you a cloak to fit you, who are now a New Moon, and then a Full Moon, and then again neither one nor the other?"

THE KINGDOM OF THE LION

THE BEASTS OF THE FIELD AND FOREST HAD A LION AS THEIR king. He was neither wrathful, cruel, nor tyrannical, but just and gentle as a king could be. He made during his reign a royal proclamation for a general assembly of all the birds and beasts, and drew up conditions for an universal league, in which the Wolf and the Lamb, the Panther and the Kid, the Tiger and the Stag, the Dog and the Hare, should live together in perfect peace and amity. The Hare said; "Oh, how I have longed to see this day, in which the weak shall take their place without fear by the side of the strong."

THE MULES AND THE ROBBERS

TWO MULES WELL LADEN WITH PACKS WERE TRUDGING ALONG. One carried panniers filled with money, the other, sacks weighted with grain. The Mule carrying the treasure walked with head erect, as if conscious of the value of his burden, and tossed up and down the clear-toned bells fastened to his neck. His companion followed with quiet and easy steps.

Suddenly Robbers rushed from their hiding-places upon them, and in the scuffle with their owners, wounded with a sword the Mule carrying the treasure, which they greedily seized upon, while they took no notice of the grain.

The Mule which had been robbed and wounded, bewailed his misfortunes. The other replied; "I am indeed glad that I was thought so little of, for I have lost nothing, nor am I hurt with any wound."

THE BULL AND THE CALF

A BULL WAS STRIVING WITH ALL HIS MIGHT TO SQUEEZE HIMself through a narrow passage which led to his stall. A young Calf came up, and offered to go before and show him the way by which he could manage to pass. "Save yourself the trouble," said the Bull; "I knew that way long before you were born."

THE DOGS AND THE FOX

SOME DOGS FOUND THE SKIN OF A LION AND BEGAN TO TEAR IT to pieces with their teeth. A Fox, seeing them, said; "If this lion were alive, you would soon find out that his claws were stronger than your teeth."

It is easy to kick a man that is down.

THE COBBLER TURNED DOCTOR

UNABLE TO MAKE A LIVING BY HIS TRADE, A COBBLER, RENDERED desperate by poverty, began to practise medicine in a town in which he was not known. He sold a drug that he claimed was an antidote to all poisons, and obtained a great name for himself by long-winded puffs and advertisements.   He happened to fall sick himself of a serious illness, on which the Governor of the town determined to test his skill.   For this purpose he called for a cup, and, while filling it with water, pretended to mix poison with the Cobbler's antidote, and commanded him to drink it, on the promise of a reward.

The Cobbler, under the fear of death, confessed that he had no knowledge of medicine, and was only made famous by the stupid clamours of the crowd.   At this the Governor called a public assembly, and thus addressed the citizens; "Of what folly have you been guilty?   You have not hesitated to entrust your heads to a man, whom no one would employ to make even the shoes for their feet."

THE VINE AND THE GOAT

THERE WAS A VINE TEEMING WITH RIPE FRUIT AND TENDER shoots, when a wanton Goat came up and gnawed the bark, and browsed upon the young leaves.   "I will revenge myself on you," said the Vine, "for this insult; for when in a few days you are brought as a victim to the altar, the juice of my grapes shall be the dew of death upon your forehead."

Retribution though late comes at last.

THE SICK LION

A LION, NO LONGER ABLE, FROM THE WEAKNESS OF OLD AGE, to hunt for his prey, laid himself up in his den, and, breathing with great difficulty, and speaking with a low voice, gave out that he was very ill indeed.   The report soon spread among the beasts, and there was great lamentation for the sick Lion.   One after the other came to see him; but, catching him thus alone, and in his own den, the Lion made an easy prey of them, and grew fat upon his diet.

The Fox, suspecting the truth of the matter, came at length to make his visit of inquiry, and standing at some distance, asked his Majesty how he did? "Ah, my dearest friend," said the Lion, "is it you? Why do you stand so far from me? Come, sweet friend, and pour a word of consolation in the poor Lion's ear, who has but a short time to live."

"Bless you!" said the Fox, "but excuse me if I cannot stay; for, to tell the truth, I feel quite uneasy at the mark of the footsteps that I see here, all pointing towards your den, and none returning outwards."

Affairs are easier of entrance than of exit; and it is but common prudence to see our way out before we venture in.

THE COCK AND THE JEWEL

AS A COCK WAS SCRATCHING UP THE STRAW IN A FARM-YARD, in search of food for the hens, he hit upon a Jewel that by some chance had found its way there. "Ho!" said he, "you are a very fine thing, no doubt, to those who prize you; but give me a barley-corn before all the pearls in the world."

THE ASS CARRYING SALT

A CERTAIN HUCKSTER WHO KEPT AN ASS, HEARING THAT SALT was to be had cheap at the sea-side, drove down his Ass thither to buy some. Having loaded the beast as much as he could bear, he was driving him home, when, as they were passing a slippery ledge of rock, the Ass fell into the stream below, and the Salt being melted, the Ass was relieved of his burden, and having gained the bank with ease, pursued his journey onward, light in body and in spirit.

The Huckster soon afterwards set off for the sea-shore for some more Salt, and loaded the Ass, if possible, yet more heavily than before. On their return, as they crossed the stream into which he had formerly fallen, the Ass fell down on purpose, and by the dissolving of the Salt, was again released from his load.

The master, provoked at the loss, and thinking how he might cure him of this trick, on his next journey to the coast freighted the beast with a load of sponges. When they arrived at the same stream as before, the Ass was at his old tricks again, and rolled himself into the water; but the sponges becoming thoroughly wet, he found to his cost, as he proceeded homewards, that instead of lightening his burden, he had more than doubled its weight.

The same measures will not suit all circumstances; and we may play the same trick once too often.

THE HEN AND THE SWALLOW

A HEN, FINDING THE EGGS OF A VIPER, AND CAREFULLY KEEPING them warm, nourished them until they hatched. A swallow, observing what she had done, said; "You silly creature! Why have you hatched these vipers, which, when they shall have grown, will inflict injury on all, beginning with yourself?"

THE PEACOCK AND JUNO

THE PEACOCK MADE COMPLAINT TO JUNO THAT, WHILE THE nightingale pleased every ear with his song, he, the proud Peacock, no sooner opened his mouth than he became a laughing-stock to all who heard him. The Goddess, to console him, said; "But you far excel in beauty and in size. The splendour of the emerald shines in your neck, and you unfold a tail gorgeous with painted plumage."

"But for what purpose have I," said the bird, "this dumb beauty so long as I am surpassed in song?"   "The lot of each," replied Juno, "has been assigned by the will of the Fates—to you, beauty; to the eagle, strength; to the nightingale, song; to the raven, favourable, and to the crow, unfavourable expectations. These are all contented with the endowments allotted to them."

THE ASTRONOMER

AN ASTRONOMER USED TO WALK OUT EVERY NIGHT TO GAZE upon the stars.   It happened one night that, as he was wandering in the outskirts of the city, with his whole thoughts rapt up in the skies, he fell into a well.   On his holloaing and calling out, one who heard his cries ran up to him, and when he had listened to his story, said; "My good man, while you are trying to pry into the mysteries of heaven, you overlook the common objects that are under your feet."

THE FOX AND THE CROW

A CROW HAD SNATCHED A GOODLY PIECE OF CHEESE OUT OF A window, and flew with it into a high tree, intent to enjoy her prize   A Fox spied the dainty morsel, and thus he planned his approaches.

"O Crow," said he, "how beautiful are thy wings, how bright thine eye! how graceful thy neck! thy breast is the breast of an eagle! thy claws—I beg pardon—thy talons, are a match for all the beasts of the field.   O! that such a bird should be dumb, and want only a voice!"

The Crow, pleased with the flattery, and chuckling to think how she would surprise the Fox with her caw, opened her mouth: —down dropped the cheese! which the Fox snapping up, observed, as he walked away, "that whatever he had remarked of her beauty, he had said nothing yet of her brains."

Men seldom flatter without some private end in view; and they who listen to such music may expect to have to pay the piper.

THE DOG'S HOUSE

IN THE WINTER TIME, A DOG ROLLED HIMSELF TOGETHER AND coiled up in as small a space as possible. On account of the cold, he determined to make himself a house. When the summer returned again he lay asleep, stretched at his full length, and appeared to himself to be of a great size, and concluded that it would be neither an easy nor a necessary work to make himself such a house as would accommodate him.

THE COUNTRYMAN AND THE SNAKE

A COUNTRYMAN RETURNING HOME ONE WINTER'S DAY, FOUND a Snake by the hedge-side, half dead with cold. Taking compassion on the creature, he laid it in his bosom and brought it home to his fire-side to revive it. No sooner had the warmth restored it, than it began to attack the children of the cottage. Upon this the Countryman, whose compassion had saved its life, took up a club and laid the Snake dead at his feet.

THE EAGLE AND THE FOX

AN EAGLE AND A FOX HAD LONG LIVED TOGETHER AS GOOD neighbours; the Eagle at the summit of a high tree, the Fox in a hole at the foot of it. One day, however, while the Fox was abroad, the Eagle made a swoop at the Fox's cub, and carried it off to her nest, thinking that her lofty dwelling would secure her from the Fox's revenge.

The Fox, on her return home, upbraided the Eagle for this breach of friendship, and begged earnestly to have her young one again; but finding that her entreaties were of no avail, she snatched a torch from an altar-fire that had been lignted hard by, and involving the whole tree in flame and smoke, soon made the Eagle restore, through fear for herself and her own young ones, the cub which she had just now denied to her most earnest prayers.

The tyrant, though he may despise the tears of the oppressed, is never safe from their vengeance.

THE OXEN AND THE AXLE-TREES

AS SOME OXEN WERE DRAGGING A WAGGON ALONG A HEAVY ROAD, the axle-trees set up a tremendous creaking. "Brute!" cried the driver to the waggon; "why do you groan, when they who are drawing all the weight are silent?"

Those who cry loudest are not always the most hurt.

THE WOLF AND THE LAMB

AS A WOLF WAS LAPPING AT THE HEAD OF A RUNNING BROOK, he spied a stray Lamb paddling, at some distance, down the stream. Having made up his mind to seize her, he bethought himself how he might justify his violence. "Villain!" said he, running up to her; "how dare you muddle the water that I am drinking?" "Indeed," said the Lamb humbly, "I do not see how

I can disturb the water, since it runs from you to me, not from me to you."

"Be that as it may," replied the Wolf, "it was but a year ago that you called me many ill names." "Oh, Sir!" said the Lamb, trembling, "a year ago I was not born." "Well," replied the Wolf, "if it was not you, it was your father, and that is all the same; but it is no use trying to argue me out of my supper." And without another word he fell upon the poor helpless Lamb and tore her to pieces.

THE CROW AND THE SERPENT

A CROW, IN GREAT WANT OF FOOD, SAW A SERPENT ASLEEP IN a sunny nook, and flying down, greedily seized him. The Serpent turning about, bit the Crow with a mortal wound; the Crow in the agony of death exclaimed; "O unhappy me! who have found in that which I deemed a happy windfall the source of my destruction."

THE COLLIER AND THE FULLER

A COLLIER, WHO HAD MORE ROOM IN HIS HOUSE THAN HE wanted for himself, proposed to a Fuller to come and take up his quarters with him. "Thank you," said the Fuller, "but I must decline your offer; for I fear that as fast as I whiten my goods you will blacken them again."

There can be little liking where there is no likeness.

THE FOX AND THE STORK

A FOX ONE DAY INVITED A STORK TO DINNER, AND BEING DIS-posed to divert himself at the expense of his guest, provided nothing for the entertainment but some thin soup in a shallow dish. This the Fox lapped up very readily, while the Stork, unable to gain a mouthful with her long narrow bill, was as hungry at the end of dinner as when she began. The Fox meanwhile professed his regret at seeing her eat so sparingly, and feared that the dish was not seasoned to her mind.

The Stork said little, but begged that the Fox would do her the honour of returning her visit; and accordingly he agreed to dine with her on the following day. He arrived true to his appointment, and the dinner was ordered forthwith; but when it was served up, he found to his dismay that it was contained in a narrow-necked vessel, down which the Stork readily thrust her long neck and bill, while he was obliged to content himself with licking the neck of the jar. Unable to satisfy his hunger, he retired with as good a grace as he could, observing that he could hardly find fault with his entertainer, who had only paid him back in his own coin.

THE BOY AND THE SCORPION

A BOY WAS HUNTING LOCUSTS UPON A WALL, AND HAD CAUGHT a great number of them; when, seeing a Scorpion, he mistook it for another Locust, and was just hollowing his hand to catch it, when the Scorpion, lifting up his sting, said; "I wish you had done it, for I would soon have made you drop me, and the Locusts into the bargain."

THE LARK AND HER YOUNG ONES

THERE WAS A BROOD OF YOUNG LARKS IN A FIELD OF CORN, which was just ripe, and the mother, looking every day for reapers, left word, whenever she went out in search of food, that her young ones should report to her all the news they heard. One day, while she was absent, the master came to look at the state of the crop. "It is full time," said he, "to call in all my neighbours and get my corn reaped."

When the old Lark came home, the young ones told their

mother what they had heard, and begged her to remove them forthwith. "Time enough," said she; "if he trusts his neighbours, he will have to wait awhile yet for his harvest." Next day, however, the owner came again, and finding the sun still hotter and the corn more ripe, and nothing done, "There is not a moment to be lost," said he; "we cannot depend upon our neighbours; we must call in our relations"; and, turning to his son, "Go call your uncles and cousins, and see that they begin to-morrow."

In still greater fear, the young ones repeated to their mother the farmer's words. "If that be all," said she, "do not be frightened, for the relations have got harvest work of their own; but take particular notice what you hear the next time, and be sure you let me know."

She went abroad the next day, and the owner coming as before, and finding the grain falling to the ground from over-ripeness, and still no one at work, called to his son. "We must wait for our neighbours and friends no longer; do you go and hire some reapers to-night, and we will set to work ourselves to-morrow." When the young ones told their mother this, "Then," said she, "it is time to be off, indeed; for when a man takes up his business himself, instead of leaving it to others, you may be sure that he means to set to work in earnest."

THE TWO WALLETS

EVERY MAN CARRIES TWO WALLETS, ONE BEFORE AND ONE BEhind, and both full of faults. But the one before, is full of his neighbour's faults; the one behind, of his own. Thus it happens that men are blind to their own faults, but never lose sight of their neighbour's.

THE MONKEY AND THE DOLPHIN

IT WAS AN OLD CUSTOM AMONG SAILORS TO CARRY ABOUT WITH them little Maltese lap-dogs, or Monkeys, to amuse them on the voyage; so it happened once upon a time that a man took with

him a Monkey as a companion on board ship. While they were off Sunium, the famous headland of Attica, the ship was caught in a violent storm, and being capsized, all on board were thrown in the water, and had to swim for land as best they could. And among them was the Monkey.

A Dolphin saw him struggling, and, taking him for a man, went to his assistance and bore him on his back straight for shore. When they had just got opposite Piræus, the harbour of Athens, the Dolphin asked the Monkey if he were an Athenian?

"Yes," answered the Monkey, "assuredly, and of one of the first families in the place." "Then, of course, you know Piræus," said the Dolphin. "Oh, yes," said the Monkey, who thought it was the name of some distinguished citizen, "he is one of my most intimate friends." Indignant at so gross a deceit and false-hood, the Dolphin dived to the bottom, and left the lying Monkey to his fate.

THE BOYS AND THE FROGS

A TROOP OF BOYS WERE PLAYING AT THE EDGE OF A POND, WHEN, perceiving a number of Frogs in the water, they began to pelt at them with stones. They had already killed many of the poor creatures, when one more hardy than the rest putting his head above the water, cried out to them; "Stop your cruel sport, my lads; consider, what is Play to you is Death to us."

THE PORKER AND THE SHEEP

A YOUNG PORKER TOOK UP HIS QUARTERS IN A FOLD OF SHEEP. One day the shepherd laid hold of him, when he squeaked and struggled with all his might and main. The Sheep reproached him for crying out, and said, "The master often lays hold of us, and we do not cry." "Yes," replied he, "but our case is not the same; for he catches you for the sake of your wool, but me for my fry."

THE PILGRIM AND THE SWORD

A PILGRIM ON HIS WAY FOUND A SWORD, AND ASKED OF THE Sword, "What is he that hath lost thee?" And the Sword answered to the Pilgrim, "A man alone hath lost me, but many a one have I lost."

And therefore an evil man may be lost, but ere he be lost he may well harm many a one.

THE EAGLE AND THE BEETLE

A HARE BEING PURSUED BY AN EAGLE, BETOOK HIMSELF FOR refuge to the nest of a Beetle, whom he entreated to save him. The Beetle therefore interceded with the Eagle, begging of him not to kill the poor suppliant, and pleaded with him, by mighty Jupiter, not to break the laws of hospitality because he was so small an animal. But the Eagle, in wrath, gave the Beetle a flap of his wing, and straightway seized upon the Hare and devoured him.

When the Eagle flew away, the Beetle flew after him, to learn where his nest was, and getting into it, he rolled the Eagle's eggs out of it one by one, and broke them. The Eagle, grieved and enraged to think that any one should attempt so audacious a thing, built his nest the next time in a higher place; but there too the Beetle got at it again, and served him in the same manner as before. Upon this the Eagle, being at a loss what to do, flew up to Jupiter, his Lord and King, and placed the third brood of eggs, as a sacred deposit, in his lap, begging him to guard them for him. But the Beetle, having made a little ball of dirt, flew up with it and dropped it in Jupiter's lap; who, rising up on a sudden to shake it off, and forgetting the eggs, threw them down, and they were again broken. Jupiter being informed by the Beetle that he had done this to be revenged upon the Eagle, who had not only wronged him, but had acted impiously towards Jove himself, told the Eagle, when he came to him, that the Beetle was the aggrieved party, and that he complained not without reason. But being unwilling that the race of Eagles should be diminished, he advised the Beetle to come to peace with the Eagle. As the Beetle would not agree to this, Jupiter transferred the Eagle's breeding to another season, when there are no Beetles to be seen.

No one can slight the laws of hospitality with impunity; and there is no station or influence, however powerful, that can protect the oppressor, in the end, from the vengeance of the oppressed.

MERCURY AND THE SCULPTOR

MERCURY HAVING A MIND TO KNOW IN WHAT ESTIMATION HE was held among men, disguised himself as a traveller, and going into a Sculptor's workshop, began asking the price of the different statues he saw there. Pointing to an image of Jupiter, he asked how much he wanted for that. "A drachma," said the image-maker. Mercury laughed in his sleeve, and asked, "How much for this of Juno?" The man wanted a higher price for that. Mercury's eye now caught his own image. "Now, will this fellow," thought he, "ask me ten times as much for this, for I am the messenger of heaven, and the source of all his gain." So he put the question to him, what he valued that Mercury at. "Well," says the Sculptor, "if you will give me my price for the other two, I will throw that into the bargain."

They who are over-anxious to know how the world values them, will seldom be set down at their own price.

THE TRAVELLERS AND THE BEAR

TWO FRIENDS WERE TRAVELLING ON THE SAME ROAD TOGETHER, when they met with a Bear. The one in great fear, without a thought of his companion, climbed up into a tree, and hid himself. The other seeing that he had no chance, single-handed, against the Bear, had nothing left but to throw himself on the ground and feign to be dead; for he had heard that the Bear will never touch a dead body.

As he thus lay, the Bear came up to his head, nuzzling and snuffing at his nose, and ears, and heart, but the man immovably held his breath, and the beast supposing him to be dead, walked away. When the Bear was fairly out of sight, his companion came down out of the tree, and asked what it was that the Bear whispered to him; "for," says he, "I observed he put his mouth very close to your ear." "Why," replied the other, "it was no great secret; he only bade me have a care how I kept company with those who, when they get into a difficulty, leave their friends in the lurch."

THE ASS, THE COCK, AND THE LION

AN ASS AND A COCK LIVED IN A FARM-YARD TOGETHER. ONE day a hungry Lion passing by and seeing the Ass in good condition, resolved to make a meal of him. Now, they say that there is nothing a Lion hates so much as the crowing of a Cock; and at that moment the Cock happening to crow, the Lion straightway made off with all haste from the spot.

The Ass, mightily amused to think that a Lion should be frightened at a bird, plucked up the courage and galloped after him, delighted with the notion of driving the king of beasts before him. He had, however, gone no great distance, when the Lion turned sharply round upon him, and made an end of him in a trice.

Presumption begins in ignorance and ends in ruin.

THE STAG, THE WOLF, AND THE SHEEP

A STAG ASKED A SHEEP TO LEND HIM A MEASURE OF WHEAT, AND said that the Wolf would be his surety. The Sheep, fearing some fraud was intended, excused herself, saying; "The Wolf is accustomed to seize what he wants, and to run off; and you, too, can quickly outstrip me in your rapid flight. How then shall I be able to find either of you, when the day of payment comes?"

Two blacks do not make one white.

THE PROPHET

A WIZARD, SITTING IN THE MARKET-PLACE, TOLD THE FORTUNES of the passers-by. A person ran up in great haste, and announced to him that the doors of his house had been broken open, and that all his goods were being stolen. He sighed heavily, and hastened away as fast as he could run. A neighbour saw him running, and said; "Oh! you fellow there! You say you can foretell the fortunes of others; how is it you did not foresee your own?"

THE VAIN JACKDAW

A JACKDAW, AS VAIN AND CONCEITED AS JACKDAW COULD BE, picked up the feathers which some Peacock had shed, stuck them amongst his own, and despising his old companions, introduced himself with the greatest assurance into a flock of those beautiful birds. They, instantly detecting the intruder, stripped him of his borrowed plumes, and falling upon him with their beaks, sent him about his business.

The unlucky Jackdaw, sorely punished and deeply sorrowing, betook himself to his former companions, and would have flocked with them again as if nothing had happened. But they, recollecting what airs he had given himself, drummed him out of their society, while one of those whom he had so lately despised, read him this lecture: "Had you been contented with what nature made you, you would have escaped the chastisement of your betters and also the contempt of your equals."

THE ASS AND THE FROGS

AN ASS, CARRYING A LOAD OF WOOD, PASSED THROUGH A POND. As he was crossing through the water he lost his footing, and stumbled and fell, and not being able to rise on account of his load, he groaned heavily. Some Frogs frequenting the pool heard his lamentation, and said; "What would you do if you had to live here always as we do, when you make a fuss about a mere fall into the water?"

Men often bear little grievances with less courage than they do large misfortunes.

THE FLEA AND THE WRESTLER

A FLEA SETTLED UPON THE BARE FOOT OF A WRESTLER, AND bit him; on which the Wrestler called loudly upon Hercules for help. The Flea a second time lighted upon his foot, when he groaned and said; "O Hercules! if you will not help me against a Flea, how can I hope for your assistance against greater antagonists?"

THE LION AND HIS THREE COUNCILLORS

THE LION CALLED THE SHEEP TO ASK HER IF HIS BREATH SMELT: she said Ay; he bit off her head for a fool. He called the Wolf, and asked him: he said No; he tore him in pieces for a flatterer. At last he called the Fox, and asked him. Truly he had got a cold, and could not smell.

Wise men say nothing in dangerous times.

THE BOY AND THE NETTLE

A BOY PLAYING IN THE FIELDS GOT STUNG BY A NETTLE. HE ran home to his mother, telling her that he had but touched that nasty weed, and it had stung him. "It was just your touching it, my boy," said the mother, "that caused it to sting you; the next time you meddle with a Nettle, grasp it tightly, and it will do you no hurt."

Do boldly what you do at all.

THE MAN AND HIS TWO WIVES

IN DAYS WHEN A MAN WAS ALLOWED MORE WIVES THAN ONE, a middle-aged bachelor, who could be called neither young nor old, and whose hair was only just beginning to turn grey, must needs fall in love with two women at once, and marry them both. The one was young and blooming, and wished her husband to appear as youthful as herself; the other was somewhat more advanced in age, and was as anxious that her husband should appear a suitable match for her.

So, while the young one seized every opportunity of pulling out the good man's grey hairs, the old one was as industrious in plucking out every black hair she could find.   For a while the man was highly gratified by their attention and devotion, till he found one morning that, between the one and the other, he had not a hair left.

He that submits his principles to the influence and caprices of opposite parties will end in having no principles at all.

THE LEOPARD AND THE FOX

A LEOPARD AND A FOX HAD A CONTEST WHICH WAS THE FINER creature of the two.   The Leopard put forward the beauty of its numberless spots; but the Fox replied; "It is better to have a versatile mind than a variegated body."

THE WOLF AND THE SKULL

A WOLF FOUND A DEAD MAN'S HEAD, WHICH HE TURNED UPside down with his foot.   And he said, "Ah ha! how fair hast thou been, and pleasant.   And now thou hast in thee neither wit nor beauty; and thou art without voice and without thought."   Therefore men ought not only to behold the beauty and fairness of the body, but also the goodness and the courage.

THE KITE AND THE PIGEONS

SOME PIGEONS HAD LONG LIVED IN FEAR OF A KITE, BUT BY BEING always on the alert, and keeping near their dove-house, they had contrived hitherto to escape the attacks of the enemy.   Finding his sallies unsuccessful, the Kite betook himself to craft: "Why," said he, "do you prefer this life of continual anxiety, when, if you would only make me your king, I would secure you from every attack that could be made upon you?" The Pigeons, trusting to his professions, called him to the throne; but no sooner was he established there than he exercised his power by devouring a pigeon a day. Whereupon one that yet awaited his turn, said no more than; "It serves us right."

THE BOASTING TRAVELLER

A MAN WHO HAD BEEN TRAVELLING IN FOREIGN PARTS, ON HIS return home was always bragging and boasting of the great feats he had accomplished in different places. In Rhodes, for instance, he said he had taken such an extraordinary leap, that no man could come near him, and he had witnesses there to prove it. "Possibly," said one of his hearers; "but if this be true, just suppose this to be Rhodes, and then try the leap again."

THE KID AND THE WOLF

A KID BEING MOUNTED ON THE ROOF OF A LOFTY HOUSE, AND seeing a Wolf pass below, began to revile him. The Wolf merely stopped to reply; "Coward! it is not you who revile me, but the place on which you are standing."

VENUS AND THE CAT

A CAT HAVING FALLEN IN LOVE WITH A YOUNG MAN, BESOUGHT Venus to change her into a girl, in the hope of gaining his affections. The Goddess, taking compassion on her weakness, changed her into a fair damsel; and the young man, enamoured of her beauty, led her home as his bride.

As they were sitting in their chamber, Venus, wishing to know whether in changing her form she had also changed her nature, set down a Mouse before her. The Girl, forgetful of her new condition, started from her seat, and pounced upon the Mouse as if she would have eaten it on the spot; whereupon the Goddess, provoked at her frivolity, straightway turned her into a Cat again.

What is bred in the bone, will never out of the flesh.

THE CAMEL

WHEN MAN FIRST SAW THE CAMEL, HE WAS SO FRIGHTENED at his vast size that he fled away. After a time, perceiving the meekness and gentleness of his temper, he summoned courage enough to approach him. Soon afterwards, observing that he was an animal altogether deficient in spirit, he assumed such boldness as to put a bridle in his mouth, and to set a child to drive him.

Use serves to overcome dread.

THE SINGING KITES

THE KITES OF OLD TIME HAD, EQUALLY WITH THE SWANS, THE privilege of song. But having heard the neigh of the horse, they were so enchanted with the sound, that they tried to imitate it; and, in trying to neigh, they forgot how to sing.

The desire for imaginary benefits often involves the loss of present blessings.

THE SWALLOW AND THE RAVEN

THE SWALLOW AND THE RAVEN CONTENDED WHICH WAS THE finer bird. The Raven ended by saying, "Your beauty is but for the summer, but mine will stand many winters."

Durability is better than show.

THE HE-GOAT AND THE WOLF

A WOLF SOME TIME RAN AFTER A HE-GOAT, AND THE HE-GOAT, for to save himself, leapt upon a rock; and the Wolf besieged him. And after when they had dwelled there two or three days, the Wolf began to wax hungry and the He-goat to have thirst. And thus the Wolf went to eat, and the He-goat went to drink. And as the He-goat drank he saw his shadow in the water; and, spying and beholding his shadow, said such words within himself; "Thou hast so fair legs, so fair a beard, and so fair horns, and hast fear of the Wolf! If it happen that he come again, I shall correct him well and shall keep him well, that he shall have no might over me."

And the Wolf, which held his peace and hearkened what was said, took him by one leg, thus saying; "What words be these which thou sayest, brother He-goat?" And when the He-goat saw that he was taken, he began to say to the Wolf; "Ha! my lord, I say nothing, and have pity on me! I know well that it is to my blame." And the Wolf took him by the neck and strangled him. And therefore it is great folly when the feeble maketh war against the powerful and strong.

THE CROW AND THE PITCHER

A CROW, READY TO DIE WITH THIRST, FLEW WITH JOY TO A Pitcher, which he saw at a distance. But when he came up to it, he found the water so low that with all his stooping and straining he was unable to reach it. Thereupon he tried to break the Pitcher; then to overturn it; but his strength was not sufficient to do either. At last, seeing some small pebbles at hand, he dropped a great many of them, one by one, into the Pitcher, and so raised the water to the brim, and quenched his thirst.

THE FALCONER AND THE PARTRIDGE

A FALCONER HAVING TAKEN A PARTRIDGE IN HIS NET, THE BIRD cried out sorrowfully, "Let me go, good Master Falconer, and I promise you I will decoy other Partridges into your net."

"No," said the man, "whatever I might have done, I am determined now not to spare you; for there is no death too bad for him who is ready to betray his friends."

THE MOLE AND HER MOTHER

SAID A YOUNG MOLE TO HER MOTHER, "MOTHER, I CAN SEE." So, in order to try her, her Mother put a lump of frankincense before her, and asked her what it was. "A stone," said the young one. "O, my child!" said the Mother, "not only do you not see, but you cannot even smell."

Brag upon one defect, and betray another.

THE MISER

A MISER, TO MAKE SURE OF HIS PROPERTY, SOLD ALL THAT HE had and converted it into a great lump of gold, which he hid in a hole in the ground, and went continually to visit and inspect it.

This roused the curiosity of one of his workmen, who, suspecting that there was a treasure, when his master's back was turned, went to the spot, and stole it away.

When the Miser returned and found the place empty, he wept and tore his hair. But a neighbour who saw him in this extravagant grief, and learned the cause of it, said; "Fret thyself no longer, but take a stone and put it in the same place, and think that it is your lump of gold; for, as you never meant to use it, the one will do you as much good as the other."

The worth of money is not in its possession, but in its use.

THE FOX AND THE MASK

A FOX HAD STOLEN INTO THE HOUSE OF AN ACTOR, AND IN RUMmaging among his various properties, laid hold of a highly-finished Mask. "A fine-looking head, indeed!" cried he; "what a pity it is that it has no brains!"

A fair outside is but a poor substitute for inward worth.

THE DOG INVITED TO SUPPER

A GENTLEMAN, HAVING PREPARED A GREAT FEAST, INVITED A Friend to supper; and the Gentleman's Dog, meeting the Friend's Dog, "Come," said he, "my good fellow, and sup with us to-night."

The Dog was delighted with the invitation, and as he stood by and saw the preparation for the feast, said to himself; "Capital fare indeed! this is, in truth, good luck. I shall revel in dainties, and I will take good care to lay in an ample stock to-night, for I may have nothing to eat to-morrow."

As he said this to himself, he wagged his tail, and gave a sly look at his friend who had invited him. But his tail wagging to and fro caught the cook's eye, who seeing a stranger, straightway seized him by the legs, and threw him out of the window. When he reached the ground, he set off yelping down the street; upon which the neighbours' Dogs ran up to him, and asked him how he liked his supper. "I'faith," said he, with a sorry smile, "I hardly know, for we drank so deep that I can't even tell you which way I got out of the house."

They who enter by the back-stairs may expect to be shown out at the window.

THE PEASANT AND THE APPLE-TREE

A PEASANT HAD IN HIS GARDEN AN APPLE-TREE, WHICH BORE no fruit, but only served as a perch for the sparrows and grasshoppers. He resolved to cut it down, and, taking his axe in hand, made a bold stroke at its roots. The grasshoppers and sparrows entreated him not to cut down the tree that sheltered them, but to spare it, and they would sing to him and lighten his labours. He paid no attention to their request, but gave the tree a second and a third blow with his axe. When he reached the hollow of the tree, he found a hive full of honey. Having tasted the honeycomb, he threw down his axe, and, looking on the tree as sacred, took great care of it.

Self-interest alone moves some men.

THE BEES, THE DRONES, AND THE WASP

SOME BEES HAD BUILT THEIR COMB IN THE HOLLOW TRUNK OF an oak. The Drones asserted that it was their doing, and belonged to them. The cause was brought into court before Judge Wasp.

Knowing something of the parties, he thus addressed them:— "The plaintiffs and defendants are so much alike in shape and colour as to render the ownership a doubtful matter, and the case has very properly been brought before me. The ends of justice, and the object of the court, will best be furthered by the plan which I propose. Let each party take a hive to itself, and build up a new comb, that from the shape of the cells and the taste of the honey, the lawful proprietors of the property in dispute may appear." The Bees readily assented to the Wasp's plan. The Drones declined it. Whereupon the Wasp gave judgment:— "It is clear now who made the comb, and who cannot make it; the Court adjudges the honey to the Bees."

THE LION AND THE BULLS

THREE BULLS FED IN A FIELD TOGETHER IN THE GREATEST PEACE and amity. A Lion had long watched them in the hope of making a prize of them, but found there was little chance for him so long as they kept all together. He therefore began secretly to spread evil and slanderous reports of one against the other, till he had fomented a jealousy and distrust amongst them. No sooner did the Lion see that they avoided one another, and fed each by himself apart, than he fell upon them singly, and so made an easy prey of them all.

The quarrels of friends are the opportunities of foes.

THE HORSE AND THE LOADED ASS

A MAN WHO KEPT A HORSE AND AN ASS WAS WONT IN HIS JOURneys to spare the Horse, and put all the burden upon the Ass's back. The Ass, who had been some while ailing, besought the Horse one day to relieve him of part of his load. "For if," said he, "you would take a fair portion, I shall soon get well again; but if you refuse to help me, this weight will kill me."

The Horse, however, bade the Ass get on, and not trouble him with his complaints. The Ass jogged on in silence, but presently, overcome with the weight of his burden, dropped down dead, as he had foretold. Upon this, the master coming up, unloosed the load from the dead Ass, and putting it upon the Horse's back, made him carry the Ass's carcase in addition.

"Alas, for my ill nature!" said the Horse; "by refusing to bear my just portion of the load, I have now to carry the whole of it, with a dead weight into the bargain."

A disobliging temper carries its own punishment along with it.

THE GULL AND THE KITE

A GULL HAD POUNCED UPON A FISH, AND IN ENDEAVOURING to swallow it got choked, and lay upon the deck for dead. A Kite who was passing by and saw him, gave him no other comfort than; "It serves you right. For what business have the fowls of the air to meddle with the fish of the sea?"

THE WOLF AND THE SHEPHERDS

A WOLF LOOKING INTO A HUT AND SEEING SOME SHEPHERDS comfortably regaling themselves on a joint of mutton, "A pretty row," said he, "would these men have made if they had caught me at such a supper!"

Men are too apt to condemn in others the very things that they practise themselves.

THE OWL AND THE BIRDS

AN OWL, IN HER WISDOM, COUNSELLED THE BIRDS, WHEN THE acorn first began to sprout, to pull it up by all means out of the ground, and not allow it to grow, because it would produce the mistletoe, from which a bird poison would be extracted, by which

they would be captured. The Owl next advised them to pluck up the seed of the flax, which men had sown, as it was a plant which brought no good to them. And, lastly, the Owl, seeing an archer approach, predicted that this man, being on foot, would contrive darts armed with feathers, which should fly faster than the wings of the Birds themselves.

The Birds gave no credence to these warning words, but considered the Owl to be beside herself, and said that she was mad. But afterwards, finding her words were true, they wondered at her knowledge, and deemed her to be the wisest of birds. Hence it is that when she appears they flock to her as knowing all things; while she no longer gives them advice, but in solitude laments their past folly.

THE MICE AND THE WEASELS

THE MICE AND THE WEASELS HAD LONG BEEN AT WAR WITH each other, and the Mice were constantly being defeated. At length at a meeting, solemnly called, they agreed that their defeat was attributable to nothing but their want of discipline, and they determined accordingly to elect regular Commanders for the time to come. So they chose those whose valour and gallantry most recommended them to the important post.

The new Commanders, proud of their position, and desirous of being as conspicuous as possible, bound horns upon their foreheads as a sort of crest and mark of distinction. Not long after a battle ensued. The Mice, as before, were soon put to flight; the common herd escaped into their holes; but the Commanders, not being able to get in from the length of their horns, were every one caught and devoured.

There is no distinction without its accompanying danger.

THE FLIES AND THE HONEY-POT

A POT OF HONEY HAVING BEEN UPSET IN A GROCER'S SHOP, THE Flies came around it in swarms to eat it up, nor would they move from the spot while there was a drop left. At length their feet became so clogged that they could not fly away, and stifled in the luscious sweets they exclaimed; "Miserable creatures that we are, who for the sake of an hour's pleasure, have thrown away our lives!"

THE DOG AND THE SHADOW

A DOG HAD STOLEN A PIECE OF MEAT OUT OF A BUTCHER'S SHOP, and was crossing a river on his way home, when he saw his own shadow reflected in the stream below. Thinking that it was another dog with another piece of meat, he resolved to make himself master of that also; but in snapping at the supposed treasure, he dropped the bit he was carrying, and so lost all.

THE OLD WOMAN AND THE PHYSICIAN

AN OLD WOMAN, WHO HAD BECOME BLIND, CALLED IN A PHYSI-cian, and promised him, before witnesses, that if he would restore her eyesight, she would give him a most handsome reward, but that if he did not cure her, and her malady remained, he should receive nothing. The agreement being concluded, the Physician tampered from time to time with the old lady's eyes, and meanwhile, bit by bit, carried off her goods.

At length after a time he set about the task in earnest and cured her, and thereupon asked for the stipulated fee. But the old Woman, on recovering her sight, saw none of her goods left in the house. When, therefore, the Physician importuned her in vain for payment, and she continually put him off with excuses, he summoned her at last before the Judges.

Being now called upon for her defence, she said, "What this man says is true enough; I promised to give him his fee if my sight were restored, and nothing if my eyes continued bad. Now then he says that I am cured, but I say just the contrary; for when my malady first came on, I could see all sorts of furniture and goods in my house; but now, when he says he has restored my sight, I cannot see one jot of either."

He who plays a trick must be prepared to take a joke.

THE THIRSTY PIGEON

A PIGEON SEVERELY PRESSED BY THIRST, SEEING A GLASS OF WATER painted upon a sign, supposed it to be real. So dashing down at it with all her might, she struck against the board, and, breaking her wing, fell helpless to the ground, where she was quickly captured by one of the passers-by.

Great haste is not always good speed.

THE LION IN LOVE

IT HAPPENED IN THE DAYS OF OLD THAT A LION FELL IN LOVE with a Woodman's daughter; and had the folly to ask her of her father in marriage. The Woodman was not much pleased with the offer, and declined the honour of so dangerous an alliance. But upon the Lion threatening him with his royal displeasure, the poor man, seeing that so formidable a creature was not to be denied, hit at length upon this expedient; "I feel greatly flattered," said he, "with your proposal; but, noble sir, what great teeth you have got! and what great claws you have got! where is the damsel that would not be frightened at such weapons as these? You must have your teeth drawn and your claws pared before you can be a suitable bridegroom for my daughter."

The Lion straightway submitted, for what will not a body do for love? and then called upon the father to accept him as a son-in-law. But the Woodman, no longer afraid of the tamed and disarmed bully, seized a stout cudgel and drove the unreasonable suitor from his door.

THE SWALLOW IN CHANCERY

A SWALLOW HAD BUILT HER NEST UNDER THE EAVES OF A COURT of Justice. Before her young ones could fly, a Serpent gliding out of his hole ate them all up. When the poor bird returned to her nest and found it empty, she began a pitiable wailing; but a neighbour suggesting, by way of comfort, that she was not the first bird who had lost her young, "True," she replied, "but it is not my little ones that I mourn, but that I should have been wronged in that very place where the injured fly for justice."

THE FOX AND THE HEDGEHOG

A FOX, WHILE CROSSING OVER A RIVER, WAS DRIVEN BY A STREAM into a narrow gorge, and lay there for a long time unable to get out, covered with myriads of horse-flies that had fastened themselves upon him. A Hedgehog, who was wandering in that direction, saw him, and, taking compassion on him, asked him if he should drive away the flies that were so tormenting him. But the Fox begged him to do nothing of the sort.

"Why not?" asked the Hedgehog. "Because," replied the Fox, "these flies that are upon me now, are already full, and draw but little blood, but should you remove them, a swarm of fresh and hungry ones will come, who will not leave a drop of blood in my body."

THE TWO SOLDIERS AND THE ROBBER

TWO SOLDIERS TRAVELLING TOGETHER, WERE ATTACKED BY A Robber. One fled away; the other stood his ground, and defended himself with his stout right hand. The Robber being slain, the timid companion runs up and draws his sword, and then, throwing back his travelling cloak, says; "I'll at him, and I'll take care he shall learn whom he has attacked."

On this he who had fought with the Robber made answer; "I only wish that you had helped me just now, even if it had been only with those words, for I should have been the more encouraged, believing them to be true; but now put up your sword in its sheath, and hold your equally useless tongue, till you can deceive others who do not know you. I, indeed, who have experienced with what speed you run away, know right well that no dependence can be placed on your valour."

THE FATHER AND HIS TWO DAUGHTERS

A MAN WHO HAD TWO DAUGHTERS MARRIED ONE TO A GARDENER, the other to a Potter. After a while he paid a visit to the Gardener's, and asked his daughter how she was, and how it fared with her. "Excellently well," said she; "we have everything that we want; I have but one prayer, that we may have a heavy storm of rain to water our plants."

Off he set to the Potter's, and asked his other daughter how matters went with her. "There is not a thing we want," she replied; "and I only hope this fine weather and hot sun may continue, to bake our tiles."

"Alack," said the Father, "if you wish for fine weather, and your sister for rain, which am I to pray for myself?"

THE TWO MEN WHO WERE ENEMIES

TWO MEN WHO WERE ENEMIES SAILED ON THE SAME VESSEL. Determined to keep as far apart as possible, one seated himself in the stern, and the other in the prow of the ship. A violent storm having arisen, and the vessel being in great danger of sinking, the one in the stern inquired of the pilot which of the two ends of the ship would go down first. On his replying that he supposed it would be the prow, then said the Man; "Death would not be grievous to me, if I could only see my Enemy die before me."

THE GOATHERD AND THE GOATS

IT WAS A STORMY DAY, AND THE SNOW WAS FALLING FAST, WHEN a Goatherd drove his Goats, all white with snow, into a desert cave for shelter. There he found that a herd of Wild-goats, more numerous and larger than his own, had already taken possession. So, thinking to secure them all, he left his own Goats to take care of themselves, and threw the branches which he had brought for them to the Wild-goats to browse on. But when the weather cleared up, he found his own Goats had perished from hunger, while the Wild-goats were off and away to the hills and woods. So the Goatherd returned a laughing-stock to his neighbours, having failed to gain the Wild-goats, and having lost his own.

They who neglect their old friends for the sake of new, are rightly served if they lose both.

THE GEESE AND THE CRANES

SOME GEESE AND SOME CRANES FED TOGETHER IN THE SAME field. One day the sportsmen came suddenly down upon them. The Cranes being light of body, flew off in a moment and escaped; but the Geese, weighed down by their fat, were all taken.

In civil commotions, they fare best who have least to fetter them.

THE ASS AND THE LAP-DOG

THERE WERE AN ASS AND A LAP-DOG WHO BELONGED TO THE same master. The Ass was tied up in the stable, and had plenty of corn and hay to eat, and was as well off as Ass could be. The little Dog was always sporting and gambolling about, caressing and fawning upon his master in a thousand amusing ways, so that he became a great favourite, and was permitted to lie in his master's lap.

The Ass, indeed, had enough to do; he was drawing wood all day, and had to take his turn at the mill at night. But while he grieved over his own lot, it galled him more to see the Lap-dog living in such ease and luxury; so thinking that if he acted a like part to his master, he should fare the same, he broke one day from his halter, and rushing into the hall began to kick and prance about in the strangest fashion; then swishing his tail and mimicking the frolics of the favourite, he upset the table where his master was at dinner, breaking it in two and smashing all the crockery; nor would he leave off till he jumped upon his master, and pawed him with his rough-shod feet.

The servants, seeing their master in no little danger, thought it was now high time to interfere, and having released him from the Ass's caresses, they so belaboured the silly creature with sticks and staves, that he never got up again; and as he breathed his last, exclaimed; "Why could not I have been satisfied with my natural position, without attempting, by tricks and grimaces, to imitate one who was but a puppy after all!"

THE FARMER AND THE CRANES

SOME CRANES SETTLED DOWN IN A FARMER'S FIELD THAT WAS newly sown. For some time the Farmer frightened them away by brandishing an empty sling at them. But when the Cranes found that he was only slinging to the winds, they no longer minded him, nor flew away. Upon this the Farmer slung at them with stones, and killed a great part of them. "Let us be off," said the rest, "to the land of the Pygmies, for this man means to threaten us no longer, but is determined to get rid of us in earnest."

THE STAG IN THE OX-STALL

A HUNTED STAG, DRIVEN OUT OF THE THICKET AND DISTRACTED by fear, made for the first farm-house he saw, and hid himself in an Ox-stall which happened to be open. As he was trying to conceal himself under the straw, "What can you mean," said an Ox, "by running into such certain destruction as to trust yourself to the haunts of man?" "Only do you not betray me," said the Stag, "and I shall be off again on the first opportunity."

Evening came on; the herdsman foddered the cattle, but observed nothing. The other farm-servants came in and out. The Stag was still safe. Presently the bailiff passed through; all seemed right. The Stag now feeling himself quite secure began to thank the Oxen for their hospitality. "Wait a while," said one of them, "we indeed wish you well, but there is yet another person, one with a hundred eyes; if he should happen to come this way I fear your life will be still in jeopardy."

While he was speaking, the Master, having finished his supper, came round to see that all was safe for the night, for he thought that his cattle had not of late looked as well as they ought. Going up to the rack, "Why so little fodder here?" says he. "Why is there not more straw?" And "How long, I wonder, would it take to sweep down these cobwebs!" Prying and observing, here and there and everywhere, the Stag's antlers, jutting from out the straw, caught his eye, and calling in his servants he instantly made prize of him.

THE MONKEY AND THE CAMEL

AT A GREAT MEETING OF THE BEASTS, THE MONKEY STOOD UP to dance. Having greatly distinguished himself, and being applauded by all present, it moved the spleen of the Camel, who came forward and began to dance also; but he made himself so utterly absurd, that all the Beasts in indignation set upon him with clubs and drove him out of the ring.

THE EAGLE AND THE ARROW

A BOWMAN TOOK AIM AT AN EAGLE AND HIT HIM IN THE HEART. As the Eagle turned his head in the agonies of death, he saw that the Arrow was winged with his own feathers. "How much sharper," said he, "are the wounds made by weapons which we ourselves have supplied!"

JUPITER AND THE CAMEL

WHEN THE CAMEL, IN DAYS OF YORE, BESOUGHT JUPITER TO grant him horns, for that it was a great grief to him to see other animals furnished with them, while he had none; Jupiter not only refused to give him the horns he asked for, but cropped his ears short for his importunity.

By asking too much, we may lose the little that we had before.

THE LION, THE MOUSE, AND THE FOX

A LION, FATIGUED BY THE HEAT OF A SUMMER'S DAY, FELL FAST asleep in his den. A Mouse ran over his mane and ears, and woke him from his slumbers. He rose up and shook himself in great wrath, and searched every corner of his den to find the Mouse. A Fox, seeing him, said, "A fine Lion you are, to be frightened of a Mouse." "'Tis not the Mouse I fear," said the Lion, "I resent his familiarity and ill-breeding."

Little liberties are great offences.

THE LION, THE ASS, AND THE FOX HUNTING

THE LION, THE ASS, AND THE FOX FORMED A PARTY TO GO OUT hunting. They took a large booty, and when the sport was ended bethought themselves of having a hearty meal. The Lion bade the Ass allot the spoil. So dividing it into three equal parts, the Ass begged his friends to make their choice; at which the

Lion, in great indignation, fell upon the Ass, and tore him to pieces. He then bade the Fox make a division; who, gathering the whole into one great heap, reserved but the smallest mite for himself. "Ah! friend," said the Lion, "who taught you to make so equitable a division?" "I wanted no other lesson," replied the Fox, "than the Ass's fate."

Better be wise by the misfortunes of others than by your own.

THE HEDGE AND THE VINEYARD

A FOOLISH YOUNG HEIR WHO HAD JUST COME INTO POSSESSION of his wise father's estate, caused all the Hedges about his Vineyard to be grubbed up, because they bore no grapes. The throwing down of the fences laid his grounds open to man and beast, and all his vines were presently destroyed. So the simple fellow learnt, when it was too late, that he ought not to expect to gather grapes from brambles, and that it was quite as important to protect his Vineyard as to possess it.

THE PANTHER AND THE SHEPHERDS

A PANTHER, BY SOME MISCHANCE, FELL INTO A PIT. THE Shepherds discovered him, threw sticks at him, and pelted him with stones, while some of them, moved with compassion towards one about to die even though no one should hurt him, threw in some food to prolong his life. At night they returned home, not dreaming of any danger, but supposing that on the morrow they should find him dead.

The Panther, however, when he had recruited his feeble strength, freed himself with a sudden bound from the pit, and hastened home with rapid steps to his den. After a few days he came forth and slaughtered the cattle, and, killing the Shepherds who had attacked him, raged with angry fury.

Then they who had spared his life, fearing for their safety, surrendered to him their flocks, and begged only for their lives; to whom the Panther made this reply; "I remember alike those who sought my life with stones, and those who gave me food— lay aside, therefore, your fears. I return as an enemy only to those who injured me."

THE RAVEN AND THE SWAN

A RAVEN ENVIED A SWAN THE WHITENESS OF HER PLUMAGE; and, thinking that its beauty was owing to the water in which she lived, he deserted the altars where he used to find his livelihood, and betook himself to the pools and streams. There he plumed and dressed himself and washed his coat, but all to no purpose, for his plumage remained as black as ever, and he himself soon perished for want of his usual food.

Change of scene is not change of nature.

THE LION AND THE FOX

A FOX AGREED TO WAIT UPON A LION IN THE CAPACITY OF A servant. Each for a time performed the part belonging to his station; the Fox used to point out the prey, and the Lion fell upon it and seized it. But the Fox, beginning to think himself as good a beast as his master, begged to be allowed to hunt the game instead of finding it. His request was granted, but as he was in the act of making a descent upon a herd, the huntsmen came out upon him, and he was himself made the prize.

THE RICH MAN AND THE TANNER

A RICH MAN LIVED NEAR A TANNER, AND NOT LIKING THE UN-pleasant smell of the tan-yard, he pressed his neighbour to go away. The Tanner put off his departure from time to time, saying that he would remove soon. But, as he still continued to stay, it came to pass, as time went on, the rich man became accustomed to the smell, and made no further complaints.

THE THIEF AND THE DOG

A THIEF COMING TO ROB A HOUSE WOULD HAVE STOPPED THE barking of a Dog by throwing bread to him. "Away with you!" said the Dog; "I had my suspicions of you before, but this excess of civility assures me that you are a rogue."

A bribe in hand betrays mischief at heart.

JUPITER AND THE BEE

IN DAYS OF YORE, WHEN THE WORLD WAS YOUNG, A BEE THAT had stored her combs with a bountiful harvest, flew up to heaven to present as a sacrifice an offering of honey. Jupiter was so de-lighted with the gift, that he promised to give her whatsoever she should ask for. She therefore besought him, saying; "O glorious Jove, maker and master of me, poor Bee, give thy servant a sting, that when any one approaches my hive to take the honey, I may kill him on the spot."

Jupiter, out of his love to man, was angry at her request, and thus answered her: "Your prayer shall not be granted in the way you wish, but the sting which you ask for you shall have; and when any one comes to take away your honey and you attack him, the wound shall be fatal not to him but to you, for your life shall go with your sting."

THE OLD MAN AND DEATH

AN OLD MAN THAT HAD TRAVELLED A LONG WAY WITH A HUGE bundle of sticks, found himself so weary that he cast it down, and called upon Death to deliver him from his most miserable existence. Death came straightway at his call, and asked him what he wanted. "Pray, good sir," says he, "do me but the favour to help me up with my burden again."

It is one thing to call for Death, and another to see him coming.

THE FOX AND THE COCK

A FOX CAME TOWARD A COCK AND SAID TO HIM, "I WOULD FAIN know if thou canst as well sing as thy father did." And then the Cock shut his eyes and began to cry and sing. And the Fox took and carried him away. And the people of the town cried, "The Fox beareth away the Cock!" And then the Cock said thus to the Fox, "My lord, understandest thou not what the people saith, that thou bearest away their Cock? Tell to them that it is thine and not theirs." And as the Fox said, "It is not yours, but it is mine," the Cock escaped from the Fox's mouth and flew upon a tree.

Then the Cock said to the Fox, "Thou liest; for I am theirs and not thine." And the Fox began to hit earth with his mouth and head, saying, "Mouth, thou hast spoken too much! Thou shouldest have eaten the Cock had not thy words been over many."

And therefore over much talking harmeth, and too much crowing smarteth.

THE WOLF AND THE CRANE

A WOLF HAD GOT A BONE STUCK IN HIS THROAT, AND IN THE greatest agony ran up and down, beseeching every animal he met to relieve him; at the same time hinting at a very handsome reward to the successful operator. A Crane, moved by his entreaties and promises, ventured her long neck down the Wolf's throat, and drew out the bone. She then modestly asked for the promised reward. To which, the Wolf, grinning and showing his teeth, replied with seeming indignation; "Ungrateful creature! to ask for any other reward than that you have put your head in a Wolf's jaws, and brought it safe out again!"

THE CRAB AND HER MOTHER

SAID AN OLD CRAB TO A YOUNG ONE; "WHY DO YOU WALK SO crooked, child? walk straight!" "Mother," said the young Crab, "show me the way, will you? and when I see you taking a straight course, I will try and follow."

THE FROGS ASKING FOR A KING

IN THE DAYS OF OLD, WHEN THE FROGS WERE ALL AT LIBERTY IN the lakes, and had grown quite weary of following every one his own devices, they assembled one day together, and with no little clamour petitioned Jupiter to let them have a King to keep them in better order, and make them lead more honest lives. Jupiter, knowing the vanity of their hearts, smiled at their request, and threw down a Log into the lake, which by the splash and commotion it made, sent the whole commonwealth into the greatest terror and amazement. They rushed under the water and into the mud, and dared not come within ten leaps' length of the spot where it lay.

At length one Frog bolder than the rest ventured to pop his head above the water, and take a survey of their new King at a respectful distance. Presently, when they perceived the Log lie stock-still, others began to swim up to it and around it; till by degrees, growing bolder and bolder, they at last leaped upon it, and treated it with the greatest contempt.

Dissatisfied with so tame a ruler, they forthwith petitioned Jupiter a second time for another and more active King. Upon which he sent them a Stork, who no sooner arrived among them than he began laying hold of them and devouring them one by one as fast as he could, and it was in vain that they endeavoured to escape him.

Then they sent Mercury with a private message to Jupiter, beseeching him that he would take pity on them once more; but Jupiter replied, that they were only suffering the punishment due to their folly, and that another time they would learn to let well alone, and not be dissatisfied with their natural condition.

THE COUNTRY MOUSE AND THE TOWN MOUSE

ONCE UPON A TIME A COUNTRY MOUSE WHO HAD A FRIEND IN town invited him, for old acquaintance sake, to pay him a visit in the country. The invitation being accepted in due form, the Country Mouse, though plain and rough and somewhat frugal in his nature, opened his heart and store, in honour of hospitality and an old friend. There was not a carefully stored-up morsel that he did not bring forth out of his larder, peas and barley, cheese-parings and nuts, hoping by quantity to make up what he feared was wanting in quality, to suit the palate of his dainty guest.

The Town Mouse, condescending to pick a bit here and a bit there, while the host sat nibbling a blade of barley-straw, at length exclaimed; "How is it, my good friend, that you can endure the dullness of this unpolished life? You are living like a toad in a hole. You can't really prefer these solitary rocks and woods to streets teeming with carriages and men. On my honour, you are wasting your time miserably here. We must make the most of life while it lasts. A mouse, you know, does not live for ever. So come with me and I'll show you life and the town."

Overpowered with such fine words and so polished a manner, the Country Mouse assented; and they set out together on their journey to town. It was late in the evening when they crept stealthily into the city, and midnight ere they reached the great house, where the Town Mouse took up his quarters. Here were couches of crimson velvet, carvings in ivory, everything in short that denoted wealth and luxury. On the table were the remains of a splendid banquet, to procure which all the choicest shops in the town had been ransacked the day before. It was now the turn of the courtier to play the host; he places his country friend on purple, runs to and fro to supply all his wants, presses dish upon dish and dainty upon dainty, and as though he were waiting on a king, tastes every course ere he ventures to place it before his rustic cousin.

The Country Mouse, for his part, affects to make himself quite at home, and blesses the good fortune that had wrought such a change in his way of life; when, in the midst of his enjoyment, as he is thinking with contempt of the poor fare he has forsaken, on a sudden the door flies open, and a party of revellers returning from a late entertainment, bursts into the room. The affrighted friends jump from the table in the greatest of consternation and hide themselves in the first corner they can reach. No sooner do they venture to creep out again than the barking of dogs drives them back in still greater terror than before.

At length, when things seemed quiet, the Country Mouse stole out from his hiding place, and bidding his friend good-bye, whispered in his ear; "Oh, my good sir, this fine mode of living may do for those who like it; but give me my barley-bread in peace and security before the daintiest feast where Fear and Care are in waiting."

THE ASS AND HIS DRIVER

AN ASS THAT WAS BEING DRIVEN ALONG THE ROAD BY HIS MASTER, started on ahead, and, leaving the beaten track, made as fast as he could for the edge of a precipice. When he was just on the point of falling over, his Master ran up, and, seizing him by the tail, endeavoured to pull him back; but the Ass resisting and pulling the contrary way, the man let go his hold, saying, "Well, Jack, if you will be master, I cannot help it. A wilful beast must go his own way."

THE HORSE AND HIS RIDER

A SOLDIER TOOK THE UTMOST PAINS WITH HIS CHARGER. AS long as the war lasted, he looked upon him as his fellow-helper in all emergencies, and fed him carefully with hay and corn. When the war was over, he only allowed him chaff to eat, and made him carry heavy loads of wood, and subjected him to much slavish drudgery and ill-treatment.

War, however, being again proclaimed, and the trumpet summoning him to his Standard, the Soldier put on his charger the military trappings, and mounted, in his heavy coat of mail. The Horse fell down straightway under the weight, no longer equal to the burden, and said to his master; "You must now go to the war on foot, for you have transformed me from a Horse into an Ass; and how can you expect that I can again turn in a moment from an Ass to a Horse?"

HERCULES AND THE WAGGONER

AS A COUNTRYMAN WAS CARELESSLY DRIVING HIS WAGGON along a miry lane, his wheels stuck so deep in the clay that the horses came to a stand-still. Upon this the man, without making the least effort of his own, began to call upon Hercules to come and help him out of his trouble. But Hercules bade him lay his shoulder to the wheel, assuring him that Heaven only aided those who endeavoured to help themselves.

THE MONKEYS AND THEIR MOTHER

THE MONKEY, IT IS SAID, HAS TWO YOUNG ONES AT A BIRTH. The mother fondles one, and nurses it with the greatest affection and care; but hates and neglects the other. It happened once on a time that the young one which was caressed and loved was smothered by the too great affection of the mother, while the despised one grew up in spite of the neglect to which it was exposed.

The best intentions will not always ensure success.

THE FOX WITHOUT A TAIL

A FOX BEING CAUGHT IN A TRAP, WAS GLAD TO SAVE HIS NECK by leaving his tail behind him; but upon coming abroad into the world, he began to be so sensible of the disgrace such a defect would bring upon him, that he almost wished he had died rather than come away without it. However, resolving to make the best of a bad matter, he called a meeting of the rest of the Foxes, and proposed that all should follow his example. "You have no notion," said he, "of the ease and comfort with which I now move about: I could never have believed it if I had not tried it myself; but really, when one comes to reason upon it, a tail is such an ugly, inconvenient, unnecessary appendage, that the only wonder is that, as Foxes, we could have put up with it so long. I propose, therefore, my worthy brethren, that you all profit by the experience that I am most willing to afford you, and that all Foxes from this day forward cut off their tails."

Upon this one of the oldest stepped forward, and said, "I rather think, my friend, that you would not have advised us to part with our tails, if there were any chance of recovering your own."

THE ASS AND THE OLD SHEPHERD

A SHEPHERD WATCHED HIS ASS FEEDING IN A MEADOW. BEING suddenly alarmed by the cries of the enemy, he appealed to the Ass to fly with him, lest they should both be captured. The Ass lazily replied; "Why should I, pray? Do you think it likely the conqueror will place on me two sets of panniers?" "No," rejoined the Shepherd. "Then," said the Ass, "as long as I carry the panniers, what matters it to me whom I serve?"

In a change of government the poor change nothing beyond the name of their master.

THE LABOURER AND THE SNAKE

A SNAKE, HAVING MADE HIS HOLE CLOSE TO THE PORCH OF A cottage, inflicted a severe bite on the Cottager's infant son, of which he died, to the great grief of his parents. The father resolved to kill the Snake, and the next day, on its coming out of its hole for food, took up his axe; but, making too much haste to hit him, missed his head, and cut off only the end of his tail. After some time the Cottager, afraid lest the Snake should bite him also, endeavoured to make peace, and placed some bread and salt beside his hole. The Snake, slightly hissing, said; "There can henceforth be no peace between us; for whenever I see you I shall remember the loss of my tail, and whenever you see me you will be thinking of the death of your son."

No one truly forgets injuries in the presence of him who caused the injury.

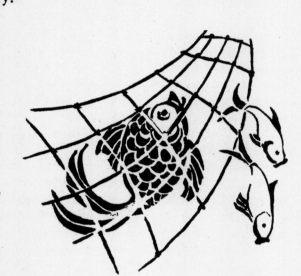

THE GREAT AND THE LITTLE FISHES

A FISHERMAN WAS DRAWING UP A NET WHICH HE HAD CAST into the sea, full of all sorts of fish. The Little Fish escaped through the meshes of the net, and got back into the deep, but the Great Fish were all caught and hauled into the ship.

Our insignificance is often the cause of our safety.

THE MOUNTEBANK AND THE COUNTRYMAN

A CERTAIN WEALTHY PATRICIAN, INTENDING TO TREAT THE Roman people with some theatrical entertainment, publicly offered a reward to any one who would produce a novel spectacle. Incited by emulation, artists arrived from all parts to contest the prize, among whom a well-known witty Mountebank gave out that he had a new kind of entertainment that had never yet been produced on any stage. This report being spread abroad, brought the whole city together.

The theatre could hardly contain the number of spectators. And when the artist appeared alone upon the stage, without any apparatus, or any assistants, curiosity and suspense kept the spectators in profound silence. On a sudden he thrust down his head into his bosom, and mimicked the squeaking of a young pig, so naturally, that the audience insisted upon it that he had one under his cloak, and ordered him to be searched; which being done, and nothing appearing, they loaded him with the most extravagant applause.

A Countryman among the audience observing what passed; "Oh!" says he, "I can do better than this," and immediately gave out that he would perform the next day.

Accordingly, on the morrow, a yet greater crowd was collected. Prepossessed, however, in favour of the Mountebank, they came rather to laugh at the Countryman than to pass a fair judgment on him. They both came out upon the stage. The Mountebank grunts away first, and calls forth the greatest clapping and applause. Then the Countryman, pretending that he concealed a little pig under his garments, and he had, in fact, really got one, pinched its ear till he made it squeak. The people cried out that the Mountebank had imitated the pig much more naturally, and hooted to the Countryman to quit the stage; but he, to convict them to their face, produced a real pig from his bosom. "And now, gentlemen, you may see," said he, "what a pretty sort of judges you are!"

It is easier to convince a man against his senses than against his will.

THE BEEVES AND THE BUTCHERS

THE BEEVES, ONCE ON A TIME, DETERMINED TO MAKE AN END of the Butchers, whose whole art, they said, was conceived for their destruction. So they assembled together, and had already whetted their horns for the contest, when a very old Ox, who had long worked at the plough, thus addressed them; "Have a care, my friends, what you do. These men, at least, kill us with decency and skill, but if we fall into the hands of botchers instead of butchers, we shall suffer a double death; for be well assured, men will not go without beef, even though they were without butchers."

THE FOX AND THE THORN-BUSH

A FOX, TO ESCAPE THE PERIL OF THE CHASE, LEAPT INTO A Thorn-bush, whose thorns hurt him sore. Thereupon the Fox, weeping in his anguish, said to the Thorn-bush; "I am come to thee as to my refuge; and thou hast hurted me to the death." And then the Thorn-bush said to the Fox; "Thou hast erred; and well thou has beguiled thyself. For thou thought to have taken me as thou art accustomed to take chickens and hens."

THE MAN, THE HORSE, THE OX, AND THE DOG

A HORSE, OX, AND DOG, DRIVEN TO GREAT STRAITS BY THE COLD, sought shelter and protection from Man. He received them kindly, lighted a fire, and warmed them. He allowed the Horse to eat of his oats, gave the Ox abundance of hay, and fed the Dog with meat from his own table.

Grateful for these favours, they determined to repay him to the best of their ability. They divided for this purpose the term of his life between them, and each endowed one portion of it with the qualities which chiefly characterized himself.

The Horse chose his earliest years, and endowed them with his own attributes; hence every man is in youth impetuous, headstrong, and obstinate in maintaining his own opinion. The Ox took under his patronage the next term of life, and therefore man in his middle age is fond of work, devoted to labour, and resolute to amass wealth, and to husband his resources. The end of life was reserved to the Dog, wherefore the old man is often snappish, irritable, hard to please, and selfish, tolerant only of his own household, but averse to strangers, and to all who do not administer to his comfort or to his necessities.

THE HORSE AND THE STAG

A HORSE HAD THE WHOLE RANGE OF A MEADOW TO HIMSELF; but a Stag coming and damaging the pasture, the Horse, anxious to have his revenge, asked a Man if he could not assist him in punishing the Stag. "Yes," said the Man, "only let me put a bit in your mouth, and get upon your back, and I will find the weapons." The Horse agreed, and the man mounted accordingly; but instead of getting his revenge, the Horse has been from that time forward the slave of Man.

Revenge is too dearly purchased at the price of liberty.

THE WOLF AND THE GOAT

A WOLF SEEING A GOAT FEEDING ON THE BROW OF A HIGH PRECI-pice where he could not come at her, besought her to come down lower, for fear she should miss her footing at that dizzy height; "And moreover," said he, "the grass is far sweeter and more abundant here below." But the Goat replied; "Excuse me; it is not for my dinner that you invite me, but for your own."

THE FARMER AND HIS SONS

A FARMER BEING ON THE POINT OF DEATH, AND WISHING TO show his sons the way to success in farming, called them to him, and said; "My children, I am now departing from this life, but all that I have to leave you, you will find in the vineyard."

The sons, supposing that he referred to some hidden treasure, as soon as the old man was dead, set to work with their spades and ploughs and every implement that was at hand, and turned up the soil over and over again. They found indeed not treasure; but the vines, strengthened and improved by this thorough tillage, yielded a finer vintage than they had ever yielded before, and more than repaid the young husbandmen for all their trouble. So truly is industry in itself a treasure.

THE HEIFER AND THE OX

A HEIFER THAT RAN WILD IN THE FIELDS, AND HAD NEVER FELT the yoke, upbraided an Ox at plough for submitting to such labour and drudgery. The Ox said nothing, but went on with his work. Not long after, there was a great festival. The Ox got his holiday: but the Heifer was led off to be sacrificed at the altar. "If this be the end of your idleness," said the Ox, "I think that my work is better than your play. I had rather my neck felt the yoke than the axe."

THE LAMB AND THE WOLF

A LAMB PURSUED BY A WOLF TOOK REFUGE IN A TEMPLE. UPON this the Wolf called out to him, and said, that the priest would slay him if he caught him. "Be it so," said the Lamb, "it is better to be sacrificed to God, than to be devoured by you."

THE COUNTRY MAID AND HER MILK-CAN

A COUNTRY MAID WAS WALKING ALONG WITH A CAN OF MILK upon her head, when she fell into the following train of reflections. "The money for which I shall sell this milk will enable me to increase my stock of eggs to three hundred. These eggs, allowing for what may prove addle, and what may be destroyed by vermin, will produce at least two hundred and fifty chickens.

The chickens will be fit to carry to market just at the time when poultry is always dear; so that by the new year I cannot fail of having money enough to purchase a new gown. Green—let me consider—yes, green becomes my complexion best, and green it shall be. In this dress I will go to the fair, where all the young fellows will strive to have me for a partner; but no—I shall refuse every one of them, and with a disdainful toss turn from them."

Transported with this idea, she could not forbear acting with her head the thought that thus passed in her mind; when—down came the can of milk! and all her imaginary happiness vanished in a moment.

THE HARE AND THE TORTOISE

A HARE JEERED AT A TORTOISE FOR THE SLOWNESS OF HIS PACE. But he laughed and said, that he would run against her and beat her any day she would name. "Come on," said the Hare, "you shall soon see what my feet are made of."

So it was agreed that they should start at once. The Tortoise went off jogging along, without a moment's stopping, at his usual steady pace. The Hare, treating the whole matter very lightly, said she would first take a little nap, and that she should soon overtake the Tortoise. Meanwhile the Tortoise plodded on, and the Hare oversleeping herself, arrived at the goal, only to see that the Tortoise had got in before her.

THE HERDSMAN AND THE LOST BULL

A HERDSMAN, WHO HAD LOST A BULL, WENT ROAMING THROUGH the forest in search of it. Being unable to find it, he began to vow to all the Nymphs of the forest and the mountain, to Mercury and to Pan, that he would offer up a lamb to them, if he could only discover the thief. At that moment, gaining a high ridge of ground, he sees a Lion standing over the carcase of his beautiful Bull. And now the unhappy man vows the Bull into the bargain, if he may only escape from the thief's clutches.

THE FLY AND THE DRAUGHT-MULE

A FLY SAT ON THE AXLE-TREE OF A CHARIOT, AND ADDRESSING the Draught-mule, said; "How slow you are! Why do you not go faster? See if I do not prick your neck with my sting."

The Draught-mule replied; "I do not heed your threats. I only care for him who sits above you, and who quickens my pace with his whip, or holds me back with the reins. Away, therefore, with your insolence, for I know well when to go fast, and when to go slow."

THE THIEF AND HIS MOTHER

A SCHOOLBOY STOLE A BOOK FROM ONE OF HIS SCHOOLFELLOWS, and brought it home to his mother. Instead of chastising him, she rather encouraged him in the deed. In course of time the boy, now grown into a man, began to steal things of greater value, till at length being caught in the very act, he was bound and led to execution.

Perceiving his mother following among the crowd, wailing and beating her breast, he begged the officers to be allowed to speak one word in her ear. When she quickly drew near and applied her ear to her son's mouth, he seized the lobe of it tightly between his teeth and bit it off. Upon this she cried out lustily, and the crowd joined her in upbraiding the unnatural son, as if his former evil ways had not been enough, but that his last act must be a deed of impiety against his mother. But he replied; "It is she who is the cause of my ruin; for if when I stole my schoolfellow's book and brought it to her, she had given me a sound flogging, I should never have so grown in wickedness as to come to this untimely end."

THE WOLF AND THE HORSE

AS A WOLF WAS ROAMING OVER A FARM, HE CAME TO A FIELD OF oats, but not being able to eat them, he left them and went his way. Presently meeting with a Horse, he bade him come with him into the field; "For," says he, "I have found some capital oats; and I have not tasted one, but have kept them all for you, for the very sound of your teeth is music to my ear."

But the Horse replied: "A pretty fellow! if Wolves were able to eat oats, I suspect you would not have preferred your ears to your appetite."

Little thanks are due to him who only gives away what is of no use to himself.

THE DOVE AND THE CROW

A DOVE THAT WAS KEPT SHUT UP IN A CAGE WAS CONGRATULAT-ing herself upon the number of her family. "Cease, good soul," said a Crow, "to boast on that subject; for the more young ones you have, so many more slaves will you have to groan over."

What are blessings in freedom are curses in slavery.

THE ASS AND HIS MASTERS

AN ASS, THAT BELONGED TO A GARDENER, AND HAD LITTLE TO EAT and much to do, besought Jupiter to release him from the Gardener's service, and give him another master. Jupiter, angry at his discontent, made him over to a Potter. He had now heavier burdens to carry than before, and again appealed to Jupiter to relieve him, who accordingly contrived that he should be sold to a Tanner.

The Ass having now fallen into worse hands than ever, and daily observing how his master was employed, exclaimed with a groan; "Alas, wretch that I am! it had been better for me to have remained content with my former masters, for now I see that my present owner not only works me harder while living, but will not even spare my hide when I am dead!"

He that is discontented in one place will seldom be happy in another.

THE FIR-TREE AND THE BRAMBLE

A FIR-TREE WAS ONE DAY BOASTING ITSELF TO A BRAMBLE. "YOU are of no use at all; but how could barns and houses be built without me?"

"Good sir," said the Bramble, "when the woodmen come here with their axes and saws, what would you give to be a Bramble and not a Fir?"

A humble lot in security is better than the dangers that encompass the high and haughty.

THE GNAT AND THE BULL

A GNAT THAT HAD BEEN BUZZING ABOUT THE HEAD OF A BULL, at length settling himself down upon his horn, begged his pardon for incommoding him: "but if," says he, "my weight at all inconveniences you, pray say so and I will be off in a moment." "Oh, never trouble your head about that," says the Bull, "for 'tis all one to me whether you go or stay; and, to say the truth, I did not know you were there."

The smaller the Mind the greater the Conceit.

THE MISCHIEVOUS DOG

THERE WAS A DOG SO WILD AND MISCHIEVOUS, THAT HIS MASTER was obliged to fasten a heavy clog about his neck, to prevent him biting and worrying his neighbours. The Dog, priding himself upon his badge, paraded in the market-place, shaking his clog to attract attention. But a sly friend whispered to him; "The less noise you make, the better; your mark of distinction is no reward of merit, but a badge of disgrace!"

Men often mistake notoriety for fame, and would rather be remarked for their vices or follies than not be noticed at all.

THE TREES AND THE AXE

A WOODMAN CAME INTO A FOREST TO ASK THE TREES TO GIVE him a handle for his Axe. It seemed so modest a request that the principal Trees at once agreed to it, and it was settled among them that the plain homely Ash should furnish what was wanted.

No sooner had the Woodman fitted the staff to his purpose, than he began laying about him on all sides, felling the noblest Trees in the wood. The Oak now seeing the whole matter too late, whispered to the Cedar, "The first concession has lost all; if we had not sacrificed our humble neighbour, we might have yet stood for ages ourselves."

THE FARMER AND THE DOGS

A FARMER, DURING A SEVERE WINTER, BEING SHUT UP BY THE snow in his farm-house, and sharply pressed for food, which he was unable to get about to procure, began consuming his own sheep. As the hard weather continued, he next ate up his goats. And at last—for there was no break in the weather—he betook himself to the plough-oxen. Upon this, the Dogs said to one another, "Let us be off; for since the master, as we see, has had no pity on the working oxen, how is it likely he will spare us?"

When our neighbour's house is on fire, it is time to look to our own.

THE TORTOISE AND THE EAGLE

A TORTOISE, DISSATISFIED WITH HIS LOWLY LIFE, WHEN HE BE-
held so many of the birds, his neighbours, disporting themselves
in the clouds, and thinking that, if he could but once get up into
the air, he could soar with the best of them, called one day upon
an Eagle and offered him all the treasures of Ocean if he could
only teach him to fly.

The Eagle would have declined the task, assuring him that the
thing was not only absurd but impossible, but being further
pressed by the entreaties and promises of the Tortoise, he at
length consented to do for him the best he could. So taking
him up to a great height in the air and loosing his hold upon
him; "Now, then!" cried the Eagle. But the Tortoise, before
he could answer him a word, fell plump upon a rock and was
dashed to pieces.

THE HUSBANDMAN AND THE STORK

A HUSBANDMAN FIXED A NET IN HIS FIELD TO CATCH THE CRANES that came to feed on his new-sown corn. When he went to examine the net, and see what Cranes he had taken, a Stork was found among the number. "Spare me," cried the Stork, "and let me go. See I am no Crane. See I have eaten none of your corn. I am a poor innocent Stork, as you may see—the most pious and dutiful of birds. I honour and succour my father and mother. I—"

But the Husbandman cut him short. "All this may be true enough, I dare say, but this I know, that I have caught you with those who were destroying my crops, and you must suffer with the company in which you are taken."

THE OLIVE-TREE AND THE FIG-TREE

THE OLIVE-TREE RIDICULED THE FIG-TREE BECAUSE, WHILE SHE was green all the year round, the Fig-tree changed its leaves with the seasons. A shower of snow fell upon them, and, finding the Olive full of foliage, it settled upon its branches, and, breaking them down with its weight, at once despoiled it of its beauty and killed the tree; but finding the Fig-tree without leaves, it fell through the branches to the ground and did not injure it at all.

THE DOG, THE COCK, AND THE FOX

A DOG AND A COCK HAVING STRUCK UP AN ACQUAINTANCE, WENT out on their travels together. Nightfall found them in a forest; so the Cock, flying up on a tree, perched among the branches, while the Dog dozed below at the foot. As the night passed away and the day dawned, the Cock, according to his custom, set up a shrill crowing.

A Fox hearing him, and thinking to make a meal of him, came and stood under the tree, and thus addressed him; "Thou art a good little bird, and most useful to thy fellow-creatures. Come down, then, that we may sing and rejoice together." The

Cock replied; "Go, my good friend, to the foot of the tree, and call the sacristan to toll the bell." But as the Fox went to call him, the Dog jumped out in a moment, and seized the Fox and made an end of him.

They who lay traps for others are often caught by their own bait.

THE FISHERMAN

A FISHERMAN WENT TO A RIVER TO FISH; AND WHEN HE HAD laid his nets across the stream, he tied a stone to a long cord, and beat the water on either side of the net, to drive the fish into the meshes. One of the neighbours that lived thereabout seeing him thus employed, went up to him and blamed him exceedingly for disturbing the water, and making it so muddy as to be unfit to drink. "I am sorry," said the Fisherman, "that this does not please you, but it is by thus troubling the waters that I gain my living."

THE SICK KITE

A KITE, WHO HAD BEEN LONG VERY ILL, SAID TO HIS MOTHER; "Don't cry, mother; but go and pray to the gods that I may recover from this dreadful disease and pain." "Alas! child," said the mother, "which of the gods can I entreat for one who has robbed all their altars?"

Death-bed repentance is poor amends for the errors of a lifetime.

THE EAGLE AND THE JACKDAW

AN EAGLE MADE A SWOOP FROM A HIGH ROCK, AND CARRIED OFF a lamb. A Jackdaw, who saw the exploit, thinking that he could do the like, bore down with all the force he could muster upon a ram, intending to bear him off as a prize. But his claws becoming entangled in the wool, he made such a fluttering in his efforts to escape, that the shepherd, seeing through the whole matter, came up and caught him, and having clipped his wings, carried him home to his children at nightfall.

"What bird is this, father, that you have brought us?" exclaimed the children. "Why," said he, "if you ask himself, he will tell you that he is an Eagle; but if you will take my word for it, I know him to be but a Jackdaw."

THE BALD KNIGHT

A CERTAIN KNIGHT GROWING OLD, HIS HAIR FELL OFF, AND HE became bald; to hide which imperfection, he wore a wig. But as he was riding out hunting, with some others, a sudden gust of wind blew off the wig, and exposed his bald pate. The company could not forbear laughing at the accident; and he himself laughed as loud as anybody, saying; "How was it to be expected that I should keep strange hair upon my head, when my own would not stay there?"

THE BELLY AND ITS MEMBERS

IN FORMER DAYS, WHEN ALL A MAN'S LIMBS DID NOT WORK together as amicably as they do now, but each had a will and way of its own, the Members generally began to find fault with the Belly for spending an idle luxurious life, while they were wholly occupied in labouring for its support, and ministering to its wants and pleasures; so they entered into a conspiracy to cut off its supplies for the future. The Hands were no longer to carry food to the Mouth, nor the Mouth to receive the food, nor the Teeth to chew it.

They had not long persisted in this course of starving the Belly into subjection, ere they all began, one by one, to fail and flag, and the whole body to pine away. Then the Members were convinced that the Belly also, cumbersome and useless as it seemed, had an important function of its own; that they could no more do without it than it could do without them; and that if they would have the constitution of the body in a healthy state, they must work together, each in his proper sphere, for the common good of all.

THE DOG AND HIS MASTER

A CERTAIN MAN WAS SETTING OUT ON A JOURNEY, WHEN, SEEING his Dog standing at the door, he cried out to him, "What are you gaping about? Get ready to come with me." The Dog, wagging his tail, said, "I am all right, Master; it is you who have to pack up."

JUPITER, NEPTUNE, MINERVA, AND MOMUS

JUPITER, NEPTUNE, AND MINERVA, AS THE STORY GOES, ONCE contended which of them should make the most perfect thing. Jupiter made a Man; Pallas made a House; and Neptune made a Bull; and Momus—for he had not yet been turned out of Olympus—was chosen judge to decide which production had the greatest merit.

He began by finding fault with the Bull, because his horns were not below his eyes, so that he might see when he butted with them. Next he found fault with the Man, because there was no window in his breast that all might see his inward thoughts and feelings. And lastly he found fault with the House, because it had no wheels to enable its inhabitants to remove from bad neighbours. But Jupiter forthwith drove the critic out of heaven, telling him that a fault-finder could never be pleased, and that it was time to criticise the works of others when he had done some good thing himself.

THE SEA-SIDE TRAVELLERS

AS SOME TRAVELLERS WERE MAKING THEIR WAY ALONG THE SEA-shore, they came to a high cliff, and looking out upon the sea saw a Faggot floating at a distance, which they thought at first must be a large Ship; so they waited, expecting to see it come into harbour. As the Faggot drifted nearer to the shore, they thought it no longer to be a Ship, but a Boat. But when it was at length thrown on the beach, they saw that it was nothing but a Faggot after all.

Dangers seem greatest at a distance; and coming events are magnified according to the interest or inclination of the beholder.

MERCURY AND THE WOODMAN

A WOODMAN WAS FELLING A TREE ON THE BANK OF A RIVER, AND by chance let slip his axe into the water, when it immediately sunk to the bottom. Being thereupon in great distress, he sat down by the side of the stream and lamented his loss bitterly. But Mercury, whose river it was, taking compassion on him, appeared at the instant before him; and hearing from him the cause of his sorrow, dived to the bottom of the river, and bringing up a golden axe, asked the Woodman if that were his. Upon the man's denying it, Mercury dived a second time, and brought up one of silver. Again the man denied that it was his. So diving a third time, he produced the identical axe which the man had lost. "That is mine!" said the Woodman, delighted to have recovered his own;

and so pleased was Mercury with the fellow's truth and honesty, that he at once made him a present of the other two.

The man goes to his companions, and giving them an account of what had happened to him, one of them determined to try whether he might not have the like good fortune. So repairing to the same place, as if for the purpose of cutting wood, he let slip his axe on purpose into the river, and then sat down on the bank, and made a great show of weeping. Mercury appeared as before, and hearing from him that his tears were caused by the loss of his axe, dived once more into the stream; and bringing up a golden axe, asked him if that was the axe he had lost. "Aye, surely," said the man, eagerly; and he was about to grasp the treasure, when Mercury, to punish his impudence and lying, not only refused to give him that, but would not so much as restore him his own axe again.

THE ASS'S SHADOW

A YOUTH, ONE HOT SUMMER'S DAY, HIRED AN ASS TO CARRY HIM from Athens to Megara. At mid-day the heat of the sun was so scorching, that he dismounted, and would have sat down to repose himself under the shadow of the Ass. But the driver of the Ass disputed the place with him, declaring that he had an equal right to it with the other.

"What!" said the Youth, "did I not hire the Ass for the whole journey?" "Yes," said the other, "you hired the Ass, but not the Ass's Shadow." While they were thus wrangling and fighting for the place, the Ass took to his heels and ran away.

THE DANCING MONKEYS

A PRINCE HAD SOME MONKEYS TRAINED TO DANCE. BEING naturally great mimics of men's actions, they showed themselves most apt pupils; and, when arrayed in their rich clothes and masks, they danced as well as any of the courtiers. The spectacle was often repeated with great applause, till on one occasion a courtier, bent on mischief, took from his pocket a handful of nuts, and threw them upon the stage.

The Monkeys at the sight of the nuts forgot their dancing, and became—as indeed they were—Monkeys instead of actors, and pulling off their masks, and tearing their robes, they fought with one another for the nuts. The dancing spectacle thus came to an end, amidst the laughter and ridicule of the audience.

THE FROG AND THE OX

AN OX, GRAZING IN A SWAMPY MEADOW, CHANCED TO SET HIS foot among a parcel of young Frogs, and crushed nearly the whole brood to death. One that escaped ran off to his mother with the dreadful news; "And, O mother!" said he, "it was a beast—such a big four-footed beast!—that did it."

"Big?" quoth the old Frog, "how big? was it as big"—and she puffed herself out to a great degree—"as big as that?" "Oh!" said the little one, "a great deal bigger than that." "Well, was it so big?" and she swelled herself out yet more.

"Indeed, mother, but it was; and if you were to burst yourself, you would never reach half its size." Provoked at such a disparagement of her powers, the old Frog made one more trial, and burst herself indeed.

So men are ruined by attempting a greatness to which they have no claim.

THE DOLPHINS AND THE SPRAT

THE DOLPHINS AND THE WHALES WERE AT WAR WITH ONE ANother, and while the battle was at its height, the Sprat stepped in and endeavoured to separate them. But one of the Dolphins cried out, "Let us alone, friend! We had rather perish in the contest, than be reconciled by you."

THE HARES AND THE FROGS

ONCE UPON A TIME, THE HARES, DRIVEN DESPERATE BY THE many enemies that compassed them about on every side, came to the sad resolution that there was nothing left for them but to make away with themselves, one and all. Off they scudded to a lake hard by, determined to drown themselves as the most miserable of creatures.

A shoal of Frogs seated upon the bank, frightened at the approach of the Hares, leaped in the greatest alarm and confusion into the water. "Nay, then, my friends," said a Hare that was foremost, "our case is not so desperate yet; for here are other poor creatures more faint-hearted than ourselves."

THE HOUSE-DOG AND THE WOLF

A LEAN HUNGRY WOLF CHANCED ONE MOONSHINY NIGHT TO fall in with a plump well-fed House-Dog. After the first compliments were passed between them, "How is it, my friend," said the Wolf, "that you look so sleek? How well your food agrees with you! and here am I striving for my living night and day, and can hardly save myself from starving."

"Well," says the Dog, "if you would fare like me, you have only to do as I do." "Indeed!" says he, "and what is that?" "Why," replies the Dog, "just to guard the master's house and keep off the thieves at night." "With all my heart; for at present I have but a sorry time of it. This woodland life, with its frosts and rains, is sharp work for me. To have a warm roof over my head and a bellyful of victuals always at hand will, methinks, be no bad exchange." "True," says the Dog; "therefore you have nothing to do but to follow me."

Now as they were jogging on together, the Wolf spied a mark in the Dog's neck, and having a strange curiosity, could not forbear asking what it meant. "Pooh! nothing at all," says the Dog. "Nay, but pray—" says the Wolf. "Oh! a mere trifle, perhaps the collar to which my chain is fastened—"

"Chain!" cries the Wolf in surprise; "you don't mean that you cannot rove when and where you please?" "Why, not exactly perhaps; you see I am looked upon as rather fierce, so they sometimes tie me up in the day-time, but I assure you I have perfect liberty at night, and the master feeds me off his own plate, and the servants give me their tid-bits, and I am such a favourite, and—but what is the matter? where are you going?"

"Oh, good-night to you," says the Wolf; "you are welcome to your dainties; but for me, a dry crust with liberty against a king's luxury with a chain."

THE WIDOW AND THE HEN

A WIDOW WOMAN KEPT A HEN THAT LAID AN EGG EVERY MORNing. Thought the woman to herself, "If I double my Hen's allowance of barley, she will lay twice a day." So she tried her plan, and the Hen became so fat and sleek, that she left off laying at all.

THE NURSE AND THE WOLF

A WOLF, ROVING ABOUT IN SEARCH OF FOOD, PASSED BY A DOOR where a child was crying and its Nurse chiding it. As he stood listening he heard the Nurse say, "Now leave off crying this instant, or I'll throw you out to the Wolf." So thinking that the old woman would be as good as her word, he waited quietly about the house, in expectation of a capital supper.

But as it grew dark and the child became quiet, he again heard the Nurse, who was now fondling the child, say, "There's a good dear then; if the naughty Wolf comes for my child, we'll beat him to death, we will." The Wolf, disappointed and mortified, thought it was now high time to be going home, and, hungry as a wolf indeed, muttered as he went along: "This comes of heeding people who say one thing and mean another!"

THE MAN AND THE LION

ONCE UPON A TIME A MAN AND A LION WERE JOURNEYING together, and came at length to high words, which was the braver and stronger creature of the two. As the dispute waxed warmer they happened to pass by, on the road-side, a statue of a man strangling a lion. "See there," said the man; "what more undeniable proof can you have of our superiority than that?" "That," said the Lion, "is your version of the story; let us be the sculptors, and for one lion under the feet of a man, you shall have twenty men under the paw of a lion."

THE ONE-EYED DOE

A DOE THAT HAD BUT ONE EYE USED TO GRAZE NEAR THE SEA, and that she might be the more secure from attack, kept her eye towards the land against the approach of the hunters, and her blind side towards the sea, whence she feared no danger. But some sailors rowing by in a boat and seeing her, aimed at her from the water and shot her. When at her last gasp, she sighed to herself: "Ill-fated creature that I am! I was safe on the land-side whence I expected to be attacked, but find an enemy in the sea to which I most looked for protection."

Our troubles often come from the quarter whence we least expect them.

THE SICK STAG

A STAG THAT HAD FALLEN SICK, LAY DOWN ON THE RICH HERB-age of a lawn, close to a wood-side, that she might obtain an easy pasturage. But so many of the beasts came to see her—for she was a good sort of neighbour—that, one taking a little, and another a little, they ate up all the grass in the place. So, though recovering from the disease, she pined for want, and in the end lost both her substance and her life.

THE LIONESS

THERE WAS A GREAT STIR MADE AMONG ALL THE BEASTS, WHICH could boast of the largest family. So they came to the Lioness. "And how many," said they, "do you have at a birth?" "One," said she, grimly; "but that one is a Lion."

THE GAME-COCKS AND THE PARTRIDGE

A MAN HAD TWO GAME-COCKS IN HIS POULTRY-YARD. ONE DAY by chance he saw a tame Partridge for sale. He purchased it, and brought it home that it might be reared with his Game-cocks. On its being put into the poultry-yard they struck at it, and followed it about, so that the Partridge was grievously troubled in mind, and supposed that he was thus evilly treated because he was a stranger. Not long afterwards, he saw the Cocks fighting together, and not separating before one had well beaten the other. He then said to himself; "I shall no longer distress myself at being struck at by these Game-cocks, when I see that they cannot even refrain from quarreling with each other."

THE BLACK-SLAVE

A CERTAIN MAN BOUGHT A BLACK-SLAVE, AND THINKING THAT the colour of his skin arose from the neglect of his former master, he no sooner brought him home than he procured all manner of scouring apparatus, scrubbing-brushes, soaps, and sand-paper, and set to work with his servants to wash him white again. They drenched and rubbed him for many an hour, but all in vain; his skin remained as black as ever; while the poor wretch all but died from the cold he caught under the operation.

THE LION AND THE DOLPHIN

A LION WAS ROAMING ON THE SEA-SHORE, WHEN, SEEING A Dolphin basking on the surface of the water, he invited him to form an alliance with him; "For," said he, "as I am the king of the beasts, and you are the king of the fishes, we ought to be the greatest friends and allies possible." The Dolphin gladly assented; and the Lion, not long after, having a fight with a wild bull, called upon the Dolphin for his promised support. But when he, though ready to assist him, found himself unable to come out of the sea for the purpose, the Lion accused him of having betrayed him. "Do not blame me," said the Dolphin in reply, "but blame my nature, which however powerful at sea, is altogether helpless on land."

THE CAT AND THE MICE

A CAT, GROWN FEEBLE WITH AGE, AND NO LONGER ABLE TO hunt the Mice as she was wont to do, bethought herself how she might entice them within reach of her paw. Thinking that she might pass herself off for a bag, or for a dead cat at least, she suspended herself by the hind legs from a peg, in the hope that the Mice would no longer be afraid to come near her.

An old Mouse, who was wise enough to keep his distance, whispered to a friend; "Many a bag have I seen in my day, but never one with a cat's head." "Hang there, good Madam," said the other, "as long as you please, but I would not trust myself within reach of you though you were stuffed with straw."

THE ASS IN THE LION'S SKIN

AN ASS HAVING PUT ON A LION'S SKIN, ROAMED ABOUT, FRIGHTening all the silly animals he met with, and, seeing a Fox, he tried to alarm him also. But Reynard, having heard his voice, said, "Well, to be sure! and I should have been frightened too, if I had not heard you bray."

They who assume a character that does not belong to them generally betray themselves.

THE WOLF AND THE SHEPHERD

A WOLF HAD LONG HUNG ABOUT A FLOCK OF SHEEP, AND HAD done them no harm. The Shepherd, however, had his suspicions, and for a while was always on the look-out against him as an avowed enemy. But when the Wolf continued for a long time following in the train of his flock without the least attempt to annoy them, he began to look upon him more as a friend than a foe; and having one day occasion to go into the city, he intrusted the sheep to his care.

The Wolf no sooner saw his opportunity than he forthwith fell upon the sheep and worried them; and the Shepherd, on his return, seeing his flock destroyed, exclaimed, "Fool that I am! yet I deserved no less for trusting my Sheep with a Wolf!"

There is more danger from a pretended friend than from an open enemy.

THE MOUSE AND THE WEASEL

A LITTLE STARVELING MOUSE HAD MADE HIS WAY WITH SOME difficulty into a basket of corn, where, finding the entertainment so good, he stuffed and crammed himself to such an extent, that when he would have got out again, he found the hole was too small to allow his puffed-up body to pass. As he sat at the hole groaning over his fate, a Weasel, who was brought to the spot by his cries, thus addressed him; "Stop there, my friend, and fast till you are thin; for you will never come out till you reduce yourself to the same condition as when you entered."

THE HARE AND THE HOUND

A HOUND HAVING PUT UP A HARE FROM A BUSH, CHASED HER for some distance, but the Hare had the best of it, and got off. A Goatherd who was coming by jeered at the Hound, saying that Puss was the better runner of the two. "You forget," replied the Hound, "that it is one thing to be running for your dinner, and another for your life."

THE LION AND ASS HUNTING

A LION AND AN ASS MADE AN AGREEMENT TO GO OUT HUNTING together. By and by they came to a cave, where many wild goats abode. The Lion took up his station at the mouth of the cave, and the Ass, going within, kicked and brayed and made a mighty fuss to frighten them out. When the Lion had caught very many of them, the Ass came out and asked him if he had not made a noble fight, and routed the goats properly.

"Yes, indeed," said the Lion; "and I assure you, you would have frightened me too, if I had not known you to be an Ass."

When braggarts are admitted into the company of their betters, it is only to be made use of and be laughed at.

THE RIVERS AND THE SEA

ONCE UPON A TIME THE RIVERS COMBINED AGAINST THE SEA, and, going in a body, accused her, saying; "Why is it that when we Rivers pour our waters into you so fresh and sweet, you straightway render them salt and unpalatable?" The Sea, observing the temper in which they came, merely answered; "If you do not wish to become salt, please to keep away from me altogether."

Those who are most benefited are often the first to complain.

THE MICE IN COUNCIL

ONCE UPON A TIME THE MICE BEING SADLY DISTRESSED BY THE persecution of the Cat, resolved to call a meeting, to decide upon the best means of getting rid of this continual annoyance. Many plans were discussed and rejected; at last a young Mouse got up and proposed that a Bell should be hung round the Cat's neck, that they might for the future always have notice of her coming, and so be able to escape.

This proposition was hailed with the greatest applause, and

was agreed to at once unanimously. Upon which an old Mouse, who had sat silent all the while, got up and said that he considered the contriv..nce most ingenious, and that it would, no doubt, be quite successful; but he had only one short question to put, namely, which of them it was who would Bell the Cat?

It is one thing to propose, another to execute.

THE WASP AND THE SNAKE

A WASP SEATED HIMSELF UPON THE HEAD OF A SNAKE, AND, striking him again and again with his stings, wounded him to death. The Snake, being in great torment, and not knowing how to rid himself of his enemy, or to scare him away, saw a wagon heavily laden with wood, and went and purposely placed his head under the wheels, and said; "My enemy and I shall thus perish together."

THE TRAVELLERS AND THE HATCHET

TWO MEN WERE TRAVELLING ALONG THE SAME ROAD, WHEN ONE of them picking up a hatchet cries, "See what I have found!" "Do not say I," says the other, "but WE have found."

After a while, up came the men who had lost the hatchet, and charged the man who had it with the theft. "Alas," says he to his companion, "we are undone!" "Do not say WE," replies the other, "but I am undone; for he that will not allow his friend to share the prize, must not expect him to share the danger."

THE IMAGE OF MERCURY AND THE CARPENTER

A VERY POOR MAN, A CARPENTER BY TRADE, HAD A WOODEN image of Mercury, before which he made offerings day by day. He entreated the idol to make him rich: but in spite of his entreaties he became poorer and poorer. At last, being very wroth, he took his image down from its pedestal, and dashed it against the wall. When its head was knocked off, out came a stream of gold, which the Carpenter picked up, and said; "Well, I think you are altogether contradictory and unreasonable; for when I paid you honour, I reaped no benefits, but now that I maltreat you, I am loaded with an abundance of riches."

THE OLD WOMAN AND HER MAIDS

A THRIFTY OLD WIDOW KEPT TWO SERVANT-MAIDS, WHOM SHE used to call up to their work at cock-crow. The Maids disliked exceedingly this early rising, and determined between themselves to wring off the Cock's neck, as he was the cause of all their trouble by waking their mistress so early. They had no sooner done this, than the old lady, missing her usual alarum, and afraid of oversleeping herself, continually mistook the time of day, and roused them up at midnight.

Too much cunning overreaches itself.

THE OLD WOMAN AND THE WINE-JAR

AN OLD WOMAN SAW AN EMPTY WINE-JAR LYING ON THE ground. Though not a drop of the wine with which it had been filled, remained, it still yielded a grateful fragrance to the passers-by. The Old Woman, applying her nose as close as she could and snuffing with all her might and main, exclaimed, "Sweet creature! how charming must your contents once have been, when the very dregs are so delicious!"

THE FOX AND THE GOAT

A FOX HAD FALLEN INTO A WELL, AND HAD BEEN CASTING about for a long time how he should get out again; when at length a Goat came to the place, and wanting to drink, asked the fox whether the water was good, and if there was plenty of it. The Fox, avoiding the real danger of his case, replied, "Come down, my friend; the water is so good that I cannot drink enough of it, and so abundant that it cannot be exhausted."

Upon this the Goat without any more ado leaped in; when the Fox, taking advantage of his friend's horns, nimbly leaped out; and coolly remarked to the poor deluded Goat; "If you had half as much brains as you have beard, you would have looked before you leaped."

THE ARAB AND THE CAMEL

AN ARAB HAVING LOADED HIS CAMEL, ASKED HIM WHETHER HE preferred to go up hill or down hill. "Pray, Master," said the Camel dryly, "is the straight way across the plain shut up?"

THE LION AND THE GOAT

ON A SUMMER'S DAY, WHEN EVERYTHING WAS SUFFERING FROM extreme heat, a Lion and a Goat came at the same time to quench their thirst at a small fountain. They at once fell to quarrelling which should first drink of the water, till at length it seemed that each was determined to resist the other even to death.

But, ceasing from the strife for a moment, to recover breath, they saw a flock of vultures hovering over them, only waiting to pounce upon whichever of them should fall. Whereupon they instantly made up their quarrel, agreeing that it was far better for them both to become friends, than to furnish food for the crows and vultures.

THE FARMER AND THE FOX

A FARMER, HAVING A LONG GRIEVANCE AGAINST A FOX FOR ROB-bing his poultry yard, caught him at last, and, being determined to take full revenge, tied some tow well soaked in oil to his tail, and set it on fire. The Fox by a strange fatality rushed through the fields of the Farmer. It was the time of the wheat harvest; and the flames destroyed all. The Farmer reaped nothing that year.

THE BLIND MAN AND THE WHELP

A BLIND MAN WAS WONT, ON ANY ANIMAL BEING PUT INTO HIS hands, to say what it was. Once they brought to him a Wolf's whelp. He felt it all over, and being in doubt, said, "I know not whether thy father was a Dog or a Wolf; but this I know, that I would not trust thee among a flock of sheep."

Evil dispositions are early shown.

THE MARRIAGE OF THE SUN

ONCE UPON A TIME, IN A VERY WARM SUMMER, IT WAS CUR-rently reported that the Sun was going to be married. All the birds and beasts were delighted at the thought; and the Frogs, above all others, were determined to have a good holiday. But an old Toad put a stop to their festivities by observing that it was an occasion for sorrow rather than for joy. "For if," said he, "the Sun of himself now parches up the marshes so that we can hardly bear it, what will become of us if he should have half a dozen little Suns in addition?"

THE TWO FROGS

TWO FROGS DWELT IN THE SAME POOL. THE POOL BEING DRIED up under the summer's heat, they left it, and set out together to seek another home. As they went along they chanced to pass a deep well, amply supplied with water, on seeing which one of the Frogs said to the other; "Let us descend and make our abode in this well, it will furnish us with shelter and food." The other replied with greater caution; "But suppose the water should fail us, how can we get out again from so great a depth?" Do nothing without a regard to the consequences.

THE DOGS AND THE HIDES

SOME HUNGRY DOGS, SEEING SOME RAW HIDES WHICH A SKIN-ner had left in the bottom of a stream, and not being able to reach them, agreed among themselves to drink up the river to get at the prize. So they set to work, but they all burst them-selves with drinking before ever they came near the Hides.

They who aim at an object by unreasonable means, are apt to ruin themselves in the attempt.

THE HEN AND THE CAT

A CAT HEARING THAT A HEN WAS LAID UP SICK IN HER NEST, paid her a visit of condolence; and creeping up to her said; "How are you, my dear friend? what can I do for you? what are you in want of?   Only tell me, if there is anything in the world that I can bring you; but keep up your spirits, and don't be alarmed." "Thank you," said the Hen; "do you be good enough to leave me, and I have no fear but I shall soon be well."

Unbidden guests are often welcomest when they are gone.

THE TRUMPETER TAKEN PRISONER

A TRUMPETER BEING TAKEN PRISONER IN A BATTLE, BEGGED hard for quarter.   "Spare me, good sirs, I beseech you," said he, "and put me not to death without cause, for I have killed no one myself, nor have I any arms but this trumpet only." "For that very reason," said they who had seized him, "shall you the sooner die, for without the spirit to fight, yourself, you stir up others to warfare and bloodshed."

He who incites strife is worse than he who takes part in it.

THE POMEGRANATE, THE APPLE, AND THE BRAMBLE

THE POMEGRANATE AND THE APPLE HAD A CONTEST ON THE score of beauty.   When words ran high, and the strife waxed dangerous, a Bramble, thrusting his head from a neighbouring bush, cried out, "We have disputed long enough; let there be no more rivalry betwixt us."

The most insignificant are generally the most presuming.

THE TWO DOGS

A MAN HAD TWO DOGS; A HOUND, TRAINED TO ASSIST HIM IN his sports, and a House-dog, taught to watch the house.   When he returned home after a good day's sport, he always gave the House-dog a good share of his spoil.

The Hound, feeling much aggrieved at this, reproached his companion, saying; "It is very hard to have all this labour, while you, who do not assist in the chase, live on the fruits of my exertions." The House-dog replied; "Do not blame me, my friend, but find fault with the master, who has not taught me to labour, but to depend for subsistence on the labour of others."

Children are not to be blamed for the faults of their parents.

THE ASS AND THE GRASSHOPPER

AN ASS HEARING SOME GRASSHOPPERS CHIRPING, WAS DELIGHTED with the music, and determining, if he could, to rival them, asked them what it was that they fed upon to make them sing so sweetly? When they told him that they supped upon nothing but dew, the Ass betook himself to the same diet, and soon died of hunger.

One man's meat is another man's poison.

THE LION AND THE MOUSE

A LION WAS SLEEPING IN HIS LAIR, WHEN A MOUSE, NOT KNOWing where he was going, ran over the mighty beast's nose and awakened him. The Lion clapped his paw upon the frightened little creature, and was about to make an end of him in a moment, when the Mouse, in pitiable tone, besought him to spare one who had so unconsciously offended, and not stain his honourable paws with so insignificant a prey. The Lion, smiling at his little prisoner's fright, generously let him go.

Now it happened no long time after, that the Lion, while

ranging the woods for his prey, fell into the toils of the hunters; and finding himself entangled without hope of escape, set up a roar that filled the whole forest with its echo. The mouse, recognising the voice of his former preserver, ran to the spot, and without more ado set to work to nibble the knot in the cord that bound the Lion, and in a short time set the noble beast at liberty; thus convincing him that kindness is seldom thrown away, and that there is no creature so much below another but that he may have it in his power to return a good office.

THE BRAZIER AND HIS DOG

THERE WAS A CERTAIN BRAZIER WHO HAD A LITTLE DOG. WHILE he hammered away at his metal, the Dog slept; but whenever he sat down to his dinner the Dog woke up. "Sluggard cur!" said the Brazier, throwing him a bone, "you sleep through the noise of the anvil, but wake up at the first clatter of my teeth."

Men are awake enough to their own interests, who turn a deaf ear to their friends' distress.

THE BOY BATHING

A BOY WAS BATHING IN A RIVER, AND, GETTING OUT OF HIS DEPTH, was on the point of sinking, when he saw a wayfarer coming by, to whom he called out for help with all his might and main. The Man began to read the Boy a lecture for his foolhardiness, but the urchin cried out; "O, save me now, sir! and read me the lecture afterwards."

THE BOWMAN AND THE LION

A MAN WHO WAS VERY SKILFUL WITH HIS BOW, WENT UP INTO the mountains to hunt. At his approach there was instantly a great consternation and rout among all the wild beasts, the Lion alone showing any determination to fight. "Stop," said the bowman to him, "and await my messenger, who has somewhat to say to you." With that he sent an arrow after the Lion, and wounded him in the side. The Lion, smarting with anguish, fled into the depth of the thickets, but a Fox seeing him run, bade him take courage, and face his enemy. "No," said the Lion, "you will not persuade me to that; for if the messenger he sends is so sharp, what must be the power of him who sends it?"

THE THREE TRADESMEN

THERE WAS A CITY IN EXPECTATION OF BEING BESIEGED, AND A council was called accordingly to discuss the best means of fortifying it. A Bricklayer gave his opinion that no material was so good as brick for the purpose. A Carpenter begged leave to suggest that timber would be far preferable. Upon which a Currier started up, and said, "Sirs, when you have said all that can be said, there is nothing in the world like leather."

THE BULL AND THE GOAT

A BULL BEING PURSUED BY A LION, FLED INTO A CAVE WHERE a wild Goat had taken up his abode. The Goat upon this began molesting him and butting at him with his horns. "Don't suppose," said the Bull, "if I suffer this now, that it is you I am afraid of. Let the Lion be once out of sight, and I will soon show you the difference between a Bull and a Goat."

THE OLD LION

A LION WORN OUT WITH YEARS LAY STRETCHED UPON THE ground, utterly helpless, and drawing his last breath. A Boar came up, and to satisfy an ancient grudge, drove at him with his tusks. Next a Bull, determined to be revenged on an old enemy, gored him with his horns. Upon this an Ass, seeing that the old Lion could thus be treated with impunity, thought that he would show his spite also, and came and threw his heels in the Lion's face. Whereupon the dying beast exclaimed; "The insults of the powerful were bad enough but those I could have managed to bear; but to be spurned by so base a creature as thou—the disgrace of nature, is to die a double death."

THE FAWN AND HER MOTHER

A FAWN ONE DAY SAID TO HER MOTHER; "MOTHER, YOU ARE bigger than a dog, and swifter and better winded, and you have horns to defend yourself; how is it that you are so afraid of the hounds?" She smiled and said; "All this, my child, I know full well; but no sooner do I hear a dog bark, than, somehow or other, my heels take me off as fast as they can carry me."

THE HART AND THE VINE

A HART PURSUED BY HUNTERS CONCEALED HIMSELF AMONG THE branches of a Vine. The hunters passed by without discovering him, and when he thought that all was safe, he began browsing upon the leaves that had concealed him. But one of the hunters, attracted by the rustling, turned round, and guessing that their prey was there, shot into the bush and killed him. As he was dying, he groaned out these words; "I suffer justly for my ingratitude, who could not forbear injuring the Vine that had protected me in time of danger."

THE GOAT AND THE GOATHERD

A GOAT HAD STRAYED FROM THE HERD, AND THE GOATHERD was trying all he could to bring him back to his companions. When by calling and whistling he could make no impression on him, at last, taking up a stone, he struck the Goat on the horn and broke it. Alarmed at what he had done, he besought the Goat not to tell his master. But he replied; "O most foolish of Goatherds! my horn will tell the story, though I should not utter a word."

Facts speak plainer than words.

THE VIPER AND THE FILE

A VIPER ENTERING INTO A SMITH'S SHOP BEGAN LOOKING ABOUT for something to eat. At length, seeing a File, he went up to it and commenced biting at it; but the File bade him leave him alone, saying, "You are likely to get little from me, whose business it is to bite others."

THE SHEPHERD AND THE SEA

A SHEPHERD MOVED HIS FLOCK TO FEED NEAR THE SHORE, AND beholding the Sea lying in a smooth and breathless calm, he was seized with a strong desire to sail over it. So he sold all his sheep and bought a cargo of Dates, and loaded a vessel, and set sail. He had not gone far when a storm arose; his ship was wrecked, and his Dates and everything lost, and he himself with difficulty reached land.

Not long after, when the Sea was again calm, and one of his friends came up to him and was admiring its repose, he said, "Have a care, my good fellow, of that smooth surface; it is only looking out for your Dates."

THE FIGHTING-COCKS AND THE EAGLE

TWO YOUNG COCKS WERE FIGHTING AS FIERCELY AS IF THEY HAD been men. At last the one that was beaten crept into a corner of the hen-house, covered with wounds. But the conqueror, straightway flying up to the top of the house, began clapping his wings and crowing, to announce his victory. At this moment an Eagle, sailing by, seized him in his talons and bore him away; while the defeated rival came out from his hiding-place, and took possession of the dunghill for which they had contended.

THE HOUND AND THE HARE

A HOUND AFTER LONG CHASING A HARE AT LENGTH CAME UP TO her, and kept first biting and then licking her. The Hare, not knowing what to make of him, said; "If you are a friend, why do you bite me?—but if a foe, why caress me?"

A doubtful friend is worse than a certain enemy; let a man be one thing or the other, and we then know how to meet him.

THE DOCTOR AND HIS PATIENT

A DOCTOR HAD BEEN FOR SOME TIME ATTENDING UPON A SICK man, who, however, died under his hands. At the funeral the

Doctor went about among the relations, saying; "Our poor friend, if he had only refrained from wine, and attended to his inside, and used proper means, would not have been lying there." One of the mourners answered him, "My good sir, it is of no use your saying this now; you ought to have prescribed these things when your Patient was alive to take them."

The best advice may come too late.

THE BIRDCATCHER AND THE LARK

A BIRDCATCHER WAS SETTING SPRINGES UPON A COMMON, WHEN a Lark, who saw him at work, asked him from a distance what he was doing. "I am establishing a colony," said he, "and laying the foundations of my first city." Upon that, the man retired to a little distance and hid himself. The Lark, believing his assertion, soon flew down to the place, and swallowing the bait, found himself entangled in the noose; whereupon the Birdcatcher straightway coming up to him, made him his prisoner. "A pretty fellow are you!" said the Lark. "If these are the colonies you found, you will not find many emigrants."

THE FOX AND THE LION

A FOX SAW A LION CONFINED IN A CAGE, AND, STANDING NEAR him, bitterly reviled him. The Lion said to the Fox; "It is not thou who revilest me; but this mischance which has befallen me."

THE TRAVELLER AND FORTUNE

A TRAVELLER, WEARIED WITH A LONG JOURNEY, LAY DOWN overcome with fatigue on the very brink of a deep well. Being within an inch of falling into the water, Dame Fortune, it is said, appeared to him, and waking him from his slumber, thus addressed him; "Good sir, pray wake up: for had you fallen into the well, the blame would be thrown on me, and I should get an ill name among mortals; for I find that men are sure to charge their calamities to me, however much by their own folly they have really brought them on themselves."

Every one is more or less master of his own fate.

THE CHARGER AND THE ASS

A CHARGER ADORNED WITH FINE TRAPPINGS CAME THUNDERING along the road, exciting the envy of a poor Ass who was trudging along the same way with a heavy load upon his back. "Get out of my road!" said the proud Horse, "or I shall trample you under my feet." The Ass said nothing, but quietly moved on one side to let the Horse pass.

Not long afterwards the Charger was engaged in the wars, and being badly wounded in battle was rendered unfit for military service, and sent to work upon a farm. When the Ass saw him dragging with great labour a heavy waggon, he understood how little reason he had had to envy one who, by his overbearing spirit in the time of his prosperity, had lost those friends who might have succoured him in time of need.

THE WOLVES AND THE SHEEP

ONCE ON A TIME, THE WOLVES SENT AN EMBASSY TO THE SHEEP, desiring that there might be peace between them for the time to come. "Why," said they, "should we be for ever waging this deadly strife? Those wicked Dogs are the cause of all; they are incessantly barking at us, and provoking us. Send them away, and there will be no longer any obstacle to our eternal friendship and peace."

The silly Sheep listened, the Dogs were dismissed, and the flock, thus deprived of their best protectors, became an easy prey to their treacherous enemy.

THE SERPENT AND THE EAGLE

A SERPENT AND AN EAGLE WERE STRUGGLING WITH EACH OTHER in a deadly conflict. The Serpent had the advantage, and was about to strangle the bird. A countryman saw them, and running up, loosed the coil of the Serpent, and let the Eagle go free.

The Serpent, irritated at the escape of his prey, some time later let fly his poison, and injected it into the drinking horn of the countryman. The rustic, ignorant of his danger, was about to drink, when the Eagle struck his hand with his wing, and, seizing the drinking horn in his talons, carried it away.

THE MONKEY AND THE FISHERMEN

A MONKEY WAS SITTING UP IN A HIGH TREE, WHEN, SEEING some Fishermen laying their nets in a river, he watched what they were doing. The Men had no sooner set their nets, and retired a short distance to their dinner, than the Monkey came down from the tree, thinking that he would try his hand at the same sport. But in attempting to lay the nets he got so entangled in them, that being well-nigh choked, he was forced to exclaim; "This serves me right; for what business had I, who know nothing of fishing, to meddle with such tackle as this?"

THE ANT AND THE DOVE

AN ANT WENT TO A FOUNTAIN TO QUENCH HIS THIRST, AND tumbling in, was almost drowned. But a Dove that happened to be sitting on a neighbouring tree saw the Ant's danger, and plucking off a leaf, let it drop into the water before him, and the Ant mounting upon it, was presently wafted safe ashore.

Just at that time, a Fowler was spreading his net, and was in the act of ensnaring the Dove, when the Ant, perceiving his object, bit his heel. The start which the man gave made him drop his net, and the Dove, aroused to a sense of her danger, flew safe away.

One good turn deserves another.

THE WOLF, THE FOX, AND THE APE

A WOLF ACCUSED A FOX OF THEFT, BUT HE ENTIRELY DENIED the charge. An Ape undertook to judge the matter between them. When each had fully stated his case, the Ape pronounced this sentence; "I do not think you, Wolf, ever lost what you claim; and I do believe you, Fox, to have stolen what you so stoutly deny."

The dishonest, if they act honestly, get no credit.

THE ANGLER AND THE LITTLE FISH

AN ANGLER, WHO GAINED HIS LIVELIHOOD BY FISHING, AFTER A long day's toil, caught nothing but one little fish. "Spare me," said the little creature, "I beseech you; so small as I am, I shall make you but a sorry meal. I am not come to my full size yet; throw me back into the river for the present, and then, when I am grown bigger and worth eating, you may come here and catch me again."

"No, no," said the man; "I have got you now, but if you once get back into the water, you tune will be, 'Catch me, if you can.'"

A bird in the hand is worth two in the bush.

THE ASS, THE FOX, AND THE LION

AN ASS AND A FOX HAVING MADE A COMPACT ALLIANCE, WENT out into the fields to hunt. They met a lion on the way. The Fox seeing the danger, made up to the Lion, and whispered that he would betray the Ass into his power, if he would promise to bear him harmless. The Lion having agreed to do so, the Fox contrived to lead the Ass into a snare. The Lion no sooner saw the Ass secured, than he fell at once upon the Fox, reserving the other for his next meal.

THE MAN AND THE SATYR

A MAN AND A SATYR HAVING STRUCK UP AN ACQUAINTANCE sat down together to eat. The day being wintry and cold, the Man put his fingers to his mouth and blew upon them. "What's that for, my friend?" asked the Satyr. "My hands are so cold," said the Man; "I do it to warm them."

In a little while some hot food was placed before them, and the Man, raising the dish to his mouth, again blew upon it. "And what's the meaning of that, now?" said the Satyr. "Oh," replied the Man, "my porridge is so hot, I do it to cool it." "Nay, then," said the Satyr, "from this moment I renounce your friendship, for I will have nothing to do with one who blows hot and cold with the same mouth."

THE HUSBANDMAN AND THE SEA

A HUSBANDMAN SEEING A SHIP FULL OF SAILORS TOSSED ABOUT up and down upon the billows, cried out; "O Sea! deceitful and pitiless element, that destroyest all who venture upon thee!"

The Sea heard him, and assuming a woman's voice replied; "Do not reproach me; I am not the cause of this disturbance, but the Winds, that when they fall upon me will give no repose. But should you sail over me when they are away, you will say that I am milder and more tractable than your own mother earth."

THE FARMER AND THE LION

A LION ENTERED ONE DAY INTO A FARM-YARD, AND THE FARMER, wishing to catch him, shut the gate. When the Lion found that he could not get out, he began at once to attack the sheep, and then betook himself to the oxen. So the farmer, afraid for himself, now opened the gate, and the Lion made off as fast as he could.

His wife, who had observed it all, when she saw her husband in great trouble at the loss of his cattle, cried out; "You are rightly served; for what could have made you so mad as to wish to detain a creature, whom, if you saw at a distance, you would wish further off?"

Better scare a thief than snare him.

THE SHEPHERD-BOY AND THE WOLF

A SHEPHERD-BOY, WHO TENDED HIS FLOCK NOT FAR FROM A village, used to amuse himself at times in crying out "Wolf! Wolf!" Twice or thrice his trick succeeded. The whole village came running out to his assistance; when all the return they got was to be laughed at for their pains.

At last one day the Wolf came indeed. The Boy cried out in earnest. But his neighbours, supposing him to be at his old sport, paid no heed to his cries, and the Wolf devoured the Sheep. So the Boy learned, when it was too late, that liars are not believed even when they tell the truth.

THE LION, THE BEAR, AND THE FOX

A LION AND A BEAR FOUND THE CARCASE OF A FAWN, AND HAD A long fight for it. The contest was so hard and even, that, at last, both of them, half-blinded and half-dead, lay panting on the ground, without strength to touch the prize that was stretched between them. A Fox coming by at the time, and seeing their helpless condition, stepped in between the combatants and carried off the booty.

"Poor creatures that we are," cried they, "who have been exhausting all our strength and injuring one another, merely to give a rogue a dinner!"

THE TRAVELLERS AND THE PLANE-TREE

SOME TRAVELLERS, ON A HOT DAY IN SUMMER, OPPRESSED WITH the noontide sun, perceiving a Plane-tree near at hand, made straight for it, and throwing themselves on the ground rested under its shade. Looking up, as they lay, towards the tree, they said one to another; "What a useless tree to man is this barren Plane!" But the Plane-tree answered them; "Ungrateful creatures! at the very moment that you are enjoying benefit from me, you rail at me as being good for nothing."

Ingratitude is as blind as it is base.

THE FARTHING RUSHLIGHT

A RUSHLIGHT THAT HAD GROWN FAT AND SAUCY WITH TOO much grease, boasted one evening before a large company, that it shone brighter than the sun, the moon, and all the stars. At that moment, a puff of wind came and blew it out. One who lighted it again said, "Shine on, friend Rushlight, and hold your tongue; the lights of heaven are never blown out."

THE OLD HOUND

A HOUND, WHO HAD BEEN AN EXCELLENT ONE IN HIS TIME, and had done good service to his master in the field, at length became worn out with the weight of years and trouble. One day, when hunting the wild boar, he seized the creature by the ear, but his teeth giving way, he was forced to let go his hold, and the boar escaped. Upon this the huntsman, coming up, severely rated him. But the feeble Dog replied; "Spare your old servant! it was the power, not the will, that failed me. Remember rather what I was, than abuse me for what I am."

THE TWO POTS

TWO POTS, ONE OF EARTHENWARE, THE OTHER OF BRASS, WERE carried down a river in a flood. The Brazen Pot begged his companion to keep by his side, and he would protect him. "Thank you for your offer," said the Earthen Pot, "but that is just what I am afraid of; if you will only keep at a distance, I may float down in safety; but should we come in contact, I am sure to be the sufferer."

Avoid too powerful neighbours; for, should there be a collision, the weakest goes to the wall.

THE MAN BITTEN BY A DOG

A MAN WHO HAD BEEN BITTEN BY A DOG, WAS GOING ABOUT asking who could cure him. One that met him said, "Sir, if you would be cured, take a bit of bread and dip it in the blood of the wound, and give it to the dog that bit you." The Man smiled, and said, "If I were to follow your advice, I should be bitten by all the dogs in the city."

He who proclaims himself ready to buy up his enemies will never want a supply of them.

THE GOAT AND THE ASS

A MAN ONCE KEPT A GOAT AND AN ASS. THE GOAT, ENVYING the Ass on account of his greater abundance of food, said: "How shamefully you are treated; at one time grinding in the mill, and at another carrying heavy burdens." And he further advised him that he should pretend to be epileptic, and fall into a ditch, and so obtain rest. The Ass followed his advice, and, falling into a ditch, was very much bruised. His master, sending for a leech, asked his advice. He bade him place upon the wounds the liver of a Goat. They at once killed the Goat, and so healed the Ass.

THE BULL, THE LIONESS, AND THE WILD-BOAR HUNTER

A BULL, FINDING A LION'S CUB ASLEEP, GORED HIM TO DEATH with his horns. The Lioness came up, and bitterly lamented the death of her child. A Wild-boar Hunter seeing her distress, stood afar off, and said to her; "Think how many men there are who have reason to lament the loss of their children, whose deaths have been caused by you."

THE BALD MAN AND THE FLY

A LITTLE FLY PRICKED A MAN UPON HIS BALD HEAD. AND when he would have smote her she flew away. And thus he smote himself, whereof the Fly began to laugh. And the Bald Man said to her, "Ha, an evil beast! Thou demandest well thy death if I smote myself, whereof thou laughest and mockest me. But if I had hit thee thou haddest been slain." And therefore men say commonly that of the evil of others men ought not to laugh nor scorn.

THE BOY AND THE FILBERTS

A CERTAIN BOY PUT HIS HAND INTO A PITCHER WHERE GREAT plenty of Figs and Filberts were deposited; he grasped as many as his fist could possibly hold, but when he endeavoured to pull it out, the narrowness of the neck prevented him. Unwilling to lose any of them, but unable to draw out his hand, he burst into tears, and bitterly bemoaned his hard fortune. An honest fellow who stood by, gave him this wise and reasonable advice; "Grasp only half the quantity, my boy, and you will easily succeed."

THE CROW AND THE SHEEP

A TROUBLESOME CROW SEATED HERSELF ON THE BACK OF A Sheep. The Sheep, much against his will, carried her backward and forward for a long time, and at last said; "If you had treated a dog in this way, you would have had your deserts from his sharp teeth." To this the Crow replied; "I despise the weak, and yield to the strong. I know whom I may bully, and whom I must flatter; and thus I hope to prolong my life to a good old age."

THE WEASEL AND THE MICE

A WEASEL, INACTIVE FROM OLD AGE AND INFIRMITIES, WAS NOT able to catch mice as he once did. He therefore rolled himself in flour and lay down in a dark corner. A Mouse, supposing him to be food, approached him, and, being instantly caught, was squeezed to death. Another perished in a similar manner, and then a third, and still others after them. A very old Mouse, who had escaped many a trap and snare, observing from a safe distance the trick of his crafty foe, said; "Ah! you that lie there, may you prosper just in the same proportion as you are what you pretend to be!"

THE FOX AND THE MONKEY

A FOX AND A MONKEY WERE TRAVELLING TOGETHER ON THE same road. As they journeyed, they passed through a cemetery full of monuments. "All these monuments which you see," said the Monkey, "are erected in honour of my ancestors, who were in their day freedmen, and citizens of great renown."

The Fox replied; "You have chosen a most appropriate subject for your falsehoods, as I am sure none of your ancestors will be able to contradict you."

A false tale often betrays itself.

THE MULE

A MULE THAT HAD GROWN FAT AND WANTON ON TOO GREAT an allowance of corn, was one day jumping and kicking about, and at length, cocking up her tail, exclaimed, "My dam was a Racer, and I am quite as good as ever she was." But being soon exhausted with her galloping and frisking, she remembered all at once that her sire was but an Ass.

Every truth has two sides; it is well to look at both before we commit ourselves to either.

THE HUNTER AND THE FISHERMAN

A HUNTER WAS RETURNING FROM THE MOUNTAINS LOADED WITH game, and a Fisherman was at the same time coming home with his creel full of fish, when they chanced to meet by the way. The Hunter took a fancy to a dish of fish: the Fisher preferred a supper of game. So each gave to the other the contents of his own basket. And thus they continued daily to exchange provision, till one who had observed them said; "Now, by this invariable interchange, will they destroy the zest of their meal; and each will soon wish to return to his own store again."

THE WOLF AND THE LION

ONE DAY A WOLF HAD SEIZED A SHEEP FROM A FOLD, AND WAS carrying it home to his own den, when he met a Lion, who straightway laid hold of the sheep and bore it away. The Wolf, standing at a distance, cried out, that it was a great shame, and that the Lion had robbed him of his own. The Lion laughed, and said: "I suppose, then, that it was your good friend the shepherd who gave it to you."

THE WILD BOAR AND THE FOX

A WILD BOAR WAS WHETTING HIS TUSKS AGAINST A TREE, WHEN a Fox coming by asked why he did so; "For," said he, "I see no reason for it; there is neither hunter nor hound in sight, nor any other danger that I can see, at hand." "True," replied the Boar; "but when that danger does arise, I shall have something else to do than to sharpen my weapons."

It is too late to whet the sword when the trumpet sounds to draw it.

THE MOUSE AND THE BULL

A BULL WAS BITTEN BY A MOUSE, AND, PAINED BY THE WOUND, tried to capture him. The Mouse however reached his hole in safety, and the bull dug into the walls with his horns, until wearied, crouching down, he slept by the hole. The Mouse peeping out, crept up his flank, and, again biting him, retreated to his hole. The Bull rising up, and not knowing what to do, was sadly perplexed. The Mouse murmured; "The great do not always prevail. There are times when the small and lowly are the strongest to do mischief."

THE FOWLER AND THE VIPER

A FOWLER, TAKING HIS BIRD-LIME AND HIS TWIGS, WENT OUT TO catch birds. Seeing a thrush sitting upon a tree, he wished to capture it, and fitting his twigs to a proper length, he watched intently, having his whole thoughts directed towards the sky. While thus looking upwards, he unawares trod upon a Viper asleep just before his feet. The Viper, turning towards him, stung him; and he, falling into a swoon, said to himself; "Woe is me! that while I purposed to hunt another, I am myself fallen unawares into the snares of death."

THE CAT AND THE COCK

A CAT CAUGHT A COCK, AND TOOK COUNSEL WITH HIMSELF HOW he might find a reasonable excuse for eating him. He accused him of being a nuisance to men, by crowing in the night time, and not permitting them to sleep. The Cock defended himself by saying that he did this for the benefit of men, that they might rise early for their labours. The Cat replied; "Although you abound in specious apologies, I shall not remain supperless." He made a meal of him.

THE FOX AND THE WOODMAN

A FOX, HARD PRESSED BY THE HOUNDS AFTER A LONG RUN, CAME up to a man who was cutting wood, and begged him to afford him some place where he might hide himself. The man showed him his own hut, and the Fox creeping in, hid himself in a corner. The Hunters presently came up, and asking the man whether he had seen the Fox, "No," said he, but pointed with his finger to the corner. They, however, not understanding the hint, were off again immediately.

When the Fox perceived that they were out of sight, he was stealing off without saying a word. But the man upbraided him, saying, "Is this the way you take leave of your host, without a word of thanks for your safety?" "A pretty host!" said the Fox, turning round upon him; "if you had been as honest with your fingers as you were with your tongue, I should not have left your roof without bidding you farewell."

THE LION AND THE COW, THE GOAT AND THE SHEEP

THE COW, THE GOAT AND THE SHEEP WENT ONCE A-HUNTING in the chase with a Lion, and they captured a Hart. And when they came to have their part and share in it, the Lion said to them:

"My lords, I let you know that the first part is mine, because I am your lord; the second because I am stronger than you; the third because I ran more swift than you did; and whosoever touches the fourth part, he shall be my mortal enemy!"

And thus the Lion took for himself alone the Hart.

THE PEACOCK AND THE CRANE

A PEACOCK, SPREADING ITS GORGEOUS TAIL, MOCKED A CRANE that passed by, ridiculing the ashen hue of its plumage, and saying; "I am robed, like a king, in gold and purple, and all the colours of the rainbow; while you have not a bit of colour on your wings."

"True," replied the Crane, "but I soar to the heights of heaven, and lift up my voice to the stars, while you walk below, like a cock, among the birds of the dunghill."

Fine feathers don't make fine birds.

THE ANT AND THE GRASSHOPPER

ON A COLD FROSTY DAY AN ANT WAS DRAGGING OUT SOME OF the corn which he had laid up in summer time, to dry it. A Grasshopper, half-perished with hunger, besought the Ant to give him a morsel of it to preserve his life. "What were you doing," said the Ant, "this last summer?" "Oh," said the Grass-hopper, "I was not idle. I kept singing all the summer long." Said the Ant, laughing and shutting up his granary: "Since you could sing all summer, you may dance all winter."

Winter finds out what Summer lays by.

THE ASS AND THE WOLF

AN ASS, GRAZING IN A FIELD, SAW A WOLF COME FORWARD TO seize him, and immediately pretended to be lame. The Wolf, coming up, inquired the cause of his lameness. The Ass said, that passing through a hedge he trod with his foot upon a sharp thorn, and requested the Wolf to pull it out, lest when he supped on him it should injure his throat.

The Wolf consenting, and lifting up the foot, and giving his whole mind to the discovery of the thorn, the Ass with his heels kicked his teeth into his mouth, and galloped away. The Wolf, being thus fearfully injured, said; "I am rightly served, for why did I attempt the art of healing, when my father only taught me the trade of a butcher?"

THE WIDOW AND THE SHEEP

THERE WAS A CERTAIN WIDOW WHO HAD AN ONLY SHEEP; AND, wishing to make the most of his wool, she sheared him so closely that she cut his skin as well as his fleece. The Sheep, smarting under this treatment, cried out: "Why do you torture me thus? What will my blood add to the weight of the wool? If you want my flesh, Dame, send for the Butcher, who will put me out of my misery at once; but if you want fleece, send for the Shearer, who will clip my wool without drawing my blood."

THE HUNTER AND THE WOODMAN

A MAN WENT OUT LION-HUNTING INTO A FOREST, WHERE MEET-ing with a Woodman, he asked him if he had seen any tracks of a Lion, and if he knew where his lair was. "Yes," said the Man, "and if you will come with me I will show you the Lion himself." At this the Hunter, turning ghastly pale, and his teeth chattering, said, "Oh! thank you; it was the Lion's track, not himself, that I was hunting."

A coward can be a hero at a distance; it is presence of danger that tests presence of mind.

THE BIRDS, THE BEASTS, AND THE BAT

ONCE UPON A TIME THERE WAS A FIERCE WAR WAGED BETWEEN the birds and the Beasts. For a long while the issue of the battle was uncertain, and the Bat, taking advantage of his ambiguous nature, kept aloof and remained neutral.

At length when the Beasts seemed to prevail, the Bat joined their forces and appeared active in the fight; but a rally being made by the Birds, which proved successful, he was found at the end of the day among the ranks of the winning party. A peace being speedily concluded, the Bat's conduct was condemned alike by both parties, and being acknowledged by neither, and so excluded from the terms of the truce, he was obliged to skulk off as best he could, and has ever since lived in holes and corners, never daring to show his face except in the duskiness of twilight.

THE QUACK FROG

A FROG EMERGING FROM THE MUD OF A SWAMP, PROCLAIMED to all the world that he was come to cure all diseases. "Here!" he cried, "come and see a doctor, the proprietor of medicines such as man never heard of before; no, not Æsculapius himself, Jove's court-physician!"

"And how," said the Fox, "dare you set up to heal others, who are not able to cure your own limping gait, and blotched and wrinkled skin?"

Test a man's professions by his practice.

THE JACKASS IN OFFICE

AN ASS CARRYING AN IMAGE IN A RELIGIOUS PROCESSION, WAS driven through a town, and all the people who passed by made a low reverence. Upon this the Ass, supposing that they intended this worship for himself, was mightily puffed up, and would not budge another step. But the driver soon laid the stick across his back, saying at the same time; "You silly dolt! it is not you that they reverence, but the Image which you carry."

Fools take to themselves the respect that is given to their office.

LOKMAN

Arabia Biblical times

THE DOG AND THE WOLF

A DOG ONCE CHASED A WOLF, AND BOASTED OF HIS FORCE AND the lightness of his course, and the flight of the Wolf at his presence.   And the Wolf returned towards him, saying to him; "Do not think my fear was of thee, for certainly my fear is of him who was hunting with you."

THE DOGS AND THE FOX

THE DOGS ONCE FOUND THE SKIN OF A LION, AND BEGAN TO mangle it.   A Fox saw them, and said to them, "Surely, if he were alive you would find that his claws are sharper and longer than your teeth."

THE DOE AND THE LIONESS

A DOE ONCE PASSED NEAR A LIONESS, SAYING; "I HAVE MANY children in a year, and thou only hast in all thy life but one or two."   And the Lioness said to her; "It is true; nevertheless, if it be but one, yet he is a Lion."

THE WEASEL AND THE CHICKENS

A WEASEL HEARD THAT THE CHICKENS WERE SICK; THE WEASEL arose and donned the skin of a Peacock, and went to visit them, and said to them; "Health to you, O Chickens! How are you and how is your state?"

And the Chickens said to him; "We are always ill until we see your face."

THE OLD MAN AND DEATH

QUITE SPENT WITH A BURTHEN OF STICKS, AN OLD CLOWN,
To take breath a while, on a bank sat him down:
He called upon Death, and wished he would please
To shorten his life, and so give him some ease.
Straight all of a sudden, pale Death did appear,
Which made the old grumbler's teeth chatter wi' fear.
"I called you," said he, "Mr. Death, in a maggot,
But now you are here, help me up with a faggot."
  Men at a distance Death defy
  Who quake like cowards when they die.

FABLES FROM THE

TALMUD

THE HEAD AND THE TAIL

THIS IS WHAT ONCE BEFELL A SNAKE. THE TAIL SAID TO THE head; "How much longer will you lead the way and drag me behind? Let me lead and you follow after."

"Very well," the head replied, "you go first."

So the tail led the way and the head followed. Nearing a ditch filled with water, the tail fell in and dragged the head after him. At a second place where thorny bushes grew, the tail and the snake and the head, all together, were torn and scratched and wounded.

Is not the head to blame, for agreeing to be led by the tail?

THE UNGRATEFUL STAG

A GROUP OF HUNTSMEN PURSUED A STAG AND CAUGHT UP WITH him at the edge of a garden. The stag leaped over the fence and hid in a bush. The hunters searched in the garden but could not find the stag, for the leaves of the shrubs concealed him.

Seeing that their search was vain, the hunters turned to go. When the stag saw that his persecutors were departing, he began to eat the leaves that hid him. And each leaf that the stag took into his mouth, uttered a deep sigh. The twigs asked, "Why do you sigh?"

"We do not sigh over our own fate," said the leaves, "but over the unfortunate stag who devours us. We have concealed him, but now the huntsmen will surely see him and slay him."

BETWEEN WOLF AND SHEPHERD

A WOLF WENT INTO A FIELD AND STOLE A SHEEP. THE SHEPherd observing the theft, ran after. He caught up with the wolf, and seizing the sheep, pulled it towards him. The shepherd pulled this way, the wolf pulled that way, and between them the poor sheep was torn in two.

THE ASS AND THE RIDER

A MAN ONCE GALLOPED THROUGH THE STREETS OF THE CITY ON an ass. In the middle of the road played a little boy. When the ass approached the spot where the boy played he jumped over the child and did not harm him. For this the people of the town loved and honored the ass. "How clever he is," they said, "to jump over the child and do him no harm!"

But then said the rider; "I swear to you, if I had not pulled the reins, the ass would have trampled the boy."

THE ROSE BUSH AND THE APPLE TREE

NEAR AN APPLE TREE GREW A ROSE BUSH. THE ROSE BUSH SAW how much she was admired and said; "Who can compare with me, and who is as worthy as I am? My flowers are beautiful to the sight and sweet to the nostrils. True, the apple tree is bigger than I, but what pleasure does he give to mankind?"

When the apple tree heard this he said; "Even though you are worthier than I in the beauty of your blossoms and the sweetness of your smell, you are less worthy in goodness of heart and friendliness."

"Tell me," the rose bush said, "what is the evidence of your goodness?"

And the apple tree answered; "You do not give your flowers to man unless you first wound him with your thorns. But I give my fruit to all, even to those who throw stones at me."

THE MAKING OF EVE

WHEN GOD DECIDED TO CREATE EVE, HE CONSIDERED FROM WHAT part of Adam's body he should fashion her.

He said; "I will not fashion her from his head lest she be too vain. I will not fashion her from his eyes lest she be eager to see all things. I will not fashion her from his ears lest she be an eavesdropper. I will not fashion her from his mouth lest she be a gossip. I will not fashion her from his heart lest she be envious. I will not fashion her from his hands lest she grasp things that do not belong to her. I will not fashion her from his feet lest she be a gadabout.

"I will fashion her from a hidden part of his body, a part which will be covered even though he stand naked." And as each nerve and tissue he created, God said, "Be thou a modest wife, an exemplary woman."

Nevertheless, God's plans were thwarted. Woman is proud; she is eager to see all and know all; she has nine measures of talk; she is jealous; she craves for things that are not hers; and she is a gadabout.

THE LOVE OF CHILD

ONCE A FARMER LED A COW TO SLAUGHTER, BUT THE COW WOULD not go. The farmer started to drag the cow by force, but the cow planted her feet firmly in the ground and would not be moved. What did the farmer do? He brought the cow's calf and led her before, and the mother followed the calf, not by force, but of her own free will.

THE FEARS OF THE TREES

WHEN THE EARTH BEGAN TO PUT FORTH PLANTS AND TREES, gardens and forests bloomed on the face of the earth. The trees were greatly afraid of the iron in the earth. They said to each other; "The time will come when from the iron man will fashion axes, and chop us down, and make an end of us."

The iron heard the trees muttering to each other and said; "Live peaceably together and do not plot against the elements. I will not be able to harm you; for where will I get the wood for the handle of the axe?"

PHAEDRUS

Greece 1st Century

THE EAGLE, THE CROW, AND THE TORTOISE

AN EAGLE CARRIED A TORTOISE ALOFT, WHO HAD HIDDEN HER body in her horny abode and thought, in her concealment, she could not be injured in any way. A Crow came through the air, and flying near, exclaimed; "You really have carried off a rich prize in your talons; but if I don't instruct you what you must do, in vain will you tire yourself with the heavy weight."

So a share of the prey being promised her, the Crow persuades the Eagle to dash the hard shell upon a rock, that, it being broken to pieces, he may easily feed upon the meat. Induced by her words, the Eagle attends to her suggestion, and at the same time gives a large share of the banquet to his instructress, Mistress Crow.

THE PILOT AND THE MARINERS

ON A CERTAIN MAN COMPLAINING OF HIS ADVERSE FORTUNE, Aesop, for the purpose of consoling him, invented this Fable.

A ship which had been tossed by a fierce tempest, while the passengers were all in tears, and filled with apprehensions of death, on the day suddenly changing to a serene aspect, began to be borne along in safety upon the buoyant waves, and to inspire the mariners with an excess of gladness. On this, the Pilot, who had been rendered wise by experience, remarked; "We ought to be moderate in our joy, and to complain with caution; for the whole of life is a mixture of grief and joy."

SOCRATES TO HIS FRIENDS

SOCRATES HAVING LAID FOR HIMSELF THE FOUNDATION OF A small house, one of the people, no matter who, amongst such passing remarks as are usual in these cases, asked; "Why do you, so famed as you are, build so small a house?"

"I only wish," he replied, "I could fill it with real friends."

THE CAMEL AND THE FLY

A FLY, CHANCING TO SIT ON THE BACK OF A CAMEL WHO WAS going along weighed down with heavy burdens, was quite delighted with himself, as he appeared to be so much higher. After they had made a long journey, they came together in the evening to the stable. The Fly immediately exclaimed, skipping lightly to the ground; "See, I have got down directly, that I may not weary you any longer, so galled as you are."

The Camel replied; "I thank you; but neither when you were on me did I find myself oppressed by your weight, nor do I feel myself at all lightened now you have dismounted."

He who, while he is of no standing, boasts to be of a lofty one, falls under contempt when he comes to be known.

ÆSOP AT PLAY

AN ATHENIAN SEEING AESOP IN A CROWD OF BOYS AT PLAY WITH nuts, stopped and laughed at him for a madman. As soon as the Sage,—a laugher at others rather than one to be laughed at,—

perceived this, he placed an unstrung bow in the middle of the road; "Hark you, wise man," said he, "unriddle what I have done."

The people gather round. The man torments his invention a long time, but cannot make out the reason of the proposed question. At last he gives up. Upon this, the victorious Philosopher says; "You will soon break the bow, if you always keep it bent; but if you loosen it, it will be fit for use when you want it."

THE FROGS FRIGHTENED AT THE BATTLE OF THE BULLS

WHEN THE POWERFUL ARE AT VARIANCE, THE LOWLY ARE THE sufferers.

A Frog, viewing from a marsh a combat of some Bulls, "Alas!" said she, "what terrible destruction is threatening us!" Being asked by another why she said so, as the Bulls were contending for the sovereignty of the herd, and passed their lives far from them, "Their habitation is at a distance," said she, "and they are of a different kind; still, he who is expelled from the sovereignty of the meadow will take to flight, and come to the secret hiding-places in the fens, and trample and crush us with his hard hoofs. Thus does their fury concern our safety."

THE MAN AND THE WEASEL

A WEASEL, ON BEING CAUGHT BY A MAN, WISHING TO ESCAPE impending death, "Pray," said she, "do spare me, for it is I who keep your house clear of troublesome mice."

The Man answered; "If you did so for my sake, there would be a reason for thanking you, and I should have granted you the pardon you entreat. But, inasmuch as you do your best that you may enjoy the scraps which they would have gnawed, and devour the mice as well, don't think of placing your pretended services to my account." So saying, he put the wicked creature to death.

Those persons ought to recognize this as applicable to themselves, whose object is private advantage.

THE STORK, THE GOOSE, AND THE HAWK

A STORK, HAVING COME TO A WELL-KNOWN POOL, FOUND A Goose diving frequently beneath the water, and inquired why she did so. The other replied; "This is our custom, and we find our food in the mud; and then, besides, we thus find safety, and escape the attack of the Hawk when he comes against us."

"I am much stronger than the Hawk," said the Stork; "if you choose to make an alliance with me, you will be able victoriously to deride him." The Goose believing her, and immediately accepting her aid, goes with her into the fields. Forthwith comes the Hawk, and seizes the Goose in his remorseless claws and devours her, while the Stork flies off. The Goose called out after her; "He who trusts himself to so weak a protector, deserves to come to a still worse end."

THE ONLY WISE MAN

AESOP WAS COMMANDED BY HIS MASTER, WHO DESIGNED TO ENtertain the philosophers and orators, to stand at the gate and admit none but wise men. At the appointed time several came to the gate, requesting admittance. Aesop put this question to them all; "What stirs the dog?" At which they were much offended, supposing he meant to give them that appellation.

At last one came who made this reply to his question; "His ears and his tail." Aesop, satisfied with the answer, admitted him, and conducted him to his master, saying there was only one philosopher who had desired admittance. The day following, when they met at the schools, they reproached Xanthus with treating them contemptuously, by permitting his servant to stand at the gate and salute them with the opprobrious epithet of dogs. Upon which Aesop was called, and asked how he dared to affront the gentlemen.

Aesop replied to his master; "Did you not tell me that none but philosophers should be admitted?"—"And what are these?" said Xanthus; "do they not merit that character?"

"By no means," answered Aesop; "for when they came to the gate I demanded of them, what stirs the dog, and but one among them all gave me a proper answer." Hereupon all agreed that Aesop had acted strictly as his master had commanded him.

THE MAN AND THE ASS

A MAN HAVING SACRIFICED A YOUNG BOAR TO THE GOD HER-cules, to whom he owed performance of a vow made for the preservation of his health, ordered the remains of the barley to be set for the Ass. But he refused to touch it, and said; "I would most willingly accept your food, if he who had been fed upon it had not had his throat cut."

A THIEF PILLAGING THE ALTAR OF JUPITER

A THIEF LIGHTED HIS LAMP AT THE ALTAR OF JUPITER, AND then plundered it by the help of its own light. Just as he was taking his departure, laden with the results of his sacrilege, the

Holy Place suddenly sent forth these words; "Although these were the gifts of the wicked, and to me abominable, so much so that I care not to be spoiled of them, still, profane man, thou shalt pay the penalty with thy life, when hereafter, the day of punishment, appointed by fate, arrives. But, that our fire, by means of which piety worships the awful Gods, may not afford its light to crime, I forbid that henceforth there shall be any such interchange of light."

Accordingly, to this day, it is neither lawful for a lamp to be lighted at the fire of the Gods, nor yet a sacrifice kindled from a lamp.

THE DOG, THE TREASURE, AND THE VULTURE

GRUBBING UP HUMAN BONES, A DOG MET WITH A TREASURE; and, because he had offended the Gods, a desire for riches was inspired in him, that so he might pay the penalty due to the holy character of the place. Accordingly, while he was watching over the gold, forgetful of food, he was starved to death; on which a Vulture, standing over him, is reported to have said; "O Dog, you justly meet your death, who, begotten at a cross-road, and bred up on a dunghill, have suddenly coveted regal wealth."

THE PARTRIDGE AND THE FOX

ONCE ON A TIME A PARTRIDGE WAS SITTING IN A LOFTY TREE. A fox came up, and began thus to speak: "O Partridge, how beautiful is your aspect! Your beak transcends the coral; your thighs the brightness of purple. And then, if you were to sleep, how much more beauteous you would be." As soon as the silly Bird had closed her eyes, that instant the Fox seized the credulous thing.

Suppliantly she uttered these words, mingled with loud cries;

"O Fox, I beseech you, by the graceful dexterity of your exquisite skill, utter my name as before, and then you shall devour me." The Fox, willing to speak, opened his mouth, and so the Partridge escaped destruction. Then said the deluded Fox; "What need was there for me to speak?" The Partridge retorted; "And what necessity was there for me to sleep, when my hour for sleep had not come?"

This is for those who speak when there is no occasion, and who sleep when it is requisite to be on the watch.

THE DOG AND THE CROCODILE

IT HAS BEEN RELATED, THAT DOGS DRINK AT THE RIVER NILE running along, that they may not be seized by the Crocodiles. Accordingly, a Dog having begun to drink running along, a Crocodile thus addressed him; "Lap as leisurely as you like; drink on; come nearer, and don't be afraid," said he. The other replied; "Egad, I would do so with all my heart, did I not know that you are eager for my flesh."

DEMETRIUS AND MENANDER

DEMETRIUS, WHO WAS CALLED PHALEREUS, UNJUSTLY TOOK possession of the sovereignty of Athens. The mob, according to their usual practice, rush from all quarters vying with each other, and cheer him, and wish him joy. Even the chief men kiss the hand by which they are oppressed, while they silently lament the sad vicissitudes of fortune. Moreover, those who live in retirement, and take their ease, come creeping in last of all, that their absence may not injure them. Among these Menander, famous for his Comedies—which Demetrius, who did not know him, had read, and had admired the genius of the man,—perfumed with unguents, and clad in a flowing robe, came with a mincing and languid step.

As soon as the Tyrant caught sight of him at the end of the train, "What effeminate wretch," said he, "is this, who presumes to come into my presence?" Those near him made answer; "This is Menander the Poet." Changed in an instant, he exclaimed; "A more agreeable-looking man could not possibly exist."

THE ASS AND THE PRIESTS OF CYBELE

THE GALLI, PRIESTS OF CYBELE, WERE IN THE HABIT, ON THEIR begging excursions, of leading about an Ass, to carry their burdens. When he was dead with fatigue and blows, his hide being stripped off, they made themselves tambourines therewith. Afterwards, on being asked by some one what they had done with their favourite, they answered in these words; "He fancied that after death he would rest in quiet; but see, dead as he is, fresh blows are heaped upon him."

THE CRANE, THE CROW, AND THE COUNTRYMAN

A CRANE AND A CROW HAD MADE A LEAGUE ON OATH, THAT the Crane should protect the Crow against the Birds, and that the Crow should foretell the future, so that the Crane might be on her guard. After this, on their frequently flying into the fields of a certain Countryman, and tearing up by the roots what had been sown, the owner of the field saw it, and being vexed, cried out; "Give me a stone, Boy, that I may hit the Crane." When the Crow heard this, at once she warned the Crane, who took all due precaution.

On another day, too, the Crow hearing him ask for a stone, again warned the Crane carefully to avoid the danger. The Countryman, suspecting that the divining Bird heard his commands, said to the Boy; "If I say, give me a cake, do you secretly hand me a stone." The Crane came again; he bade the Boy give him a cake, but the Boy gave him a stone, with which he hit the Crane, and broke her legs.

The Crane, on being wounded, said; "Prophetic Crow, where now are your auspices? Why did you not hasten to warn your companion, as you swore you would, that no such evil might befall me?" The Crow made answer; "It is not my art that deserves to be blamed; but the purposes of double-tongued people are so deceiving, who say one thing and do another."

THE SHIPWRECK OF SIMONIDES

A LEARNED MAN HAS ALWAYS A FUND OF RICHES IN HIMSELF.

Simonides, who wrote such excellent lyric poems, the more easily to support his poverty, began to make a tour of the celebrated cities of Asia, singing the praises of victors for such reward as he might receive. After he had become enriched by this kind of gain, he resolved to return to his native land by sea; for he was born, it is said, in the island of Ceos.

Accordingly he embarked in a ship, which a dreadful tempest, together with its own rottenness, caused to wreck at sea. Some gathered together their girdles, others their precious effects, which formed the support of their existence. One who was over-inquisitive, remarked; "Are you going to save none of your property, Simonides?" He made reply; "All my possessions are about me."

A few only made their escape by swimming, for the majority, being weighed down by their burdens, perished. Some thieves too made their appearance, and seized what each person had saved, leaving him naked.　Clazomenæ, an ancient city, chanced to be near; to which the shipwrecked persons repaired.　Here a person devoted to the pursuits of literature, who had often read the lines of Simonides, and was a very great admirer of him though he had never seen him, knowing from his very language who he was, received him with the greatest pleasure into his house, and furnished him with clothes, money, and attendants.　The others meanwhile were carrying about their pictures, begging for victuals.　Simonides chanced to meet them; and, as soon as he saw them, remarked; "I told you that all my property was about me; what you have endeavoured to save is lost."

SIMONIDES PRESERVED BY THE GODS

I HAVE SAID, ABOVE, HOW GREATLY LEARNING IS ESTEEMED among men.　I will now hand down to posterity how great is the honour paid to it by the Gods.

Simonides, the very same of whom I have before made mention, agreed, at a fixed price, to write a panegyric for a certain Pugilist, who had been victorious.　Accordingly he sought retirement.　As the meagreness of his subject cramped his imagination, he used, according to general custom, the license of the Poet, and introduced the twin stars of Leda, citing them as an example of similar honours.　He finished the Poem according to contract, but received only a third part of the sum agreed upon.

On his demanding the rest, "They," said he, "will give it you whose praises occupy the other two-thirds; but, that I may feel convinced that you have not departed in anger, promise to dine with me, as I intend to-day to invite my kinsmen, in the number of whom I reckon you."

Although defrauded, and smarting under the injury, in order that he might not, by parting on bad terms, break off all friendly intercourse, he promised that he would.　At the hour named he returned, and took his place at table.　The banquet shone joyously with its cups; the house resounded with gladness, amid vast preparations, when, on a sudden, two young men, covered with dust, and dripping with perspiration, their bodies of more than human form, requested one of the servants to call Simonides to them, and say that it was of consequence to him to make no delay. The man, quite confused, called forth Simonides; and hardly had he put one foot out of the banqueting-room, when suddenly the fall of the ceiling crushed the rest, and no young men were to be seen at the gate.

THE ANT AND THE FLY

AN ANT AND A FLY WERE CONTENDING WITH GREAT WARMTH which was of the greater importance. The Fly was the first to begin; "Can you possibly compare with my endowments? When a sacrifice is made, I am the first to taste of the entrails that belong to the Gods. I pass my time among the altars, I wander through all the temples; soon as I have espied it, I seat myself on the head of a king; and I taste of the chaste kisses of matrons. I labour not, and yet enjoy the nicest of things. What like to this, good rustic, falls to your lot?"

"Eating with the Gods," said the Ant, "is certainly a thing to be boasted of; but by him who is invited, not him who is loathed as an intruder. You talk about kings and the kisses of matrons. While I am carefully heaping up a stock of grain for winter, I see you feeding on filth about the walls. You frequent the altars; yes, and are driven away as often as you come. You labour not; therefore it is that you have nothing when you stand in need of it. And, further, you boast about what modesty ought to conceal. You tease me in summer; when winter comes you are silent. While the cold is shrivelling you up and putting you to death, a well-stored abode harbours me. Surely I have now pulled down your pride enough."

THE LION, THE ROBBER, AND THE TRAVELLER

WHILE A LION WAS STANDING OVER A BULLOCK, WHICH HE HAD brought to the ground, a Robber came up, and demanded a share.

"I would give it to you," said the Lion, "were you not in the habit of taking without leave"; and so repulsed the rogue.

By chance, a harmless Traveller was led to the same spot, and on seeing the wild beast, retraced his steps; on which the Lion kindly said to him; "You have nothing to fear; boldly take the share which is due to your modesty." Then having divided the carcase, he sought the woods, that he might make room for the Man.

THE TWO BALD MEN

A BALD MAN CHANCED TO FIND A COMB IN THE PUBLIC ROAD. Another, equally destitute of hair, came up; "Come," said he, "shares, whatever it is you have found." The other showed the booty, and added withal; "The will of the Gods has favoured us, but through the malignity of fate, we have found, as the saying is, a coal instead of a treasure."

THE ASS, THE OX, AND THE BIRDS

AN ASS AND AN OX, FASTENED TO THE SAME YOKE, WERE DRAWING a waggon. While the Ox was pulling with all his might he broke his horn. The Ass swears that he experiences no help whatever from his weak companion. Exerting himself in the labour, the Ox breaks his other horn, and at length falls dead upon the ground. Presently, the Herdsman loads the Ass with the flesh of the Ox, and he breaks down amid a thousand blows, and stretched in the middle of the road, expires. The Birds flying to the prey, exclaim: "If you had shown yourself compassionate to the Ox when he entreated you, you would not have been food for us through your untimely death."

AESOP AT PLAY

AN ATHENIAN ONE DAY FOUND AESOP AT PLAY WITH A COMpany of little boys, at their childish diversions, and began to jeer and laugh at him for it. The old fellow, who was too much of a wag himself to suffer others to ridicule him, took a bow, unstrung, and laid it upon the ground. Then calling the censorious Athenian, "Now, philosopher," said he, "expound the riddle if you can, and tell us what the unstrung bow implies." The man, after racking his brains and scratching his pate about it a considerable time, to no purpose, at last gave it up, and declared he knew not what to make of it.

"Why," says Aesop, laughing, "if you keep a bow always bent, it will break presently; but if you let it go slack, it will be the fitter for use when you want it."

PILPAY

India 4th Century

THE ASS AND THE GARDENER

AN ASS HAD ONCE BY SOME ACCIDENT LOST HIS TAIL, WHICH was a grievous affliction to him; and he was everywhere seeking after it, being fool enough to think he could get it set on again, he passed through a meadow, and afterwards got into a garden. The gardener seeing him, and not able to endure the mischief he was doing in trampling down his plants, fell into a violent rage, ran to the ass, and never standing on the ceremony of a pillory, cut off both his ears, and beat him out of the ground. Thus the ass, who bemoaned the loss of his tail, was in far greater affliction when he saw himself without ears; and depend on it, that, in general, whoever he be that takes not reason for his guide, wanders about, and at length falls over precipices.

THE SCORPION AND THE TORTOISE

A TORTOISE AND SCORPION HAD CONTRACTED A GREAT INTIMACY, and bound themselves with such ties of friendship, that the one could not live without the other. These inseparable companions, one day, finding themselves obliged to change their habitation, travelled together; but in their way meeting with a large and deep river, the scorpion making a stop, said to the tortoise; "My dear friend, you are well provided for what we see before us, but how shall I get over this water?" "Never trouble yourself, my dear friend, for that," replied the tortoise, "I will carry you upon my back secure from all danger."

The scorpion, on this, without hesitation, got upon the back of the tortoise, who immediately took water and began to swim. But he was hardly got halfway across the river, when he heard a terrible rumbling upon his back; which made him ask the scorpion what he was doing? "Doing!" replied the scorpion, "why, I am whetting my sting, to try whether I can bore this horny cuirass of yours, that covers your flesh like a shield, from all injuries." "Oh, ungrateful wretch!" cried the tortoise, "wouldst thou, at a time when I am giving thee such a demonstration of my friendship, wouldst thou at such a time, pierce with thy venomous sting the defence that Nature has given me, and take away my life? It is well, however, I have it in my power, both to save myself, and reward thee as thou deservest." So saying, he sunk his back to some depth under water, threw off the scorpion, and left him to pay with his life the just forfeit of his monstrous ingratitude.

THE BIRDS CHOOSING A KING

IT ONCE HAPPENED THAT A FLIGHT OF BIRDS ASSEMBLED TO choose a king; and every different species among them put in his pretensions to the crown. At length, however, there were sevcral that gave their voices for the owl, because Minerva, the goddess of wisdom, had made choice of him as her peculiar bird. But a vast number of others being strenuous in their resolution never to obey so deformed a creature, the diet broke up, and they fell one upon another with so much fury, that several on all sides were slain.

The fight, however, probably would have lasted longer than it did, had not a certain bird, in order to part them, bethought himself of crying out to the combatants; "No more civil wars; why do you spill one another's blood in vain? Here is a raven coming; let us all agree to make him our judge and arbitrator; he is a person of judgment, and whose years have gained him experience."

The birds unanimously consented to this: and when the raven arrived, and had informed himself of the occasion of the quarrel, he thus delivered himself; "Are you such fools and madmen, gentlemen," said he, "to choose for your king a bird, that draws after him nothing but misfortune? Will you set up a fly instead of a griffin? Why do you not rather make choice of a falcon, who is eminent for his courage and agility? or a peacock, who treads with a majestic gait, and carries a train of starry eyes in his tail? Why do you not rather raise an eagle to the throne, who is the emblem of royalty; or, lastly, a griffin, who only by the motion and noise of his wings makes the mountains tremble? But though there were no such birds as these that I have named in the world, surely it were better for you to live without a king, than subject yourselves to such a horrid creature as an owl; for though he has the physiognomy of a cat, he has no wit; and, what is yet more insupportable, notwithstanding that he is so abominably ugly, he is as proud as a fine lady at a public feast; and what ought, if possible, to render him yet more despicable in our eyes, he hates the light of that magnificent body that enlivens all nature. Therefore, gentlemen, lay aside a design so prejudicial to your honour, proceed to the election of another king, and do nothing that you may hereafter repent."

THE TRAVELLING PIGEON

THERE WERE ONCE IN A CERTAIN PART OF YOUR MAJESTY'S dominions two Pigeons, a male and a female, which had been hatched from the same brood of eggs, and bred up together afterwards in the same nest, under the roof of an old building, in which they lived together in mutual content and perfect happiness, safely sheltered from all the injuries of the weather, and contented with a little water and a few tares. It is a treasure to live in a desert when we enjoy the happiness of a friend; and there is no loss in quitting for the sake of such a one all other company in the world. But it seems too often the peculiar business of destiny to separate friends.

Of these Pigeons the one was called the Beloved, the other the Lover. One day the Lover, having an eager desire to travel, imparted his design to his companion. "Must we always," said he, "live confined to a hole? No; be it with you as you please, but for my part I am resolved to take a tour about the world. Travellers every day meet with new things, and acquire experience; and all the great and learned among our ancestors have told us, that travelling is the only means to acquire knowledge. If the sword be never unsheathed, it can never show the valour of the person that wears it; and if the pen takes not its run through the extent of a page, it can never show the eloquence of the author that uses it. The heavens, by reason of their perpetual motion, exceed in glory and delight the regions beneath them; and the dull brute earth is the solid place for all creatures to tread upon, only because it is immovable. If a tree could remove itself from one place to another, it would neither be afraid of the saw nor the wedge, nor exposed to the ill usage of the wood-mongers."

"All this is true," said the Beloved; "but, my dear companion, you know not, nor have you ever yet undergone the fatigues of travel, nor do you understand what it is to live in foreign countries; and believe me, travelling is a tree, the chiefest fruit of which is labour and disquiet."

"If the fatigues of travelling are very great," answered the Lover, "they are abundantly rewarded with the pleasure of seeing a thousand rarities; and when people are once grown accustomed to labour, they look upon it to be no hardship."

"Travelling," replied the Beloved, "my dear companion, is never delightful but when we travel in company of our friends; for when we are at a far distance from them, besides that we are exposed to the injuries of the weather, we are grieved to find ourselves separated from what we love: therefore take, my dearest, the advice which my tenderness suggests to you; never leave the place where you live at ease, nor forsake the object of your dearest affection."

"If I find these hardships insupportable," replied the Lover, "believe me, I will return in a little time.   If I do not, be assured that I am happy, and let the consciousness of that make you also so."   After they had thus reasoned the case together, they went to their rest, and meeting the next morning, the Lover being immovable in his resolution, took their leaves of each other, and so parted.

The Lover left his hole, like a bird that had made his escape out of a cage; and as he went on his journey, was ravished with delight at the prospect of the mountains, rivers, and gardens which he flew over; and, arriving towards evening at the foot of a little hill, where several rivulets, shaded with lovely trees, watered the enamelled meadows, he resolved to spend the night in a place that so effectually resembled a terrestrial paradise.   But, alas! how soon began he to feel the vicissitudes of fortune! Hardly had he betaken himself to his repose upon a tree, when the air grew gloomy, and blazing gleams of lightning began to flash against his eyes, while the thunder rattled along the plains, and became doubly terrible by its echoes from the neighbouring mountains.   The rain also and the hail came down together in whole torrents, and made the poor Pigeon hop from bough to bough, beaten, wetted to the skin, and in continual terror of being consumed in a flash of lightning.   In short, he spent the night so ill, that he already heartily repented his having left his comrade.

The next morning, the sun having dispersed the clouds, the Lover was prudent enough to take his leave of the tree, with a full resolution to make the best of his way home again; he had not, however, flown fifty yards, when a Sparrow-hawk, with a keen appetite, perceiving our traveller, pursued him upon the wing. The Pigeon, seeing him at a distance, began to tremble; and, as he approached nearer, utterly despairing ever to see his friend again, and no less sorry that he had not followed her advice, protested that if ever he escaped that danger, he would never more think of travelling. In this time the Sparrow-hawk had overtaken, and was just ready to seize him and tear him in pieces, when a hungry Eagle, lancing down with a full swoop upon the Sparrow-hawk, cried out; "Hold, let me devour that Pigeon to stay my stomach, till I find something else more solid."

The Sparrow-hawk, however, no less courageous than hungry, would not, though unequal in strength, give way to the Eagle; so that the two birds of prey fell to fighting one with another, and in the meantime the poor Pigeon escaped, and perceiving a hole so small that it would hardly give entrance to a Titmouse, yet made shift to squeeze himself into it, and so spent the night in a world of fear and trouble. At the break of the day he got out again, but he had now become so weak for want of food that he could hardly fly; add to this, he had not yet half recovered himself from the fear he was in the day before. As he was, however, full of terror, looking round about him to see whether the Sparrow-hawk or the Eagle appeared, he spied a Pigeon in a field at a small distance, with a great deal of corn scattered in the place where he was feeding. The Lover, rejoiced at the sight, drew near this happy Pigeon, as he thought him, and without compliments fell to; but he had hardly pecked three grains before he found himself caught by the legs. The pleasures of this world, indeed, are generally but snares which the devil lays for us.

"Brother," said the Lover to the other Pigeon, "we are both of one and the same species; wherefore, then, did you not inform me of this piece of treachery, that I might not have fallen into these springes they have laid for us?" To which the other answered; "Forbear complaints; nobody can prevent his destiny; nor can all the prudence of man preserve him from inevitable accidents."

The Lover, on this, next besought him to teach him some expedient to free himself from the danger that threatened him.

"Poor, innocent creature," answered the other, "if I knew any means to do this, dost thou not think I would make use of it to deliver myself, that so I might not be the occasion of surprising others of my fellow-creatures? Alas! unfortunate friend, thou art but like the young Camel, who, weary with travelling, cried to his mother, with tears in his eyes; 'O mother without affection! stop a little, that I may take breath and rest myself.' To whom the mother replied; 'O son without consideration! seest thou not that my bridle is in the hand of another? Were I at liberty, I would gladly both throw down my burden and give thee my assistance; but, alas! we must both submit to what we cannot avoid or prevent.'"

Our traveller perceiving, by this discourse, that all hopes of relief from others were vain, resolved to rely only on himself, and strengthened by his own despair, with much striving and long fluttering, at length broke the snare, and taking the benefit of his unexpected good fortune, bent his flight toward his own country; and such was his joy for having escaped so great a danger, that he even forgot his hunger. However, at length passing through a village, and lighting, merely for a little rest, upon a wall that was over against a field newly sown, a countryman, that was keeping the birds from his corn, perceiving the Pigeon, flung a stone at him, and, while the poor Lover was dreaming of nothing less than of the harm that was so near him, hit him so terrible a blow, that he fell quite stunned into a deep and dry well that was at the foot of the wall. By this, however, he escaped being made the countryman's supper, who, not being able to come at his prey, left it in the well, and never thought more of it.

There the Pigeon remained all the night long in the well, with a sad heart, and a wing half broken. During the night his misfortunes would not permit him to sleep, and a thousand times over he wished himself at home with his friend; the next day, however, he so bestirred himself, that he got out of the well, and towards evening arrived at his old habitation.

The Beloved, hearing the fluttering of her companion's wings, flew forth with a more than ordinary joy to meet him; but seeing him so weak and in so bad a condition, asked him tenderly the reason of it; upon which the Lover told her all his adventures,

protesting heartily to take her advice for the future, and never to travel more.

"I have recited," concluded the Vizir, "this example to your Majesty, to dissuade you from preferring the inconveniences of travelling, to the repose that you enjoy at home, among the praises and adorations of a loyal and happy people."

"Wise Vizir," said the King, "I acknowledge it a painful thing to travel; but it is no less true that there is great and useful knowledge to be gained by it. Should a man be always tied to his own house or his own country, he would be deprived of the sight and enjoyment of an infinite number of noble things. And to continue your allegoric history of the birds, the Falcon is happy in seeing the beauties of the world, while Princes frequently carry them upon their hands, and for that honour and pleasure he quits the inglorious life of the nest. On the other hand, the Owl is condemned, because he always hides himself in ruinous buildings and dark holes, and delights in nothing but retirement. The mind of man ought to fly abroad and soar like the Falcon, not hide itself like the Owl. He that travels renders himself acceptable to all the world, and men of wisdom and learning are pleased with his conversation. Nothing is more clear and limpid than running water, while stagnating puddles grow thick and muddy. Had the famous Falcon, that was bred in the Raven's nest, never flown abroad, he would never have been so highly advanced."

THE FABLE OF THE GREEDY CAT
Which the Raven Narrates to the Falcon

THERE WAS FORMERLY AN OLD WOMAN IN A VILLAGE, EXTREMELY thin, half-starved, and meagre. She lived in a little cottage as dark and gloomy as a fool's heart, and withal as close shut up as a miser's hand. This miserable creature had for the companion of her wretched retirements a Cat meagre and lean as herself; the poor creature never saw bread, nor beheld the face of a stranger, and was forced to be contented with only smelling the mice in their holes, or seeing the prints of their feet in the dust. If by some extraordinary lucky chance this miserable animal happened to catch a mouse, she was like a beggar that discovers a treasure; her visage and her eyes were inflamed with joy, and that booty served her for a whole week; and out of the excess of her admiration, and distrust of her own happiness, she would cry out to herself; "Heavens! Is this a dream, or is it real?"

One day, however, ready to die for hunger, she got upon the ridge of her enchanted castle, which had long been the mansion of famine for cats, and spied from thence another Cat, that was stalking upon a neighbour's wall like a Lion, walking along as if she had been counting her steps, and so fat that she could hardly go. The old Woman's Cat, astonished to see a creature of her own species so plump and so large, with a loud voice, cries out to her pursy neighbour; "In the name of pity, speak to me, O happiest of the Cat kind! why, you look as if you came from one of the Khan of Kathai's feasts; I conjure ye, to tell me how or in what region it is that you get your skin so well stuffed?"

"Where?" replied the fat one; "why, where should one feed well but at a King's table? I go to the house," continued she, "every day about dinner-time, and there I lay my paws upon some delicious morsel or other, which serves me till the next, and then leave enough for an army of mice, which under me live in peace and tranquillity; for why should I commit murder for a piece of tough and skinny mouse-flesh, when I can live on venison at a much easier rate?" The lean Cat, on this, eagerly inquired the way to this house of plenty, and entreated her plump neighbour to carry her one day along with her.

"Most willingly," said the fat Puss; "for thou seest I am naturally charitable, and thou art so lean that I heartily pity thy condition." On this promise they parted; and the lean Cat returned to the old Woman's chamber, where she told her dame the story of what had befallen her.

The old Woman prudently endeavoured to dissuade her Cat from prosecuting her design, admonishing her withal to have a care of being deceived; "For, believe me," said she, "the desires of the ambitious are never to be satiated, but when their mouths are stuffed with the dirt of their graves. Sobriety and temperance are the only things that truly enrich people. I must tell you, poor silly Cat, that they who travel to satisfy their ambition, have no knowledge of the good things they possess, nor are they truly thankful to Heaven for what they enjoy, who are not contented with their fortune."

The poor starved Cat, however, had conceived so fair an idea of the King's table, that the old Woman's good morals and judicious remonstrances entered in at one ear and went out at the other; in short, she departed the next day with the fat Puss to go to the King's house; but, alas! before she got thither, her destiny had laid a snare for her. For being a house of good cheer, it was so haunted with cats, that the servants had, just at this time, orders to kill all the cats that came near it, by reason of a great robbery committed the night before in the King's larder.

The old Woman's Cat, however, pushed on by hunger, entered the house, and no sooner saw a dish of meat unobserved by the cooks, than she made a seizure of it, and was doing what for many years she had not done before, that is, heartily filling her belly; but as she was enjoying herself under the dresser-board, and feeding heartily upon her stolen morsels, one of the testy officers of the kitchen, missing his breakfast, and seeing where the poor Cat was solacing herself with it, threw his knife at her with such an unlucky hand, that it struck her full in the breast. However, as it had been the providence of Nature to give this creature nine lives instead of one, poor Puss made a shift to crawl away, after she had for some time shammed dead; but, in her flight, observing the blood come streaming from her wound, "Well," said she, "let me but escape this accident, and if ever I quit my old hold and my own mice for all the rarities in the King's kitchen, may I lose all my nine lives at once."

"I cite you this example, to show you, that it is better to be contented with what one has than to travel in search of what ambition prompts us to seek for."

"What you say," said the Falcon, "is true, and it is a very wholesome advice; but it is for mean and low spirits only to confine themselves always to a little hole. He that aspires to be a King, must begin with the conquest of a kingdom, and he that would meet a crown must go in search of it. An effeminate and lazy life can never agree with a great soul."

"You are very magnanimous, Son," replied the Raven, "and I perceive design great conquests; but let me tell you, your enterprise cannot so soon be put in execution: before you can conquer a kingdom, you must get together arms and armies, and make great preparations."

"My talons," replied the Falcon, "are instruments sufficient to bring about my design, and myself am equal to the undertaking. Sure you never heard the story of the warrior, who by his single valour became a King?"

"No," replied the Raven; "therefore let me hear it from you." On which the Falcon related it in this manner.

THE POOR MAN WHO BECAME A GREAT KING

IT BEING THE PLEASURE OF HEAVEN TO RESCUE FROM MISERY a Man who lived in extreme poverty, Providence gave him a Son, who from his infancy showed signal signs that he would one day come to be a great man. This infant became an immediate blessing to the old Man's house, for his wealth increased from day to day, from the time that the child was born. So soon as this young one could speak, he talked of nothing but swords, and bows and arrows. The Father sent him to school, and did all he could to infuse into him a good relish of learning; but he neglected his book, and devoted his thoughts to nothing but running at the ring, and other warlike exercises with the other children.

When he came to the years of discretion, "Son," said his Father to him, "thou art now past the age of childhood, and art in the greatest danger to fall into disorder and irregularity, if thou givest thyself over to thy passions. I therefore intend to prevent that accident by marrying thee betimes."

"Dear Father," replied the stripling, "for Heaven's sake, refuse me not the mistress which my youthful years have already made choice of."

"Who is that mistress?" presently replied the old Man, with great earnestness and uneasiness, for he had already looked out for him the daughter of a neighbouring hind, and agreed the matter with her father, "and what is her condition?"

"This is she," the lad made answer, showing his Father a very noble sword; "and by virtue of this I expect to become master of a throne."

The Father gave him many reasons to imagine he disapproved his intentions, and looked on them as little better than madness: many a good lecture followed during the remainder of the day; to avoid which for the future, the young hero the next morning quitted his Father's house, and travelled in search of opportunities to signalise his courage; many years he warred under the command of different Monarchs. At length, after he had everywhere signalised himself, not only by his conduct, but by his personal courage, a neighbouring Monarch, who, with his whole family, lay besieged in a small fortress, sent to him to beseech him to accept of the command of all his forces, to get them together, and endeavour to raise the siege, and relieve them; in which, if he succeeded, he would make him his adopted son, and the heir of his vast empire.

Our young warrior engaged in this, raised a vast army, fought the besiegers in their trenches, entirely conquered them, and was the gainer of a glorious victory. But, alas! the heat of the action made him not perceive that the fortress in which the King was, was in flames; some treacherous person had fired it, at the instigation of the general of the besieger's army, and the King and his whole family perished in the flames; the old Monarch just lived, however, to see his deliverer, and to settle on him the inheritance of his crown. The Royal Family being all extinct by this fatal calamity, the nobles ratified the grant, and our illustrious hero lived many years a great and glorious monarch.

"I have recited this example," said the Falcon to the Raven, "that you may understand that I also find myself born to undertake great enterprises; I have a strange foreboding within me, that I shall prove no less fortunate than this famous warrior; and for this reason can never quit my design." When the Raven perceived him so fixed in his resolution, he consented to his putting it in execution; persuaded that so noble a courage would never be guilty of idle or unworthy actions.

The Falcon having taken his leave of the Raven, and bid farewell to all his pretended brethren, left the nest and flew away; long he continued flying, and in love with liberty, and at length stopped upon a high mountain; here, looking round about him, he spied a Partridge in the fallow grounds that made all the neighbouring hills resound with her note. Presently the Falcon lanced himself upon her, and having got her in his pounce, began to tear and eat her.

"This is no bad beginning," said he to himself; "though it were for nothing but to taste such delicious food; 'tis better travelling than to lie sleeping in a nasty nest, and feed upon carrion, as my brothers do." Thus he spent three days in caressing himself with delicate morsels; but on the fourth, being on the top of another mountain, he saw a company of men that were hawking; these happened to be the King of the country with all his court; and while he was gazing upon them, he saw their Falcon in pursuit of a Heron. Upon that, pricked forward by a noble emulation, he flies with all his force, gets before the King's Falcon, and overtakes the Heron. The King, admiring this agility, commands his Falconers to make use of all their cunning to catch this noble bird, which by good luck they did. And in a little time he so entirely won the affection of the King, that he did him the honour to carry him usually upon his own hand.

"Had he always stayed in his nest," concluded the Monarch,

"this good fortune had never befallen him. And you see by this Fable, that it is no unprofitable thing to travel. It rouses the genius of people, and renders them capable of noble achievements."

Dabschelim having ended his discourse, the Vizir, after he had made his submissions, and paid his duty according to custom, came forward, and addressing himself to the King, said; "Sir, what your Majesty has said is most true, but I cannot but think yet that it is not advisable that a great, a glorious, and happy King should quit his repose for the hardship and danger of travelling."

"Men of courage," answered the King, "delight in labour, fatigue, and danger. If Kings, who have power, strip not the thorns from the rose-bushes, the poor can never gather the roses; and till Princes have endured the inconveniences of campaigns, the people can never sleep in peace. Nobody can be safe in these dominions, while thou seekest nothing but my ease."

THE DERVISE, THE FALCON, AND THE RAVEN

A CERTAIN DERVISE USED TO RELATE, THAT, IN HIS YOUTH, ONCE passing through a wood and admiring the works of the great Author of Nature, he spied a Falcon that held a piece of flesh in its beak; and hovering about a tree, tore the flesh into bits, and gave it to a young Raven that lay bald and featherless in its nest. The Dervise admiring the bounty of Providence, in rapture of admiration, cried out; "Behold, this poor bird, that is not able to seek out sustenance for himself, is not, however, forsaken of its Creator, who spreads the whole world like a table, where all creatures have their food ready provided for them! He extends His liberality so far, that the serpent finds wherewith to live upon the mountain of Gahen. Why, then, am I so greedy, and wherefore do I run to the ends of the earth, and plough up the ocean for bread? Is it not better that I should henceforward confine myself in repose to some little corner, and abandon myself to fortune?"

Upon this he retired to his cell, where, without putting himself to any farther trouble for anything in the world, he remained three days and three nights without victuals.

At last, "Servant of mine," said the Creator to him in a dream, "know thou that all things in this world have their causes; and though my providence can never be limited, my wisdom requires that men shall make use of the means that I have ordained them. If thou wouldst imitate any one of the birds thou hast seen to my glory, use the talents I have given thee, and imitate the Falcon that feeds the Raven, and not the Raven that lies a sluggard in his nest, and expects his food from another."

"This example shows us that we are not to lead idle and lazy lives upon the pretence of depending upon Providence."

On this the elder son was silenced, but the second son, taking upon him to speak, said to his Father; "You advise us, sir, to labour, and get estates and riches; but when we have heaped up a great deal of wealth, is it not also necessary that you inform us what we shall do with it?"

" 'Tis easy to acquire wealth," replied the Father, "but a difficult thing to expend it well. Riches many times prove very fatal."

THE FABLE OF THE FOX AND THE HEN
Which Damna, the Fox, Told to the Lion

"THERE WAS ONCE UPON A TIME A CERTAIN HUNGRY FOX, WHO eagerly searching about for something to appease his hunger, at length spied a Hen, that was busy scratching the earth and picking up worms at the foot of a tree. Upon the same tree there also hung a drum, which made a noise every now and then, the branches being moved by the violence of the wind, and beating upon it. The Fox was just going to fling himself upon the Hen, and make amends for a long fast, when he first heard the noise of the drum. 'O ho,' quoth he, looking up, 'are you there? I will be with ye by and by; that body, whatever it be, I promise myself must certainly have more flesh upon it than a sorry Hen.' So saying, he clambered up the tree, and in the meanwhile the Hen made her escape. The greedy and famished Fox seized his prey, and fell to work with teeth and claws upon it. But when he had torn off the head of the drum, and found there was nothing within but an empty cavity,—air instead of flesh and gristles, and a mere hollowness instead of good guts and insides,—fetching a deep sigh, 'Unfortunate wretch that I am,' cried he, 'what a delicate morsel have I lost, only for the show of a large bellyful!'

"I have recited this example," concluded he, "to the end your Majesty may not be terrified with the sound of the bellowing noise you hear, because loud and strenuous, for there is no certainty from that of its coming from a terrible beast; and if you please, I will go and see what sort of creature it is."

To this the Lion consented; nevertheless, when *Damna* was gone, he repented his having sent him. "For," said the Monarch to himself, "I should have remembered my father's excellent rule, that it is a great error in a Prince to discover his secrets to any, but especially that there are ten sorts of people who are never to be instrusted with them. These are, 1 Those whom he has used ill without a cause. 2 Those who have lost their estates or their honour at court. 3 Those who have been degraded from their employments without any hopes of ever being restored to them again. 4 Those that love nothing but sedition and disturbance. 5 Those that see their kindred or acquaintance in preferments from whence themselves have been excluded. 6 Such as, having committed any crime, have been more severely punished than others who have transgressed in the same manner. 7 Such as have done good service, and have been but ill rewarded for it. 8 Enemies reconciled by constraint. 9 Those who believe the ruin of the Prince will turn to their advantage. 10 And lastly, those who believe themselves less obliged to their Sovereign than to his enemy. And as these are together so numerous as a class of persons, I hope I have not done imprudently in discovering my secrets to *Damna*."

While the Lion was making these reflections to himself, *Damna* returned, and told him, with a smiling countenance, that the beast which made such a noise was no other than an Ox, that was feeding in a meadow, without any other design than to spend his days lazily in eating and sleeping. "And," added *Damna*, "if your Majesty thinks it convenient, I will so order the matter, that he shall be glad to come and enroll himself in the number of your servants."

The Lion was extremely pleased with *Damna's* proposals, and made him a sign to go and fetch the Ox into his presence. On this, *Damna* went to *Cohotorbe*, the Ox, and asked him from whence he came, and what accident brought him into those quarters? In answer to which, when *Cohotorbe* had related his history at large, *Damna* said; "Friend, I am very glad I have happened to see thee, for it may be in my power to do thee a singular service, by acquainting thee with the state of the place thou hast accidentally wandered into; know, then, that here lives a Lion not far off, who is the king of all the beasts of this country, and that he is, though a terrible enemy, yet a most kind and tender friend to all the beasts who put themselves under his protection. When I first saw thee here, I acquainted his Majesty with it, and he has graciously desired to see thee, and given me orders to conduct thee to his palace. If thou wilt follow me, I promise thee the favour of being admitted into his service and protection; but if thou refusest to go along with me, know that thou hast not many days to live in this place."

So soon as the Ox but heard the word Lion pronounced, he trembled for fear; but, recovering himself a little as *Damna* continued his speech, he at length made answer; "If thou wilt assure me that he shall do me no harm, I will follow him." *Damna*, at that, immediately swore to him; and *Cohotorbe*, upon the faith of his oaths, consented to go and wait upon the Lion. *Damna*, on this, ran before to give the King notice of *Cohotorbe's* coming; and our Ox, arriving soon after, made a profound reverence to the King, who received him with great kindness, and asked him what occasion had brought him into his dominions?

In answer to which, when the Ox had recounted to him all his adventures, "Remain here," said the Lion, "with us, and live in peace; for I permit all my subjects to live within my dominions in repose and tranquillity." The Ox having returned his Majesty thanks for his kind reception, promised to serve him with a real fidelity; and at length insinuated himself in such a manner into the Lion's favour, that he gained his Majesty's confidence, and became his most intimate favourite.

This, however, was matter of great affliction to poor *Damna,* who, when he saw that *Cohotorbe* was in greater esteem at court than himself, and that he was the only depository of the King's secrets, it wrought in him so desperate a jealousy, that he could not rest, but was ready to hang himself for vexation; in the fullness of his heart he flew to make his moan to his wife *Kalila.* "O wife," said he, "I have taken a world of care and pains to gain the King's favour, and all to no purpose; I brought, you may remember, into his presence the object that occasioned all his disturbances, and that very Ox is now become the sole cause of my disquiet."

To which *Kalila* answered; "Spouse, you ought not to complain of what you have done, or at least you have nobody to blame but yourself."

"It is true," said *Damna,* "that I am the cause of all my troubles; this I am too sensible of, but what I desire of you is, to prescribe me the remedy."

"I told you from the beginning," replied *Kalila,* "that for my part I would never meddle with your affairs, and now do not intend to trouble myself with the cure of your disturbances. Mind your own business yourself, and consider what course you have to take, and take it; for, as to me, I have plagues enough of my own, without making myself unhappy about the misfortunes which your own follies have brought upon you."

"Well then," replied *Damna,* "what I shall do is this; I will use all my endeavours to ruin this Ox which occasions me all my misery, and shall be contented if I but find I have as much wit as the Sparrow that revenged himself upon the Hawk." *Kalila,* upon this, desired him to recite that Fable, and *Damna* gave it to her in the following manner.

THE SPARROW AND THE SPARROW-HAWK

TWO SPARROWS HAD ONCE BUILT THEIR NESTS UNDER THE SAME hovel, where they had also laid up some small provision for their young ones; but a Sparrow-hawk, who had built his nest upon the top of a mountain, at the foot of which this hovel stood, came continually to watch at what time their eggs would be hatched; and when they were, immediately ate up the young sparrows. This was a most sensible affliction to both the parents. However, they had afterwards another brood, which they hid so among the thatch of the hovel, that the Hawk was never able to find them; these, therefore, they bred up so well, and in so much safety, that they had both of them the pleasure to see them ready to fly. The father and the mother, by their continual chirping, testified for a long time their joy for such a happiness; but all of a sudden, as the young ones began to be fledged, they fell into a profound melancholy, which was caused through extremity of fear lest the Sparrow-hawk should devour these young ones as he had done the others, as soon as they found their way out of the nest.

The eldest of the young sparrows one day, perceiving this, desired to know of the father the reason of his affliction, which the father having discovered to him, he made answer, that instead of breaking his heart with sorrow, it much better became him to seek out some way, if possible, to remove so dangerous a neighbour. All the sparrows approved this advice of the young one; and while the mother flew to get food, the father went another way in search of some cure for his sorrows. After he had flown about for some time, said he to himself; "I know not, alas! what it is I am seeking. Whither shall I fly? and to whom shall I discover my troubles?"

At length he resolved, not knowing what course to take, to address himself to the first creature he met, and to consult him about his business. This first creature chanced to be a Salamander, whose extraordinary shape at first affrighted him. However, the Sparrow would not alter his resolution, but accosted and saluted him.

The Salamander, who was very civil, gave him an obliging reception; and looking upon him with a fixed eye, "Friend," said he, "I discover much trouble in thy countenance; if it proceed from weariness, sit down and rest thyself; if from any other cause, let me know it; and if it be in my power to serve thee, command me." With that the Sparrow told his misfortunes in such moving language as raised compassion in the Salamander.

"Well," said he, "be of courage, let not these troubles any more perplex thee; I will deliver thee from this wicked neighbour this very night; only show me his nest, and then go peaceably to roost with thy young ones." This the Sparrow accordingly punctually did, and returned the Salamander many thanks for being so much concerned for his misfortunes.

No sooner was the night come, but the Salamander, determined to make good his promise, collected together a number of his fellows, and away they went in a body, with every one a bit of lighted sulphur in their mouths to the Sparrow-hawk's nest, who, not dreaming of any such thing, was surprised by the Salamanders, who threw the sulphur into the nest, and burnt the old Hawk, with all the young ones.

"This Fable teaches ye, that whoever has a design to ruin his enemy, may possibly bring it about, let him be never so weak."

"But consider, spouse," replied *Kalila*. "*Cohotorbe* is the King's chief favourite, and it will be a difficult thing, believe me, to ruin him; where prudent princes have once placed their confidence, they seldom withdraw it because of bare report. And I presume you will not be able to use any other means on this occasion."

"I will take care, however," replied *Damna,* "of this, at least, that it shall be represented to the Lion, that one of the six great things which cause the ruin of kingdoms, and which is indeed the principal, is to neglect and contemn men of wit and courage."

"That, indeed," replied *Kalila,* "is one very great one; but what, I pray, are the other five?"

"The second," continued *Damna,* "is not to punish the seditious; the third is to be too much given to women, to play, and divertissements; the fourth, the accidents attending a pestilence, a famine, or an earthquake; the fifth is being too rash and violent; and the sixth is the preferring war before peace."

"You are wise and prudent, spouse," replied *Kalila;* "but let me, though more simple, advise you in this matter; be not the carver of your own revenge; but consider that whoever meditates mischief, commonly brings it at last upon his own head. On the other side, he that studies his neighbour's welfare, prospers in everything he undertakes, as you may see by the ensuing Fable."

THE KING WHO FROM A SAVAGE TYRANT BECAME A BENIGN RULER

THERE WAS ONCE IN THE EASTERN PART OF EGYPT A KING, WHOSE reign had long been a course of savage tyranny; long had he ruined the rich and distressed the poor; so that all his subjects, day and night, implored of heaven to be delivered from him. One day, as he returned from hunting, after he had summoned his people together, "Unhappy subjects," says he to them, "my conduct has been long unjustifiable in regard to you; but that tyranny, with which I have governed hitherto, is at an end, and I assure you from henceforward you shall live in peace and at ease, and nobody shall dare to oppress you." The people were extremely overjoyed at this good news, and forbore praying against the King.

In a word, this Prince made from this time such an alteration in his conduct, that he acquired the title of the Just, and every one began to bless the felicity of his reign.

One day, when his subjects were thus settled in happiness, one of his favourites presuming to ask him the reason of so sudden and so remarkable a change, the King gave him this answer; "As I rode a-hunting the other day," said he, "I saw a series of accidents which threw me into a turn of mind that has produced this happy change, which, believe me, cannot give my people more real satisfaction than it does myself. The things that made this change in me were these; I saw a dog in pursuit of a fox, who, after he had overtaken him, bit off the lower part of his leg; however, the fox, lame as he was, made a shift to escape and get into a hole, and the dog, not able to get him out, left him there. Hardly had he gone, however, a hundred paces, when a man threw a great stone at him and cracked his skull; at the same instant the man ran in the way of a horse, that trod upon his foot and lamed him for ever; and soon after the horse's foot stuck so fast between two stones, that he broke his ankle-bone in striving to get it out. On seeing the sudden misfortunes befall those who had engaged in doing ill to others, I could not help saying to myself, Men are used as they use others; whoever does that which he ought not to do, receives what he is not willing to receive."

"This example shows you, my dear spouse, that they who do mischief to others, are generally punished themselves for it, when they least expect it: believe me, if you attempt to ruin *Cohotorbe,* you will repent of it; he is stronger than you, and has more friends."

"No matter for that, dear spouse," replied *Damna,* "wit is always beyond strength, as the following Fable will convince you."

A RAVEN, A FOX, AND A SERPENT

A RAVEN HAD ONCE BUILT HER NEST FOR MANY SEASONS together in a convenient cleft of a mountain, but however pleasing the place was to her, she had always reason enough to resolve to lay there no more; for every time she hatched, a Serpent came and devoured her young ones. The Raven complaining to a Fox that was one of her friends, said to him; "Pray tell me, what would you advise me to do to be rid of this Serpent?"

"What do you think to do?" asked the Fox.

"Why, my present intent is," replied the Raven, "to go and peck out his eyes when he is asleep, that so he may no longer find the way to my nest." The Fox disapproved this design, and told the Raven, that it became a prudent person to manage his revenge in such a manner that no mischief might befall himself in taking it; "Never run yourself," says he, "into the misfortune that once befell the Crane, of which I will tell you the Fable."

THE CRANE AND THE CRAW-FISH

A CRANE HAD ONCE SETTLED HER HABITATION BY THE SIDE OF A broad and deep lake, and lived upon such fish as she could catch in it; these she got in plenty enough for many years; but at length having become old and feeble, she could fish no longer. In this afflicting circumstance she began to reflect, with sorrow, on the carelessness of her past years; "I did ill," said she to herself, "in not making in my youth necessary provision to support me in my old age; but, as it is, I must now make the best of a bad market, and use cunning to get a livelihood as I can."

With this resolution she placed herself by the water-side, and began to sigh and look mighty melancholy. A Craw-fish, perceiving her at a distance, accosted her, and asked her why she appeared so sad? "Alas," said she, "how can I otherwise choose but grieve, seeing my daily nourishment is like to be taken from me? for I just now heard this talk between two fishermen passing this way. Said the one to the other, 'Here is great store of fish, what think you of clearing this pond?' to whom his companion answered, 'No; there is more in such a lake; let us go thither first, and then come hither the day afterwards.' This they will certainly perform; and then," added the Crane, "I must soon prepare for death."

The Craw-fish, on this, went to the fish, and told them what she had heard; upon which the poor fish, in great perplexity, swam immediately to the Crane, and addressing themselves to her, told her what they had heard, and added; "We are now in so great a consternation, that we are come to desire your protection. Though you are our enemy, yet the wise tell us, that they who make their enemy their sanctuary, may be assured of being well received; you know full well that we are your daily food; and if we are destroyed, you, who are now too old to travel in search of food, must also perish; we pray you, therefore, for your own sake, as well as ours, to consider, and tell us what you think is the best course for us to take."

To which the Crane replied; "That which you acquaint me with, I heard myself from the mouths of the fishermen; we have no power sufficient to withstand them; nor do I know any other way to secure you, but this; it will be many months before they can clear the other pond they are to go about first; and, in the meantime, I can at times, and as my strength will permit me, remove you one after another into a little pond here hard by, where there is very good water, and where the fishermen can never catch you, by reason of the extraordinary depth."

The fish approved this counsel, and desired the Crane to carry them one by one into this pond. Nor did she fail to fish up three or four every morning, but she carried them no farther than to the top of a small hill, where she ate them. And thus she feasted herself for a while.

But one day, the Craw-fish, having a desire to see this delicate pond, made known her curiosity to the Crane, who, bethinking herself that the Craw-fish was her most mortal enemy, resolved to get rid of her at once, and murder her as she had done the rest; with this design she flung the Craw-fish upon her neck, and flew towards the hill. But when they came near the place, the Craw-fish, spying at a distance the small bones of her slaughtered companions, mistrusted the Crane's intention, and laying hold of a fair opportunity, got her neck in her claw, and grasped it so hard, that she fairly saved herself, and strangled the Crane.

"This example," said the Fox, "shows you that crafty, tricking people often become victims to their own cunning."

The Raven, returning thanks to the Fox for his good advice, said, "I shall not by any means neglect your wholesome instructions; but what shall I do?"

"Why," replied the Fox, "you must snatch up something that belongs to some stout man or other, and let him see what you do, to the end he may follow you. Which that he may easily do, do you fly slowly; and when you are just over the Serpent's hole, let fall the thing that you hold in your beak or talons, whatever it be, for then the person that follows you, seeing the Serpent come forth, will not fail to knock him on the head." The Raven did as the Fox advised him, and by that means was delivered from the Serpent.

"What cannot be done by strength," said *Damna,* "is to be performed by policy."

"It is very true," replied *Kalila;* "but the mischief here is, that the Ox has more policy than you. He will, by his prudence, frustrate all your projects, and before you can pluck one hair from his tail, will flay off your skin. I know not whether you have ever heard of the Fable of the Rabbit, the Fox, and the Wolf; if not, I will tell it you, that you may make your advantage of it in the present case."

THE RABBIT, THE FOX, AND THE WOLF

A HUNGRY WOLF ONCE SPIED A RABBIT FEEDING AT THE FOOT of a tree, and was soon preparing to seize him. The Rabbit, perceiving him, would have saved his life by flight, but the Wolf threw himself in his way, and stopped his escape; so that seeing himself in the power of the Wolf, submissive and prostrate at his feet, he gave him all the good words he could think of.

"I know," said he, "that the king of all creatures wants a supply to appease his hunger, and that he is now ranging the fields in search of food; but I am but an insignificant morsel for his royal stomach; therefore let him be pleased to take my information. About a furlong from hence lives a Fox that is fat and plump, and whose flesh is as white as a capon's; such a prey will do your Majesty's business. If you please, I will go and give him a visit, and engage him to come forth out of his hole; then, if he prove to your liking, you may devour him; if not, it will be my glory that I had the honour of dying not in vain, but being a small breakfast for your Majesty."

Thus over-persuaded, the Wolf gave the Rabbit leave to seek out the Fox, and followed him at the heels. The Rabbit left the Wolf at the entrance of the hole, and crept in himself, overjoyed that he had such an opportunity to revenge himself on the Fox, from whom he had received an affront which he had for a long time pretended to have forgot. He made him a low congé, and gave him great protestations of his friendship. On the other side, the Fox was no less obliging in his answers to the Rabbit's civilities, and asked him what good wind had blown him thither.

"Only the great desire I had to see your worship," replied the Rabbit; "and there is one of my relations at the door, who is no less ambitious to kiss your hands, but he dares not enter without your permission."

The Fox on this, mistrusting there was something more than ordinary in all this civility, said to himself; "I shall find the bottom of all this presently, and then, if it proves as I suspect, I will take care to pay this pretended friend of mine in his own coin." However, not seeming to take any notice of what he suspected, "Sir," said he to the Rabbit, "your friend shall be most welcome; he does me too much honour; but," added he, "I must entreat you to let me put my chamber in a little better order to receive him."

The Rabbit, too much persuaded of the good success of his enterprise, "Poh, poh," said he, "my relation is one that never stands upon ceremony," and so went out to give the Wolf notice that the Fox had fallen into the snare. The Wolf thought he had the Fox fast already, and the Rabbit believed himself quite out of danger, as having done the Wolf such a piece of good service. But the Fox was too sharp-sighted to be thus trepanned out of his life. He had, at the entrance of his hole, a very deep trench, which he had digged on purpose to guard him against surprises of this nature. Presently, therefore, he took away the planks, which he had laid for the convenience of those that came to visit him, covered the trench with a little earth and straw, and set open a back door in case of necessity; and having thus prepared all things, he desired the Rabbit and his friend to walk in. But instead of the success of their plot, the two visitors found themselves, before they expected it, in the bottom of a very deep pit; and the Wolf, imagining that the Rabbit had a hand in the contrivance, in the heat of his fury, tore him to pieces.

"By this you see that finesse and policy signify nothing, where you have persons of wit and prudence to deal with."

"It is very true," said *Damna*; "but the Ox is now proud of his preferment, and thoughtless of danger, at least from me; for he has not the least suspicion of my hatred."

THE TWO FISHERMEN AND THE THREE FISHES

As Told by Damna, the Fox, to His Majesty, the Lion

THERE WAS ONCE IN YOUR MAJESTY'S DOMINIONS A CERTAIN pond, the water of which was very clear, and emptied itself into a neighbouring river. This pond was in a quiet place; it was remote from the highway, and there were in it three Fishes; the one of them was prudent, the second had but little wit, and the third was a mere fool.

One day, by chance, two Fishermen, in their walks, perceiving this pond, made up to it, and no sooner observed these three Fishes, which were large and fat, but they went and fetched their nets to take them. The Fishes suspecting, by what they saw of the Fishermen, that they intended no less than their destruction, began to be in a world of terror. The prudent Fish immediately resolved what course to take; he threw himself out of the pond, through the little channel that opened into the river, and so made his escape.

The next morning the two Fishermen returned; they made it their first business to stop up all the passages, to prevent the Fishes from getting out, and were making preparations for taking them. The half-witted Fish now heartily repented that he had not followed his companion; at length, however, he bethought himself of a stratagem; he appeared upon the surface of the water with his belly upward, and feigned to be dead. The Fisherman also, having taken him up, thought him really what he counterfeited himself to be, so threw him again into the water. And the last, which was the foolish Fish, seeing himself pressed by the Fishermen, sunk down to the bottom of the pond, shifted up and down from place to place, but could not avoid at last falling into their hands, and was that day made part of a public entertainment.

"This example," continued *Damna*, "shows you that you ought to prevent *Cohotorbe*, who is a traitor to your Majesty, and has, I believe, some design on your sacred person, from doing the mischief he intends, by making yourself master of his life, before he have yours at his command."

"What you say is very agreeable to reason," said the King, "but

I cannot believe that *Cohotorbe,* upon whom I have heaped so many favours, should be so perfidious as you say."

"Why, it is most true," replied *Damna,* "that he never received anything but kindness from your Majesty; but what is bred in the bone will never come out of the flesh; neither can anything come out of a vessel but what is put into it; of which the following Fable is a sufficient proof."

THE FALCON AND THE HEN

As Told by Damna, the Fox, to Cohotorbe, the Ox

"OF ALL THE ANIMALS I WAS EVER ACQUAINTED WITH," SAID A Falcon once to a Hen, "you are the most unmindful of benefits, and the most ungrateful."

"Why, what ingratitude," replied the Hen, "have you ever observed in me?"

"Can there be a greater piece of ingratitude," replied the Falcon, "than that which you commit in regard to men? By day they seek out every nourishment to fat you; and in the night you have a place always ready to roost in, where they take care that your chamber be close barred up, that nothing may trouble your repose; nevertheless, when they would catch you, you forget all their goodness to you, and basely endeavour to escape their hands; which is what I never do, I that am a wild creature, no way obliged to them, and a bird of prey. Upon the meanest of their caresses I grow tame; suffer myself to be taken, and never eat but upon their fists."

"All this is very true," replied the Hen; "but I find you know not the reason of my flight; you never saw a Falcon upon the spit; but I have seen a thousand Hens dressed with all manner of sauces."

"I have recited this Fable to show you that often they who are ambitious of a court-life, know not the inconveniences of it."

"I believe, friend," said *Damna,* "that the Lion seeks your life for no other reason than that he is jealous of your virtues."

"The fruit-trees only," replied *Cohotorbe,* "are subject to have their branches broken; Nightingales are caged because they sing more pleasantly than other birds; and we pluck the Peacocks' feathers from their tails for no other reason but because they are beautiful. Merit alone is, therefore, too often the source and origin of our misfortunes. However, I am not afraid of whatever contrivances the malice of wicked people can make to my prejudice; but shall endeavour to submit to what I cannot prevent, and imitate the Nightingale in the following Fable."

THE NIGHTINGALE AND THE COUNTRYMAN

A CERTAIN COUNTRYMAN HAD A ROSE-BUSH IN HIS GARDEN, which he made his sole pleasure and delight. Every morning he went to look upon it, in the season of its flowering, and see his roses ready to blow. One day as he was admiring, according to his custom, the beauty of the flowers, he spied a Nightingale perched upon one of the branches near a very fine flower, and plucking off the leaves of it one after another. This put him into so great a passion, that the next day he laid a snare for the Nightingale, in revenge of the wrong; in which he succeeded so well, that he took the bird, and immediately put her in a cage.

The Nightingale, very melancholy to see herself in that condition, with a mournful voice asked the Countryman the reason of her slavery. To whom he replied; "Knowest thou not that my whole delight was in those flowers, which thou wast wantonly destroying? Every leaf that thou pluckedst from that rose was as a drop of blood from my heart."

"Alas!" replied the Nightingale, "you use me very severely for having cropped a few leaves from a rose; but expect to be used harshly in the other world, for afflicting me in this manner; for there all people are used after the same manner as they here use the other animals."

The Countryman, moved with these words, gave the Nightingale her liberty again; for which she, willing to thank him, said; "Since you have had compassion in your nature, and have done me this favour, I will repay your kindness in the manner it deserves. Know therefore," continued she, "that at the foot of yonder tree, there lies buried a pot full of gold; go and take it, and Heaven bless you with it."

The Countryman digged about the tree, and, finding the pot, astonished at the Nightingale's sagacity in discovering it, "I wonder," said he to her, "that, being able to see this pot, which was buried underground, you could not discover the net that was spread for your captivity."

"Know you not," replied the Nightingale, "that, however sharp-sighted or prudent we are, we can never escape our destiny?"

"By this example you see that, when we are conscious of our own innocence, we are wholly to resign ourselves up to our fate."

"It is very true," replied *Damna;* "the Lion, however, according to the most just observation of the captive Nightingale in your Fable, in seeking your destruction, cannot but incur divine punishment; and, desirous as he is to augment his grandeur by your fall, I am apt to think that what once befell the Hunter will be his destiny."

THE HUNTER, THE FOX, AND THE LEOPARD

"A CERTAIN HUNTER ONCE," SAID DAMNA, PURSUING HIS DIScourse, "espied, in the middle of a field, a Fox, who looked with so engaging an aspect, and had on a skin so fair and lovely, that he had a great desire to take him alive. With this intent he found out his hole, and just before the entrance into it dug a very deep trench, which he covered with slender twigs and straw, and, having laid on it a piece of smoking lamb's flesh, just cut up, went and hid himself in a corner out of sight. The Fox, returning to his hole, and observing at a distance what the Hunter had left for his breakfast, presently ran to see what dainty morsel it was. When he came to the trench, he would fain have been tasting the delicate entertainment; but the fear of some treachery would not permit him to fall to; and, in short, finding he had strong reasons to suspect some ill design towards him, he was cunning enough to remove his lodging, and take up other quarters.

"In a moment after he was gone, as fortune would have it, came a hungry Leopard, who, being tempted by the savoury odour of the yet warm and smoking flesh, made such haste to fall to, that he tumbled into the trench. The Hunter, hearing the noise of the falling Leopard, immediately threw himself into the trench, without looking into it, never questioning but that it was the Fox he had taken; but there found, instead of him the Leopard, who tore him in pieces, and devoured him.

"This Fable teaches us, that, however earnestly we may wish for any event, providence and wisdom ought to regulate our desires."

"I did very ill, indeed," replied *Cohotorbe*, "to accept the Lion's offer of favour and friendship, and now heartily wish I had been content with an humbler fortune."

"It is not enough," replied *Damna*, interrupting him, "to repent and bewail your past life; your business is now to endeavour to moderate the Lion's passion."

"I am assured of his natural good will to me," replied the Ox, *Cohotorbe*; "but traitors and flatterers will do their utmost to change his favour into hatred, and I am afraid they will bring about their designs."

"You are perfectly in the right," said *Damna*; "but, for my part, were I in your condition, I would defend my life; and, if I must perish, fall like a warrior, not like a victim of justice at the gallows. He that dies with his sword in his hand, renders himself famous. It is not good to begin a war; but, when we are attacked, it is ignominious to surrender ourselves like cowards into the enemy's hand."

"This is right and proper counsel," replied *Cohotorbe*; "but we ought to know our strength before we engage in a combat and attack our enemy."

"An enemy," said *Damna*, the Fox, "I very well know, is at no time to be despised."

"However," replied *Cohotorbe*, "I will not begin the combat; but if the Lion attacks me, I will endeavour to defend myself."

"Well," answered *Damna*, "that you may know when to be

upon your guard, let me give you this caution; when you see him lash the ground with his tail, and roll his eyes angrily about, you may be sure he will immediately be upon you."

"I thank you for your advice," replied *Cohotorbe;* "and when I observe the signs which you have, so like a friend, informed me of, I shall prepare myself to receive him."

Here they parted; and *Damna,* overjoyed at the success of his enterprise, ran to *Kalila,* who asked him how his design went forward. "I thank my fates," cried *Damna,* "I am just going to triumph over my enemy." After this short confabulation, the two Foxes went to court, where soon after *Cohotorbe* arrived.

The Lion no sooner beheld him, but he thought him guilty; and *Cohotorbe,* casting his eyes upon the Lion, made no question, from what he saw, but that his Majesty had resolved his ruin; so that both the one and the other manifesting those signs which *Damna* had described to each, there began a most terrible combat, wherein the Lion killed the Ox, but not, however, without a great deal of trouble and hazard.

When all was over, "O! what a wicked creature thou art!" cried *Kalila* to *Damna;* "thou hast here, for thine own sake, endangered the King's life; thy end will be miserable for contriving such pernicious designs; and that which happened to a cheat, who was the cully of his own knaveries, will one day befall thee."

THE GARDENER AND THE BEAR

As Told to Damna, the Fox, by his Wife Kalila

THERE WAS ONCE, IN THE EASTERN PARTS OF OUR COUNTRY, a Gardener, who loved gardening to that degree that he wholly absented himself from the company of men, to the end he might give himself up entirely to the care of his flowers and plants. He had neither wife nor children; and from morning till night he did nothing but work in his garden, so that it lay like a terrestrial paradise. At length, however, the good man grew weary of being alone, and took a resolution to leave his garden in search of good company.

As he was, soon after, walking at the foot of a mountain, he spied a Bear, whose looks had in them nothing of a savage fierceness natural to that animal, but were mild and gentle. This bear was also weary of being alone, and came down from the mountain, for no other reason but to see whether he could meet with any one that would join society with him. So soon, therefore, as these two saw each other, they began to have a friendship one for another; and the Gardener first accosted the Bear, who, in return, made him a profound reverence. After some compliments passed between them, the Gardener made the Bear a sign to follow him, and carrying him into his garden, regaled him with a world of very delicious fruit, which he had carefully preserved; so that at length they entered into a very strict friendship together; insomuch that when the Gardener was weary of working, and lay down to take a little nap, the Bear, out of affection, stayed all the while by him, and kept off the flies from his face.

One day as the Gardener lay down to sleep at the foot of a tree, and the Bear stood by, according to his custom, to drive away the flies, it happened that one of those insects did light upon the Gardener's mouth, and still as the Bear drove it away from one side, it would light on the other; which put the Bear into such a passion, that he took up a great stone to kill it. It is true he did kill the fly; but at the same time he broke out two or three

of the Gardener's teeth. From whence men of judgment observe, that it is better to have a prudent enemy than an ignorant friend.

"This example shows that we should take care whom we are concerned with; and I am of opinion that your society is no less dangerous than the company of the Bear."

"This is an ill comparison," replied *Damna;* "I hope I am not so ignorant, but that I am able to distinguish between what is baneful and what is beneficial to my friend."

"Why, I know very well indeed," replied *Kalila,* "that your transgressions are not the failings of ignorance; but I know, too, that you can betray your friends, and that when you do so, it is not without long premeditation; witness the contrivances you made use of to set the Lion and the poor Ox together by the ears; but after this I cannot endure to hear you pretend to innocence. In short, you are like the man that would make his friend believe that rats eat iron."

THE MERCHANT AND HIS FRIEND

"A CERTAIN MERCHANT," SAID KALILA, PURSUING HER DIScourse, "had once a great desire to make a long journey. Now in regard that he was not very wealthy, 'It is requisite,' said he to himself, 'that before my departure I should leave some part of my estate in the city, to the end that if I meet with ill luck in my travels, I may have wherewithal to keep me at my return.' To this purpose he delivered a great number of bars of iron, which were a principal part of his wealth, in trust to one of his friends, desiring him to keep them during his absence; and then, taking his leave, away he went. Some time after, having had but ill luck in his travels, he returned home; and the first thing he did was to go to his Friend, and demand his iron: but his Friend, who owed several sums of money, having sold the iron to pay his own debts, made him this answer; 'Truly, friend,' said he, 'I put your iron into a room that was close locked, imagining it would have been there as secure as my own gold; but an accident has happened which nobody could have suspected, for there was a rat in the room which ate it all up.'

"The Merchant, pretending ignorance, replied, 'It is a terrible misfortune to me indeed; but I know of old that rats love iron extremely; I have suffered by them many times before in the same manner, and therefore can the better bear my present affliction.' This answer extremely pleased the Friend, who was glad to hear the Merchant so well inclined to believe that a rat had eaten his iron; and to remove all suspicions, desired him to dine with him the next day. The Merchant promised he would, but in the meantime he met in the middle of the city one of his Friend's children; the child he carried home, and locked up in a room. The next day he went to his Friend, who seemed to be in great affliction, which he asked him the cause of, as if he had been perfectly ignorant of what had happened.

" 'O, my dear friend,' answered the other, 'I beg you to excuse me, if you do not see me so cheerful as otherwise I would be; I have lost one of my children; I have had him cried by sound of trumpet, but I know not what is become of him.'

" 'O!' replied the Merchant, 'I am grieved to hear this; for yesterday in the evening, as I parted from hence, I saw an owl in the air with a child in his claws; but whether it were yours I cannot tell.'

" 'Why, you most foolish and absurd creature!' replied the Friend, 'are you not ashamed to tell such an egregious lie? An owl, that weighs at most not above two or three pounds, can he carry a boy that weighs above fifty?'

" 'Why,' replied the Merchant, 'do you make such a wonder at that? as if in a country where one rat can eat an hundred tons' weight of iron, it were such a wonder for an owl to carry a child that weighs not over fifty pounds in all!' The Friend, upon this, found that the Merchant was no such fool as he took him to be, begged his pardon for the cheat which he designed to have put upon him, restored him the value of his iron, and so had his son again.

"This Fable shows," continued *Kalila*, "that these fine-spun deceits are not always successful; but as to your principles, I can easily see that if you could be so unjust as to deceive the Lion, to whom you were so much indebted for a thousand kindnesses, you will with much more confidence put your tricks upon those to whom you are less obliged. This is the reason why I think your company is dangerous."

While *Damna* and *Kalila* were thus confabulating together, the Lion, whose passion was now over, made great lamentations for *Cohotorbe*, saying that he began to be sensible of his loss, because of his extraordinary endowments. "I know not," added he, "whether I did ill or well in destroying him, or whether what was reported of him was true or false." Thus musing for a while in a studious melancholy, at length he repented of having punished a subject who might, for aught he knew, be innocent. *Damna*, observing that the Lion was seized with remorse of conscience, left *Kalila*, and accosted the King with a most respectful humility.

"Sir," said he, "what makes your Majesty so pensive? Consider that here your enemy lies at your feet; and fix your eyes upon such an object with delight."

"When I think upon *Cohotorbe's* virtues," said the Lion, "I cannot but bemoan his loss. He was my support and my comfort, and it was by his prudent counsel that my people lived in repose."

"This indeed was once the case," replied *Damna;* "but his revolt was therefore the more dangerous; and I am grieved to see your Majesty bewail the death of an unfaithful subject. It is true he was profitable to the public; but in regard he had a design upon your person, you have done no more than what the wisest have already advised, which is to cut off a member that would prove the destruction of the whole body." These admonitions of *Damna's* for the present gave the Lion a little comfort; but notwithstanding all, *Cohotorbe's* innocence crying continually afterwards in the Monarch's breast for vengeance, roused at last some thoughts in him, by which he found means to discover the long chain of villainies *Damna* had been guilty of. He that will reap wheat must never sow barley. He only that does good actions, and thinks just thoughts, will be happy in this world, and cannot fail of rewards and blessings in the other.

THE PRINCE AND HIS MINISTER

The Fable Which the Lion's Mother Told to Him

THERE WAS ONCE A PRINCE WHO WAS VERY MUCH FAMED throughout all these countries; he was a great conqueror, and was potent, rich, and just. One day as he rode a-hunting, said he to his Minister; "Put on thy best speed; I will run my horse against thine, that we may see which is the swiftest: I have a long time had a strange desire to make this trial."

The Minister, in obedience to his master, spurred his horse, and rode full speed, and the King followed him. But when they were got at a great distance from the grandees and nobles that accompanied them, the King, stopping his horse, said to the Minister; "I had no other design in this but to bring thee to a place where we might be alone; for I have a secret to impart to thee, having found thee more faithful than any other of my servants. I have a jealousy that the Prince, my brother, is framing some contrivance against my person, and for that reason I have made choice of thee to prevent him; but be discreet."

The Minister on this swore he would be true to him; and when they had thus agreed, they stayed till the company overtook them, who were in great trouble for the King's person. The Minister, however, notwithstanding his promises to the King, upon the first opportunity he had to speak with the King's brother, disclosed to him the design that was brewing to take away his life. And this obliged the young Prince to thank him for his information, promise him great rewards, and take some precautions in regard to his own safety.

Some few days after, the King died, and his brother succeeded him. But when the Minister who had done him this signal service expected now some great preferment, the first thing he did, after he was advanced to the throne, was to order him to be put to death. The poor wretch immediately upbraided him with the service he had done him. "Is this," said he, "the recompense for my friendship to you? This the reward which you promised me?"

"Yes," answered the new King; "whoever reveals the secrets

of his prince deserves no less than death; and since thou hast committed so foul a crime, thou deservest to die. Thou betrayedst a king who put his confidence in thee, and who loved thee above all his court; how is it possible, therefore, for me to trust thee in my service?" It was in vain for the Minister to allege any reasons in his own justification; they would not be heard, nor could he escape the stroke of the executioner.

"You see by this Fable, son," continued the old Lioness, "that secrets are not to be disclosed."

"But, my dear mother," answered the King, "he that intrusted you with this secret desires it should be made known, seeing he is the first that makes the discovery; for if he could not keep it himself, how could he desire another to be more reserved? Let me conjure you," continued he, "if what you have to say be true, put me out of my pain."

The mother seeing herself so pressed, "Then," said she, "I must inform you of a criminal unworthy of pardon; for though it be the saying of wise men that a king ought to be merciful, yet there are certain crimes that ought never to be forgiven. It is *Damna* I mean," pursued the matron Lioness, "who, by his false insinuations, wrought *Cohotorbe's* fall." And having so said, she retired, leaving the Lion in a deep astonishment. Some time he pondered with himself on this discovery, and afterwards summoned an assembly of the whole court. *Damna*, taking umbrage at this—as guilty consciences always make people cowards,—comes to one of the King's favourites, and asks him if he knew the reason of the Lion's calling such an assembly; which the Lion's mother overhearing, "Yes," said she, "it is to pronounce thy death; for thy artifice and juggling politics are now, though too late, discovered."

"Madam," answered *Damna*, "they who render themselves worthy of esteem and honour at court by their virtues, never fail of enemies. O! that we," added he, "would act no otherwise than as the Almighty acts in regard to us; for He gives to every one according to his desert; but we, on the other side, frequently punish those who are worthy of reward, and as often cherish those that deserve our indignation. How much was I to blame to quit my solitude, merely to consecrate my life to the King's service, to meet with this reward! Whoever," continued he, "dissatisfied with what he has, prefers the service of princes before his duty to his Creator, will be sure, I find, early or late, to repent in vain."

THE BLIND MAN WHO TRAVELLED WITH ONE OF HIS FRIENDS

The Fable Which the True Hermit Told the Court Hermit

"THERE WERE ONCE," SAYS THE FABLE, "TWO MEN THAT travelled together, one of whom was blind. These two companions being, in the course of their journey, one time, surprised by night upon the road, entered into a meadow, there to rest themselves till morning; and as soon as day appeared, they rose, got on horseback, and continued their journey. Now, the blind Man, instead of his whip, as ill fate would have it, had picked up a Serpent that was stiff with cold; but having it in his hand, as it grew a little warm, he felt it somewhat softer than his whip, which pleased him very much; he thought he had gained by the change, and therefore never minded the loss. In this manner he travelled some time; but when the sun began to appear and illuminate the world, his Companion perceived the Serpent, and with loud cries, 'Friend,' said he, 'you have taken up a Serpent instead of your whip; throw it out of your hand, before you feel the mortal caresses of the venomous animal!'

"But the blind Man, no less blind in his intellect than in his body, believing that his friend had only jested with him to get away his whip, 'What!' said he, 'do you envy my good luck? I lost my whip that was worth nothing, and here my kind fortune has sent me a new one. Pray do not take me for such a simpleton but that I can distinguish a Serpent from a whip.'

"With that his friend replied; 'Companion, I am obliged by the laws of friendship and humanity to inform you of your danger; and therefore let me again assure you of your error, and conjure you, if you love your life throw away the Serpent.'

"To which the blind Man, more exasperated than persuaded;

'Why do you take all this pains to cheat me, and press me thus to throw away a thing which you intend, as soon as I have done so, to pick up yourself?' His Companion, grieved at his obstinacy, entreated him to be persuaded of the truth, swore he had no such design, and protested to him that what he held in his hand was a real and poisonous Serpent. But neither oaths nor protestations would prevail; the blind Man would not alter his resolution. The sun by this time began to grow high, and his beams having warmed the Serpent by degrees, he began to crawl up the blind Man's arm, which he immediately after bit in such a venomous manner, that he gave him his death wound.

"This example teaches us, brother," continued the pious Hermit, "that we ought to distrust our senses; and that it is a difficult task to master them, when we are in possession of the thing that flatters our fancy."

This apposite Fable, and judicious admonition, awakened the Court-Hermit from his pleasing dream. He opened his eyes, and surveyed the hazards that he ran at court; and bewailing the time which he had vainly spent in the service of the world, he passed the night in sighs and tears. His friend constantly attended him, and rejoiced at making him a convert; but, alas! day being come, the new honours that were done him destroyed all his repentance. At this melancholy sight, the pious stranger, with tears in his eyes, and many prayers for his lost brother, as he accounted him, took his leave of the court, and retired to his cell. On the other hand, the courtier began to thrust himself into all manner of business, and soon became unjust, like the people of the world.

One day, in the hurry of his affairs, he rashly and inconsiderately condemned to death a person, who, according to the laws and customs of the country, ought not to have suffered capital punishment. After the execution of the sentence, his conscience teased him with reproaches that troubled his repose for some time; and, at length, the heirs of the person whom he had unjustly condemned, with great difficulty, obtained leave of the King to inform against the Hermit, whom they accused of injustice and oppression; and the council, after mature debate upon the informations, ordered that the Hermit should suffer the same punishment which he had inflicted upon the person deceased. The Hermit made use of all his credit and his riches to save his life. But all availed not, and the decree of the council was executed.

"I must confess," said *Damna*, "that, according to this example, I ought long since to have been punished for having quitted my solitude to serve the Lion; notwithstanding that, I can safely appeal to Heaven, that I am guilty of no crime against any person yet."

Damna here gave over speaking, and his eloquence was admired by all the court. Different opinions were formed of him by the different persons present; and as for the Lion, he held down his head, turmoiled with so many various thoughts, that he knew not what to resolve, nor what answer to give. While the Lion, however, was in this dilemma, and all the courtiers kept silence, a certain creature, called *Siagousch*, who was one of the most faithful servants the King had, stepped forward, and spoke to this effect:

"O thou most wicked wretch! all the reproaches which thou throwest upon those that serve kings, turn only to thy own shame; for besides that it does no way belong to thee to enter into these affairs, know that an hour of service done to the King is worth a hundred years of prayers. Many persons of merit have we seen, that have quitted their little cells to go to court, where, serving princes, they have eased the people, and secured them from tyrannical oppressions."

THREE ENVIOUS PERSONS THAT FOUND MONEY

As Told by the Lion to his Mother

THREE MEN ONCE WERE TRAVELLING THE SAME ROAD, AND SOON by that means became acquainted. As they were journeying on, said the eldest to the rest; "Pray tell me, fellow-travellers, why you leave your settled homes to wander in foreign countries?"

"I have quitted my native soil," answered one, "because I could not endure the sight of some people whom I hated worse than death; and this hatred of mine, I must confess, was not founded on any injury done me by them; but arose from my own temper, which, I own it, cannot endure to see another happy."

"Few words will give you my answer," replied the second; "for the same distemper torments my breast, and sends me a-rambling about the world."

"Friends," replied the eldest, "then let us all embrace; for I find we are all three troubled with the same disease."

On these reciprocal confessions they soon became acquainted, and, being of the same humour, immediately closed in an union together. One day, as they travelled through a certain deep hollow way, they spied a bag of money, which some traveller had dropped in the road. Presently they all three alighted, and cried one to another; "Let us share this money and return home again, where we may be merry and enjoy ourselves."

But this they only said in dissimulation; for every one being unwilling that his companion should have the least benefit, they were truly each of them at a stand, whether it were not best to go on without meddling with the bag, to the end the rest might do the same; being well contented not to be happy themselves, lest another should be so also. In conclusion, they stopped a whole day and night in the same place to consider what they should do. At the end of which time, the King of the country riding a-hunting with all his court, the chase led him to this place. He rode up to the three men, and asked them what they did with the money that lay on the ground. And being thus surprised, and dreading some ill consequence if they equivocated, they all frankly told the truth.

"Sir," said they, "we are all three turmoiled with the same passion, which is envy. This passion has forced us to quit our native country, and still keeps us company wherever we go; and a great act of kindness would it be in any one, if it were possible, that he would cure us of this accursed passion, which, though we cannot but carry in our bosoms, yet we hate and abhor."

"Well," said the King, "I will be your doctor; but before I can do anything, it is requisite that every one of you should inform me truly in what degree this passion prevails over him, to the end that I may apply a remedy in proper proportion of strength."

"My envy, alas!" said the first, "has got such a head, that I cannot endure to do good to any man living."

"You are an honest man in comparison with me," cried the second; "for I am so far from doing good to another myself, that I mortally hate that anybody else should do another man good."

Said the third, "You both are children in this passion to me; neither of you possesses the quality of envy in a degree to be compared with me; for I not only cannot endure to oblige, nor to see any other person obliged, but I even hate that anybody should do myself a kindness."

The King was so astonished to hear them talk at this rate, that he knew not what to answer. At length, after he had considered some time, "Monsters, and not men, that ye are," said he; "you deserve, not that I should let you have the money, but punishment, if that can be adequate to your tempers." At the same time he commanded the bag to be taken from them, and condemned them to punishments they justly merited. He that could not endure to do good, was sent into the desert barefoot and without provision; he that could not endure to see good done to another, had his head chopped off, because he was unworthy to live, as being one that loved nothing but mischief; and lastly, as for him that could not endure any good to be done to himself, his life was spared, in regard his torment was only to himself; and he was put into a quarter of the kingdom where the people were of all others famous for being the best-natured, and the most addicted to the performance of good deeds and charitable actions. The goodness of these people, and the favours they conferred upon him from day to day, soon became such torment to his soul, that he died in the utmost anguish.

"By this history," continued the Lion, "you see what envy is; that it is of all vices the most abominable, and most to be expelled out of all human society."

"Most true," replied the Mother; "and it is for that very reason that *Damna* ought to be put to death, since he is attained of so dangerous a vice."

"If he be guilty," replied the Lion, "he shall perish; but that I am not well assured of; but am resolved to be, before he is condemned."

While matters were thus carrying on at court, however, *Damna's* wife, moved with compassion, went to see him in his prison, and read him this curtain-lecture; "Did I not tell you," said she, "that it behoved you to take care of going on with the execution of your enterprise; and that people of judgment and discretion never begin a business till they have warily considered what will be the issue of it? A tree is never to be planted, spouse," continued she, "before we know what fruit it will produce."

While *Kalila* was thus upbraiding *Damna,* there was in the prison a Bear, of whom they were not aware, and who, having overheard them, resolved to make use of what his ears had furnished him withal, as occasion should direct him.

The next day, betimes in the morning, the council met again, where, after every one had taken his place, the Mother of the Lion thus began; "Let us remind your Majesty," said she, "that we ought no more to delay the punishment of a capital offender than to hurry on the condemnation of the innocent; and that a King that forbears the punishment of a malefactor is guilty of no less a crime than if he had been a confederate with him." The old lady spoke this with much earnestness; and the Lion, considering that she spoke nothing but reason, commanded that *Damna* should be immediately brought to his trial. On this, the chief justice, rising from his seat, made the accustomed speech on such occasions, and desired the several members of the council to speak, and give their opinion freely, boldly, and honestly, in this matter; saying, withal, that it would produce three great advantages; first, that truth would be found out, and justice done; secondly, that wicked men and traitors would be punished; and thirdly, that the kingdom would be cleared of knaves and impostors, who by their artifices troubled the repose of it. But, notwithstanding the eloquence of the judge, as nobody then present knew the depth of the business, none opened their mouths to speak.

This gave *Damna* an occasion to defend himself with so much the greater confidence and intrepidity.

"Sir," said he, rising slowly from his seat, and making a profound reverence to his Majesty and the court, "had I committed the crime of which I stand accused, I might draw some colour of advantage from the general silence; but I find myself so innocent, that I wait with indifference the end of this assembly. Nevertheless, I must needs say this, that seeing nobody has been pleased to deliver his sentiments upon this affair, it is a certain sign that all believe me innocent. Let me not, sacred sir, be blamed for speaking in my own justification; I am to be excused in that, since it is lawful for every one to defend himself. Therefore," said he, pursuing his discourse, "I beseech all this illustrious company to say in the King's presence whatever they know concerning me; but let me caution them at the same time to have a care of affirming anything but what is true, lest they find themselves involved in what befell the ignorant Physician; of whom, with your Majesty's permission, I will relate the Fable."

THE IGNORANT PHYSICIAN

THERE WAS ONCE, IN A REMOTE PART OF THE EAST, A MAN WHO was altogether void of knowledge, yet presumed to call himself a Physician. He was so ignorant that he knew not the colic from the dropsy, nor could he distinguish rhubarb from bezoar. He never visited a patient twice; for his first coming always killed him. On the other hand, there was in the same province another Physician, of such art that he cured the most desperate diseases by the virtue of the several herbs of the country, of which he had a perfect knowledge. Now this learned man became blind, and not being able to visit his patients, at length retired into a desert, there to live at his ease.

The ignorant Physician no sooner understood that the only man he looked upon with an envious eye was retired out of the way, but he began boldly to display his ignorance under the opinion of manifesting his knowledge.   One day the King's daughter fell sick, upon which the wise Physician was sent for; because, that besides he had already served the court, people knew that he was much more able than his pompous successor.   The wise Physician being in the Princess's chamber, and understanding the nature of her disease, ordered her to take a certain pill composed of such ingredients as he prescribed.   Presently they asked him where the drugs were to be had.

"Formerly," answered the Physician, "I have seen them in such and such boxes in the King's cabinet; but what confusion there may have been since among those boxes I know not."   Upon this the ignorant Physician pretended that he knew the drugs very well, and that he also knew where to find and how to make use of them.

"Go then," said the King, "to my cabinet, and take what is requisite."   Away went the ignorant Physician, and fell to searching for the box; but as many of the boxes were alike, and because he knew not the drugs when he saw them, he was not able to find the right ones.   He rather chose, in the puzzle of his judgment, to take a box at a venture than to acknowledge his ignorance.   But he never considered that they who meddle with what they understand not are likely to repent it; for in the box which he had picked out there was a most deadly poison.   Of this he made up the pills, which he caused the Princess to take, who died immediately after; on which the King commanded the foolish Physician to be apprehended and condemned to death.

"This example," pursued *Damna*, "teaches us that no man ought to say or do a thing which he understands not."

"A man may, however, perceive by your physiognomy," said one of the assistants, interrupting him, "notwithstanding these fine speeches, that you are a sly companion, one that can talk better than you can act; and therefore I pronounce that there is little heed to be given to what you say."

The judge on this asked him that spoke last what proof he could produce of the certainty of what he averred.   "Physiognomists," answered he, "observe, that they who have their eyebrows parted, their left eye blared, and bigger than the right, the nose turned towards the left side, and who, counterfeiting your hypocrites, cast their eyes always toward the ground, are generally traitors and sycophants; and therefore, *Damna* having all these marks, from what I know of the art, I thought I might safely give that character of him which I have done, without injury to truth."

"Your art may fail you," replied *Damna;* "for it is our Creator alone who forms us as He pleases, and gives us such a physiognomy as He thinks fitting, and for what purposes He best knows. And permit me to add, that, if what you say were true, and every man carried written in his forehead what he had in his heart, the wicked might certainly be distinguished from the righteous at sight, and there would be no need of judges and witnesses to determine the disputes and differences that arise in civil society. In like manner it would be unjust to put some to their oaths and others to the rack, to discover the truth, because it might be evidently seen. And if the marks you have mentioned impose a necessity upon those that bear them to act amiss, would it not be palpable injustice to punish the wicked, since they are not free in their own actions? We must then conclude, according to this maxim, that if I were the cause of *Cohotorbe's* death, I am not to be punished for it, since I am not master of my actions, but was forced to it by the marks which I bear. You see, by this way of arguing, therefore, that your inferences are false." *Damna,* having thus stopped the assistant's mouth, nobody durst venture to say anything more; which forced the judge to send him back to prison, and left the King yet undetermined what to think of him.

Damna, being returned to his prison, was about to have sent a messenger to *Kalila* to come to him, when a brother Fox that was in the room by accident spared him that trouble, by informing him of *Kalila's* death, who died the day before of grief at seeing her husband entangled in such an unfortunate affair.

The news of *Kalila's* death touched *Damna* so to the quick, that, like one who cared not to live any longer, he seemed to be altogether comfortless. Upon which the Fox endeavoured to cheer him up, telling him, that if he had lost a dear and loving wife, he might, however, if he pleased to try him, find him a zealous and a faithful friend. *Damna*, on this, knowing he had no friend left that he could trust, and for that the Fox so frankly proffered him his service, accepted his kindness.

"I beseech you then," said *Damna*, "go to the court, and give me a faithful account of what people say of me; this is the first proof of friendship which I desire of you."

"Most willingly," answered the Fox; and immediately taking his leave, he went to the court to see what observations he could make, but further report of his doing there is none.

The next morning, by the break of day, the Lion's mother went to her son, and asked him what he had determined to do with *Damna*. "He is still in prison," answered the King; "and I can find nothing proved upon him yet, nor know I what to do about him."

"What a deal of difficulty is here," replied the Mother, "to condemn a traitor and a villain, who deserves more punishments than you can inflict; and yet I am afraid, when all is done, will escape by his dexterity and cunning."

"I cannot blame you for being discontented with these delays," replied the King; "for I also am so, but know not how to help myself; and if you please to be present at his next examination yourself, I will order it immediately, and you shall see what will be resolved upon." Which said, he ordered *Damna* to be sent for, that the business might be brought to a conclusion. The King's orders were obeyed, and the prisoner being brought to the bar, the chief justice put the same question as the day before, whether anybody had anything to say against *Damna*? But nobody said a word; which *Damna* observing, "I am glad to see," said he, "that in your Majesty's court there is not a single villain; few sovereign princes can say as much; but here is a proof of the truth of it before us, in that there is nobody here who will bear false witness, though it be wished by every one that something were said; and in other courts it were well if the same honour and honesty were kept up."

After *Damna* had done speaking, the Lion, looking upon his Mother, asked her opinion. "I find," answered she, "that you have a kindness for this most cunning villain; but believe me, he will, if you pardon him, cause nothing but faction and disorder in your court."

"I beseech you," replied the Lion, "to tell me who has so strongly prepossessed you against *Damna*."

"It is but too true," replied the Queen-mother, "that he has committed the crime that is laid to his charge. I know him to be guilty; but I shall not now discover the person who intrusted me with this secret. However, I will go to him, and ask him whether he will be willing that I should bring him in for a witness." And so saying, she went home immediately, and sent for the Leopard.

When he was come, "This villain whom you have accused to me," said she, "will escape the hands of justice, unless you appear yourself against him. Go, therefore," continued she, "at my request, and boldly declare what you know concerning *Damna*. Fear no danger in so honest a cause; for no ill shall befall you."

"Madam," answered the Leopard, "you know that I could wish to be excused from this; but you also know that I am ready to sacrifice my life to your Majesty's commands; dispose of me, therefore, as you please; I am ready to go wherever you command." With that she carried the Leopard to the King; to whom, "Sir," said she, "here is an undeniable witness which I have to produce against *Damna*." Then the Lion, addressing himself to the Leopard, asked him what proof he had of the delinquent's treason.

"Sir," answered the Leopard, "I was willing to conceal this truth, on purpose, for some time, to see what reasons the cunning traitor would bring to justify himself; but now it is time your Majesty knew all." On this the Leopard made a long recital of what had passed between *Kalila* and her husband; which deposition being made in the hearing of several beasts, was soon divulged far and near, and presently afterwards confirmed by a second testimony, which was the Bear's, of whom I made mention before. After this the delinquent was asked what he had now to say for himself; but he had not a word to answer. This at length determined the Lion to sentence that *Damna*, as a traitor, should be shut up between four walls, and there starved to death.

THE MAN AND THE ADDER

As Told to the Raven by the Rat

A MAN MOUNTED UPON A CAMEL ONCE RODE INTO A THICKET, and went to rest himself in that part of it from whence a caravan was just departed, and where the people having left a fire, some sparks of it, being driven by the wind, had set a bush, wherein lay an Adder, all in a flame. The fire environed the Adder in such a manner that he knew not how to escape, and was just giving himself over to destruction, when he perceived the Man already mentioned, and with a thousand mournful conjurations begged of him to save his life.

The Man, on this, being naturally compassionate, said to himself; "It is true these creatures are enemies to mankind; however, good actions are of great value, even of the very greatest when done to our enemies; and whoever sows the seed of good works, shall reap the fruit of blessings."

After he had made this reflection, he took a sack, and tying it to the end of his lance, reached it over the flame to the Adder, who flung himself into it; and when he was safe in, the traveller pulled back the bag, and gave the Adder leave to come forth, telling him he might go about his business; but hoped he would have the gratitude to make him a promise, never to do any more harm to men, since a man had done him so great a piece of service.

To this the ungrateful creature answered; "You much mistake both yourself and me; think not that I intend to be gone so calmly; no, my design is first to leave you a parting blessing, and throw my venom upon you and your Camel."

"Monster of ingratitude!" replied the Traveller, "desist a moment at least, and tell me whether it be lawful to recompense good with evil."

"No," replied the Adder, "it certainly is not; but in acting in that manner I shall do no more than what yourselves do every day; that is to say, retaliate good deeds with wicked actions, and requite benefits with ingratitude."

"You cannot prove this slanderous and wicked aspersion," replied the Traveller; "nay, I will venture to say, that if you can show me any one other creature in the world that is of your opinion, I will consent to whatever punishment you think fit to inflict on me for the faults of my fellow-creatures."

"I agree to this willingly," answered the Adder; and at the same time spying a Cow, "let us propound our question," said he, "to this creature before us, and we shall see what answer she will make."

The Man consented; and so both of them accosting the Cow, the Adder put the question to her, how a good turn was to be requited. "By its contrary," replied the Cow, "if you mean according to the custom of men; and this I know by sad experience. I belong," said she, "to a man, to whom I have long been several ways extremely beneficial. I have been used to bring him a calf every year, and to supply his house with milk, butter, and cheese; but now I am grown old, and no longer in a condition to serve him as formerly I did, he has put me in this pasture to fat me, with a design to sell me to a butcher, who is to cut my throat, and he and his friends are to eat my flesh. And is not this requiting good with evil?"

On this, the Adder taking upon him to speak, said to the Man; "What say you now? are not your own customs a sufficient warrant for me to treat you as I intend to do?"

The Traveller, not a little confounded at this ill-timed story, was cunning enough, however, to answer; "This is a particular case only, and give me leave to say, one witness is not sufficient to convict me; therefore pray let me have another."

"With all my heart," replied the Adder; "let us address ourselves to this Tree that stands here before us."

The Tree, having heard the subject of their dispute, gave his opinion in the following words; "Among men, benefits are never requited but with ungrateful actions. I protect travellers from the heat of the sun, and yield them fruit to eat, and a delightful liquor to drink; nevertheless, forgetting the delight and benefit of my shade, they barbarously cut down my branches to make sticks, and handles for hatchets, and saw my body to make planks and rafters. Is not this requiting good with evil?"

The Adder, on this, looking upon the Traveller, asked if he was satisfied. But he was in such a confusion that he knew not what to answer. However, in hopes to free himself from the danger that threatened him, he said to the Adder; "I desire only one favour more; let us be judged by the next beast we meet; give me but that satisfaction, it is all I crave; you know life is sweet; suffer me therefore to beg for the means of continuing it." While they were thus parleying together, a Fox passing by was stopped by the Adder, who conjured him to put an end to their controversy.

The Fox, upon this, desiring to know the subject of their dispute, said the Traveller: "I have done this Adder a signal piece of service, and he would fain persuade me that, for my reward, he ought to do me a mischief." "If he means to act by you as you men do by others, he speaks nothing but what is true," replied the Fox, "but, that I may be better able to judge between you, let me understand what service it is that you have done him."

The Traveller was very glad of this opportunity of speaking for himself, and recounted the whole affair to him; he told him after what manner he had rescued him out of the flames with that little sack, which he showed him.

"How!" said the Fox, laughing outright, "would you pretend to make me believe that so large an Adder as this could get into such a little sack? It is impossible!" Both the Man and the Adder, on this, assured him of the truth of that part of the story; but the Fox positively refused to believe it. At length said he; "Words will never convince me of this monstrous improbability; but if the Adder will go into it again, to convince me of the truth of what you say, I shall then be able to judge of the rest of this affair."

"That I will do most willingly," replied the Adder, and, at the same time, put himself into the sack.

Then said the Fox to the Traveller; "Now you are the master of your enemy's life; and, I believe, you need not be long in resolving what treatment such a monster of ingratitude deserves of you." With that the Traveller tied up the mouth of the sack, and with a great stone, never left off beating it till he had pounded the Adder to death; and, by that means, put an end to his fears and the dispute at once.

"This Fable," pursued the Rat, "informs us, that there is no trusting to the fair words of an enemy, for fear of falling into the like misfortunes."

THE MERCHANT, HIS WIFE, AND THE ROBBER

A MERCHANT, VERY RICH, BUT HOMELY, AND VERY DEFORMED in his person, had married a very fair and virtuous wife. He loved her passionately; but, on the other hand, she hated him, insomuch that, not being able to endure him, she lay by herself in a separate bed in the same chamber.

It happened, soon after they married, that a thief one night broke into the house, and came into the chamber. The husband was at this time asleep; but the wife being awake, and perceiving the thief, was in such a terrible fright, that she ran to her husband, and caught him fast in her arms. The husband, waking, was transported with joy to see the delight of his life clasping him in her embraces. "Bless me!" cried he, "to what am I obliged for this extraordinary happiness? I wish I knew the person to whom I owe it, that I might return him thanks."

Hardly had he uttered the words when the thief appeared, and he soon guessed the whole occasion. "Oh!" cried the merchant, "the most welcome person in the world; take whatever thou thinkest fitting; I cannot reward thee sufficiently for the good service thou hast done me."

FABLES FROM THE

GESTA RO-MANORUM

14th Century

THE GRATEFUL LION

THERE WAS A KNIGHT WHO DEVOTED MUCH OF HIS TIME TO hunting. It happened one day, as he was pursuing this diversion, that he was met by a lame lion, who showed him his foot. The knight dismounted, and drew from it a sharp thorn; and then applied an unguent to the wound, which speedily healed it. A while after this, the king of the country hunted in the same wood, and caught that lion, and held him captive for many years.

Now, the knight having offended the king, fled from his anger to the very forest in which he had been accustomed to hunt. There he betook himself to plunder, and spoiled and slew a multitude of travellers. But the king's sufferance was exhausted; he sent out an army, captured, and condemned him to be delivered to a fasting lion.

The knight was accordingly thrown into a pit, and remained in terrified expectation of the hour when he should be devoured. But the lion, considering him attentively, and remembering his former friend, fawned upon him; and remained seven days with him destitute of food. When this reached the ears of the king, he was struck with wonder, and directed the knight to be taken from the pit.

"Friend," said he, "by what means have you been able to render the lion harmless?"

"As I once rode along the forest, my lord, that lion met me lame. I extracted from his foot a large thorn, and afterwards healed the wound, and therefore he has spared me."

"Well," returned the king, "since the lion has spared you, I will for this time ratify your pardon. Study to amend your life."

The knight gave thanks to the king, and ever afterwards conducted himself with all propriety. He lived to a good old age, and ended his days in peace.

A DOVE WARNS THE CITY

IN THE REIGN OF THE EMPEROR HENRY II., A CERTAIN CITY WAS besieged by its enemies. Before they had reached its walls a dove alighted in the city, around whose neck a letter was suspended, which bore the following inscription: "The generation of dogs is at hand; it will prove a quarrelsome breed; procure aid, and defend yourselves resolutely against it."

THE BLACK PIT AND A DROP OF HONEY

BARLAAM SAYS THAT A SINNER IS LIKE A MAN WHO, BEING afraid of a unicorn, stepped backward into a deep pit. But when he had fallen he laid hold of the branch of a tree, and drew himself up.

Looking below, he espied at the foot of the tree by which he had ascended a very black well, and a horrible dragon encompassing it. The dragon appeared to expect his fall with extended jaws. Now, the tree was constantly being gnawed by two mice, of which one was white and the other black, and the man felt it shake. There were also four white vipers at its foot, which filled the whole pit with their pestilential breath.

Lifting up his eyes, the man beheld honey dropping from a bough of the tree; and, wholly forgetful of his danger, he gave himself up to the fatal sweetness.

A friend, stretching out to him a ladder, would have raised him entirely out; but, overcome by the allurement, he clung to the tree, which fell, and cast him into the jaws of the dragon. The monster, immediately descending to the lowest pit, there devoured him. He thus died a miserable death.

THE EAGLE AND THE SERPENT

PLINY MENTIONS THE STORY OF AN EAGLE THAT HAD BUILT HER nest upon a lofty rock, whose young a kind of serpent called *Perna* attempted to destroy. But finding that they were beyond her reach, she stationed herself to windward and emitted a large quantity of poisonous matter, so as to infect the atmosphere and poison the young birds.

But the eagle, led by the unerring power of instinct, took this precaution. She fetched a peculiar sort of stone called agate which she deposited in that quarter of the nest which was against the wind; and the stone by virtue of certain occult properties which it possessed, prevented the malicious intentions of the serpent from taking effect.

ARISTOTLE'S ADVICE TO ALEXANDER

WE READ THAT ALEXANDER THE GREAT WAS THE DISCIPLE OF Aristotle, from whose instructions he derived the greatest advantage. Amongst other important matters, he inquired of his master what would profit himself, and at the same time be serviceable to others.

Aristotle answered, "My son, hear with attention; and if you retain my counsel, you will arrive at the greatest honours. There are seven distinct points to be regarded. First, that you do not overcharge the balance. Secondly, that you do not feed a fire with the sword. Thirdly, stress not at the crown; nor, fourthly, eat the heart of a little bird. Fifthly, when you have once com-

menced a proper undertaking, never turn from it. Sixthly, walk
not in the highroad; and, seventhly, do not allow a prating swallow to possess your eaves."

The king carefully considered the meaning of these puzzling
directions; and, observing them, experienced their utility in his
subsequent life.

BY HIS OWN DEVICES

DIONYSIUS RECORDS THAT WHEN PERILLUS DESIRED TO BECOME
a craftsman of Phalaris, a cruel and tyrannical king who depopulated the kingdom of Agrigentum, and was guilty of many
dreadful excesses, he presented to him, already too well skilled in
cruelty, a brazen bull, which he had just constructed. In one of
its sides there was a secret door, by which those who were sentenced should enter and be burnt to death.

The idea was that the sounds produced by the agony of the
sufferer confined within should resemble the roaring of a bull;
and thus, while nothing human struck the ear, the mind should
be unimpressed by a feeling of mercy.

The king highly applauded the invention, and said, "Friend,
the value of thy industry is yet untried; more cruel even than
the people account me, thou thyself shalt be the first victim."

Indeed, there is no law more just than that "the artificer of
death should perish by his own devices," as Ovid has observed.

THE ARCHER AND THE NIGHTINGALE

AN ARCHER, CATCHING A LITTLE BIRD CALLED A NIGHTINGALE,
was about to put her to death. But, being gifted with language,
she said to him, "What will it gain you to kill me? I cannot satisfy your appetite. Let me go, and I will give you three rules,

from which you will derive great benefit, if you follow them accurately."

Astonished at hearing the bird speak, he promised her liberty on
the conditions that she had stated.

"Hear, then," said she: "never attempt impossibilities; secondly,
do not lament an irrecoverable loss; thirdly, do not credit things

that are incredible. If you keep these three maxims with wisdom, they will infinitely profit you."

The man, faithful to his promise, let the bird escape. Winging
her flight through the air, she commenced a most exquisite song;
and having finished, said to the archer, "Thou art a silly fellow,
and hast to-day lost a great treasure. There is in my bowels a
pearl bigger than the egg of an ostrich."

Full of vexation at her escape, he immediately spread his nets
and endeavoured to take her a second time; but she eluded his art.
"Come into my house, sweet bird!" said he, "and I will show thee
every kindness. I will feed thee with my own hands, and permit
thee to fly abroad at pleasure."

The nightingale answered, "Now I am certain thou art a fool,
and payest no regard to the counsel I gave thee: 'Regret not what

is irrecoverable.' Thou canst not take me again, yet thou hast spread thy snares for that purpose. Moreover, thou believest that my bowels contain a pearl larger than the egg of an ostrich, when I myself am nothing near that size! Thou art a fool; and a fool thou wilt always remain."

With this consolatory assurance she flew away. The man returned sorrowfully to his own house, but never again obtained a sight of the nightingale.

THE SUBTLE SERPENT

IN THE REIGN OF THE EMPEROR FULGENTIUS, A CERTAIN KNIGHT named Zedechias, married a very beautiful but imprudent wife. In a certain chamber of their mansion a serpent dwelt.

Now, the knight's passionate inclination for tournaments and jousting brought him to extreme poverty; he grieved immoderately, and, like one who was desperate, walked backward and forward, ignorant of what he should do.

The serpent, beholding his misery, like the ass of Balaam, was on that occasion miraculously gifted with a voice, and said to the knight, "Why do you lament? Take my advice, and you shall not repent it. Supply me every day with a certain quantity of sweet milk, and I will enrich you."

This promise pleased the knight, and he faithfully followed the instructions of his subtle friend. The consequence was that he had a beautiful son, and became exceedingly wealthy.

But it happened that his wife one day said to him, "My lord, I am sure that serpent has great riches hidden in the chamber where he dwells. Let us kill him and get possession of the whole."

The advice pleased the knight, and at the request of his wife he took a hammer and a vessel of milk to destroy the serpent. Allured by the milk, it put its head out of the hole, as it had been accustomed, and the knight lifted the hammer to strike it. The serpent, observing his intention, suddenly drew back its head; and the blow fell upon the vessel. No sooner had he done this, than his offspring died, and he lost everything that he formerly possessed.

The wife, grieved by their common loss, said to him, "Alas! I have ill counselled you; but go now to the hole of the serpent, and humbly acknowledge your offence. Perhaps you may find grace."

The knight complied, and standing before the dwelling-place of the serpent, shed many tears, and entreated that he might once more be made rich.

"I see," answered the serpent, "I see now that you are a fool, and will always be a fool. For how can I forget that blow of the hammer which you designed for me, for which reason I slew your son and took away your wealth? There can be no real peace between us."

The knight, full of sorrow, replied thus: "I promise the most unshaken fidelity, and will never think the slightest injury, provided I may this once obtain your grace."

"My friend," said the serpent, "it is the nature of my species to be subtle and venomous. Let what I have said suffice. The blow offered at my head is fresh upon my recollection; get you gone before you receive an injury."

The knight departed in great affliction, saying to his wife, "Fool that I was to take thy counsel!" But ever afterwards they lived in the greatest poverty.

THE KING, THE SERPENT, AND THE PHILOSOPHER

AN EMPEROR RODE OUT IN THE AFTERNOON TO HUNT. HAPpening to pass a certain wood, he heard a serpent, which some shepherds had caught and bound firmly to a tree, making a most horrible clamour. Moved by pity, he loosed it, and warmed its frozen body in his own bosom. No sooner, however, did the animal find itself recovered, than it began to bite its benefactor, and shot a flood of poison into the wound.

"What have you done?" said the emperor. "Wherefore have you rendered evil for good?"

The serpent, like the ass of Balaam, being suddenly endowed with voice, replied, "The tendencies which nature has implanted no one can destroy. You have done what you could; and I have only acted according to my nature. You exhibited towards me all the kindness in your power, and I have recompensed you as well as I might. I offered poison, because, except poison, I had nothing to offer. Moreover, I am an enemy to man; for through him I became punished with a curse."

As they thus contended, they entreated a philosopher to judge between them, and to state which was in the wrong.

"I know these matters," answered the umpire, "only by your relation; but I should like to see the thing itself upon which I am to pronounce judgment. Let the serpent, therefore, be bound to the tree, as he was in the first instance, and let my lord the emperor remain unbound; I shall then determine the matter between you." This was done accordingly.

"Now you are bound," said the philosopher, addressing the serpent, "loose yourself if you can."

"I cannot," said the serpent; "I am bound so fast that I can scarcely move."

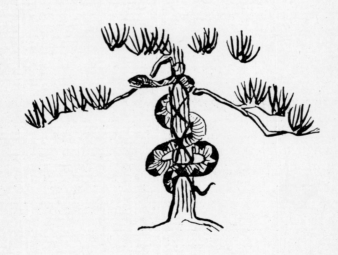

"Then die," rejoined the philosopher, "by a just sentence. You were always ungrateful to man, and you always will be. My lord, you are now free; shake the venom from your bosom, and go your way: do not repeat your folly. Remember that the serpent is only influenced by his natural propensities."

The emperor thanked the philosopher for his assistance and advice, and departed.

STORY OF THE BELL OF JUSTICE

THE EMPEROR THEODOSIUS HAD THE MISFORTUNE TO LOSE HIS sight. He put up a bell in his palace; and the law was, that whoever had any suit to make should pull the string with his own hands. When the bell rang, a judge, appointed to this end, descended and administered justice.

It chanced that a serpent made her nest immediately under the bell-rope, and in due time brought forth young. When they were old enough, one day she conducted them forth to enjoy the fresh air beyond the city. Now, while the serpent was absent, a toad entered and occupied her nest. When, therefore, the former returned with her young, she found the toad in possession, and instantly began an attack. But the latter baffled her attempts, and obstinately maintained his station.

The serpent, perceiving her inability to eject the intruder, coiled her tail around the bell-rope, and forcibly rang the bell; as though she had said, "Descend, judge, and give me justice; for the toad has wrongfully seized my nest."

The judge, hearing the bell, descended; but not seeing any one, returned. The serpent, finding her design fruitless, once more sounded the alarm. The judge again appeared, and upon this occasion, seeing the serpent attached to the bell-rope, and the toad in possession of her nest, declared the whole circumstance to the emperor.

"Go down, my lord," said the latter, "and not only drive away the toad, but kill him; let the serpent possess her right." All which was done.

On a subsequent day, as the king lay in his bed, the serpent entered the bed-chamber, carrying a precious stone in her mouth. The servants, perceiving this, informed the emperor, who gave directions that they should not harm it; "For," added he, "it will do me no injury."

The serpent, gliding along, ascended the bed, and approached the emperor's eyes, let the stone fall upon them, and immediately left the room. No sooner, however, had the stone touched the eyes than their sight was completely restored.

Infinitely rejoiced at what had happened, the emperor made inquiry after the serpent, but it was not heard of again. He carefully treasured this invaluable stone, and ended his days in peace.

THE PHILOSOPHY OF DEATH

WE READ THAT AT THE DEATH OF ALEXANDER A GOLDEN sepulchre was constructed, and that a number of philosophers assembled round it.

One said, "Yesterday, Alexander made a treasure of gold; and now gold makes a treasure of him."

Another observed, "Yesterday, the whole world was not enough to quench his ambition; to-day, three or four ells of cloth are more than sufficient."

A third said, "Yesterday, Alexander commanded the people; to-day, the people command him."

Another said, "Yesterday, Alexander could enfranchise thousands; to-day, he cannot avoid the spear of death."

Another remarked, "Yesterday, he pressed the earth; to-day, it oppresses him."

"Yesterday," continued another, "all men feared Alexander; to-day, men count him as nothing."

Another said, "Yesterday, Alexander had a multitude of friends; to-day, not one."

Still another said, "Yesterday, Alexander led on an army; to-day, that army bears him to the grave."

FABLES FROM THE

HITO-PADESHA

Sanskrit 15th Century

THE ASS IN THE TIGER SKIN

SAID THE KING TO THE BIRDS; "THE ASS, WHO HAD BEEN FED on good corn, and fell to braying ignorantly in the hide of a Tiger, was slain for his impertinence."

"How happened that?" said the Birds.

"There is," answered the King, "in a certain town a fuller, whose Ass, weakened by carrying heavy loads, was like an animal wanting to die. The master, therefore, carried him in a Tiger's skin, and left him in a wood in a field of corn. The owners of the field, taking him at a distance for a Tiger, fled; but one of them, covering himself with a piece of cloth of an Ass's colour, stooped down to bend his bow; and the Ass perceiving him, thought he was another Ass, and began braying, and ran towards him. But the keeper of the cornfield knowing, by his voice, that he was only an Ass, killed him with ease."

THE MONKEYS AND THE BELL

A NOISE ONLY, WHEN THE CAUSE OF IT IS UNKNOWN, MUST NOT be dreaded. One day a thief, escaping from a house in which he had stolen a Bell, was killed and eaten by a tiger on the top of this mountain; and the Bell, which had dropped from his hand, was taken up by some Monkeys, who from time to time made it sound. The people of the town having discovered that a man had been killed, and hearing continuously the noise of the Bell, said that the Cruel Demon had in his rage eaten him, and they all fled from the town.

It came into the head of a certain woman that the Bell was only sounded by Monkeys; and she went to the Prince, saying; "If you will advance me a large sum of money, I will make the Demon quiet." The King gave her a treasure, and she, having paid adoration to a certain quarter of the globe, made idols, and formed circles, and acquired great reputation for sanctity; she then took such fruits as Monkeys love, and having entered the forest, scattered them about, which the Monkeys perceiving, quitted the Bell, and eagerly devoured the fruits. The woman took up the Bell, and went with it to the palace of the King, where all the people did her reverence.

Hence a noise only, when the cause of it is unknown, must not be dreaded.

THE MOUSE AND THE SAINT

A MEAN PERSON, RAISED TO A HIGH DEGREE, SEEKS THE RUIN OF his lord; as the Mouse, having attained the form and force of a Tiger, went to kill the Saint. For there is in the sacred grove of the divine philosopher a Saint who is very pious; who seeing a young Mouse fall near his dwelling, from the bill of a Crow, kindly took him up, and fed him with grains of rice.

One day when the Mouse was preparing to eat, a Cat appeared, and the kind Saint, by the power of his devotion, changed the Mouse into a Cat. This new animal was soon afterwards terrified by a Dog, and so he, too, was turned by the Saint into a Dog. At length, being in dread of a Tiger, he became a Tiger, through the prayers of the Saint, who then perceived the difference between a Tiger and a Rat.

All the people said; "See how the piety of the Saint has changed yon Rat into a Tiger!"

Then the ungrateful beast thought within himself; "As long as the Saint lives, they will say these spiteful things against me." With this thought, he ran towards his protector and attempted to kill him, but was changed, by a short prayer of the heaven-eyed Saint, into a Mouse again. Thus a mean person, raised to a high degree, seeks the ruin of his lord.

THE CAT AND THE VULTURE

THE CROW SAID TO THE RAT; "TO A STRANGE PERSON OF AN unknown tribe, or uncertain temper, no one should give his house; by means of a Cat, the Vulture *Jaradgabah* was slain."

"How did it happen?" said the Rat.

The Crow answered; "There stands near the *Gangà*, on a mountain called 'Vulture-fort,' a large hollow tree; high in whose trunk, his sight dim with the fear of danger, lived a Vulture, named *Jaradgabah;* by little and little he supplied his young with sustenance from his own prey, and thus the other birds of his species were supported. It happened that a Cat, named *Long-ears,* used to devour the young birds, and then to depart. The young ones saw her coming, and confounded with fear, made a noise. *Jaradgabah* heard it, and said; 'Who is coming?'

"The Cat seeing the Vulture, was alarmed, and said: 'Alas! I am destroyed. I cannot now escape from this enemy; so, as a last resource, let me boldly go to him.' Having resolved on this, she went near him, and said; 'Great sir, I am thy servant!'

" 'Who art thou?' said the Vulture. 'A Cat,' said he. 'De-part far off,' said the other, 'or thou shalt be chastised.' 'Hear me, however,' replied the Cat, 'and if I deserve chastisement, then chastise me.' 'Speak on,' said the Vulture. 'I live here,' said the Cat, 'near the *Gangà,* in which I daily bathe myself; eating neither fish nor flesh, and performing the hard tasks of a holy person: thou, who art well acquainted with justice, art therefore one worthy to be trusted by me. The birds continually pray before me; and I came hither to hear a discourse on justice from thee, who art great in age and wisdom. And now tell me, thou who art so learned, why shouldst thou be prepared to beat me, who am a stranger?'

" 'Shall cats,' answered the Vulture, 'who love delicate flesh, dwell here with young birds? On that account I forbid thee.' Then the Cat, stroking her ears and touching the ground with her head, thus spoke; 'I who have learnt the *Dermasastra,* and who have performed all the difficult offices of religion, am without appetite for flesh, and I speak nothing but truth.'

"And so the Vulture trusted him, and he abode in the cavern; but some days having elapsed, he assailed the young birds, carried them off, and devoured them: during this cruel repast, on their plaintive cries, a question was asked, what he was doing?

"The Cat perceiving the discovery, left the cavern and ran away. The birds having examined the place on all sides, took up the scattered bones of their young, and suspecting that the Vulture had eaten them, united all their force, and by their first onset the Vulture was killed. For this reason I say: To a person of an unknown temper no one should give his house."

THE ELEPHANT AND THE MOON

BY USING THE GREAT NAME OF A POWERFUL KING, PROSPERITY is attained, as the Fawn found security by naming the Moon. For in the forest of Dandaca a herd of Elephants being distressed by a scarcity of rain in winter, thus addressed their king; "O sir, what remedy has our distress? Yonder is a pool used by little animals, who are bending their necks to drink it; but we, parched with thirst, whither shall we go? What can we do?"

The king of the Elephants hearing this, went to a little distance, and discovered a pond of clear water, on the borders of which were some little Antelopes, who were trodden from time to time by the feet of the Elephants. One of them thus thought within himself; "If this mighty Elephant bring his herd hither every day to quench their thirst, our whole race will be destroyed."

An old Antelope, guessing the cause of his melancholy, said; "Be not sorrowful; I will provide a remedy for this evil." With

this promise he departed, and considered how he should approach the Elephant near enough to address him without danger. "I will," said he, "climb up yon mountain and thence discourse with him." Having done as he had resolved, he thus began; "O sovereign of Elephants, I come to thee, by the command of that great monarch the Moon."

"Who art thou?" said the Elephant; "and what is thy business?"

"I am an ambassador," he answered; "I speak by order of his Lunar Majesty. In driving away the Antelopes who are appointed keepers of the pool thou hast acted improperly; we Antelopes are its guardians."

When the pretended ambassador had said this, the Elephant said with great fear; "This has been done by me through ignorance; we will not again come hither."

"Come, then," said the Antelope, "and having saluted the god who dwells here, and trembles with rage, appease him." The Elephant went, and as it was night, the Antelope showed him the reflection of the Moon quivering in the water, and commanded him to bow down.

"Great sir," said the Elephant, "my offense was through ignorance; therefore be moved to forgiveness." Saying this and making profound salutation, he went his way.

THE THREE ROGUES

ONCE THERE WAS A BRAHMIN WHO BOUGHT A GOAT IN ANOTHER village, and carrying it home on his shoulder, was seen by three Rogues, who said to one another; "If by some contrivance that goat can be taken from him, it will be great pleasure to us."

With this view they severally sat down in the road under three trees, at some distance from each other, by which the Brahmin was to pass. One of the Scoundrels called out, as he was going by; "O Brahmin! why dost thou carry that dog on thy shoulder?"

"It is not a dog," answered the Brahmin; "it is a goat for a sacrifice."

Then at a certain distance away, the second Knave put the same question to him; which when the Brahmin heard, he threw the goat down on the ground, and looking at it again and again, placed it a second time on his shoulder, and walked on with a mind waving like a swing. The Brahmin heard the same question from the third Villain, was persuaded that the goat was really a dog, and taking it from his back, threw it down, and having washed himself, returned to his home.

The three Rogues took the goat to their own house, and feasted on it. Thence he who thinks a knave as honest as himself, is deceived by him, like this Brahmin who was ruined.

THE STAG AND THE LION

HE WHO HAS KNOWLEDGE HAS FORCE. SEE HOW A PROUD LION was killed by a Stag. In the mountain named Mandara dwells a Lion called *Darganta,* who hunts the other beasts, and kills great numbers of them for his food. All the beasts being assembled, he was thus addressed by them; "Why are so many beasts killed by thee? We will give thee one every day in our turns for your food: so many ought not to be slain by thee."

"Be it so," said the Lion; and all of them, one by one, for his food daily gave a beast.

On a certain day, when the lot fell upon an old Stag, he thus thought within himself; "For the sake of our own souls, and in hope of life, homage is paid: but if I must meet this fate, what need have I to respect the Lion?" He moved, therefore, slowly step by step; and the Lion, tormented by hunger, said to him angrily; "Why dost thou come so late?"

"It is not my fault," said he, "for in the way I was forcibly seized by another Lion, till I swore to the necessity of my coming to thee; and now I approach thee with supplication."

The Lion having heard this, passionately said; "Where is that audacious animal?" The Stag led him near a deep well, and said: "Let my lord behold." Then the Lion seeing his own image in the water, proudly roared, and throwing himself down with rage, perished in the well.

LAURENTIUS

ABSTEMIUS

Italy 16th Century

A SWALLOW AND A SPIDER

A SPIDER THAT OBSERVED A SWALLOW CATCHING FLIES, FELL immediately to work upon a net to catch swallows, for she looked upon it as an encroachment upon her right: but the birds, without any difficulty, brake through the work, and flew away with the very net itself. "Well," says the Spider, "bird-catching is none of my talent, I perceive." And so she returned to her old trade of catching flies again.

A SWAN AND A STORK

A STORK THAT WAS PRESENT AT THE SONG OF A DYING SWAN told her 'twas contrary to nature to sing so much out of season; and asked her the reason of it. "Why," says the Swan, "I am now entering into a state where I shall be no longer in danger of either snares, guns, or hunger: and who would not joy at such a deliverance?"

CAPONS FAT AND LEAN

THERE WERE A GREAT MANY CRAMMED CAPONS TOGETHER IN A coop; some of them very fair and fat, and others again that did not thrive upon feeding. The Fat ones would be ever and anon making sport with the Lean, and calling them starvelings; till in the end the cook was ordered to dress so many Capons for supper, and to be sure to take the best in the pen: when it came to that once, they that had most flesh upon their backs wished they had had less, and 'twould have been better for them.

WAX AND BRICK

THERE WAS A QUESTION STARTED ONCE ABOUT WAX AND BRICK, why the one should be so brittle, and liable to be broken with every knock, and the other bear up against all injuries and weathers, so durable and firm. The Wax philosophised upon the matter, and finding out at last that it was burning made the Brick so hard, cast itself into the fire, upon an opinion that heat would harden the Wax too; but that which consolidated the one, dissolved the other.

A FLY UPON A WHEEL

"WHAT A DUST DO I RAISE!" SAYS THE FLY, "UPON THE COACH-wheel! And what a rate do I drive at," says the same Fly again, "upon the horse's back!"

A HUSBANDMAN AND CERES

A CERTAIN FARMER COMPLAINED THAT THE BEARDS OF HIS CORN cut the reapers' and the thrashers' fingers sometimes, and therefore he desired Ceres that his corn might grow hereafter without beards. The request was granted, and the little birds ate up all his grain. "Fool that I was," says he, "rather to lose the support of my life, than venture the pricking of my servants' fingers."

A COUNTRYMAN AND A HAWK

A COUNTRY FELLOW HAD THE FORTUNE TO TAKE A HAWK IN the hot pursuit of a Pigeon. The Hawk pleaded for herself, that she never did the Countryman any harm; "And therefore I hope," says she, "that you'll do me none."

"Well," says the Countryman, "and pray what wrong did the Pigeon ever do you? Now by the reason of your own argument, you must expect to be treated yourself, as you yourself would have treated this Pigeon."

A LEAGUE OF BEASTS AND FISHES

THE BEASTS ENTERED INTO A LEAGUE WITH THE FISHES AGAINST the Birds. The war was declared; but the Fishes, instead of their quota, sent their excuse, that they were not able to march by land.

A MOUSE IN A CHEST

A MOUSE THAT WAS BRED IN A CHEST, AND HAD LIVED ALL HER days upon what the dame of the house laid up in it, happened one time to drop out over the side, and to stumble upon a very delicious morsel, as she was hunting up and down to find her way in again. She had no sooner the taste of it in her mouth, but she brake out into exclamations, what a fool she had been thus long, to persuade herself that there was no happiness in the world but in that box.

THE FISHES AND THE FRYING-PAN

A COOK WAS FRYING A DISH OF LIVE FISH, AND SO SOON AS EVER they felt the heat of the pan, "There's no enduring of this," cried one, and so they all leapt into the fire; and instead of mending the matter, they were worse now than before.

A COUNTRYMAN AND A RIVER

A COUNTRYMAN THAT WAS TO PASS A RIVER SOUNDED IT UP and down to try where it was most fordable; and upon trial he made this observation on it: "Where the water ran smooth, he found it deepest; and on the contrary, shallowest where it made most noise."

A SPANIEL AND A SOW

"I WONDER," SAYS A SOW TO A SPANIEL, "HOW YOU CAN FAWN thus upon a master that gives you so many blows and twinges by the ears."

"Well," says the Dog, "but then set the good bits and the good words he gives me, against those blows and twinges, and I'm a gainer by the bargain."

JEAN DE

La FONTAINE

France 1621 -- 1695

THE MONKEY AND THE LEOPARD

THE MONKEY AND THE LEOPARD BOTH MADE A GOOD HARVEST
at the fair; each had bills pasted about the place.   One of them
said; "Gentlemen, my glory and renown are known and thoroughly acknowledged.   The king has honoured me with a visit;
and when I die he desires that a muff may be made out of my skin,
so beautiful and variegated are the spots on it."   The advertise-
ment proved attractive; every one set out to see the leopard; but
this being shortly accomplished, they soon came out again.

The Monkey on his part said; "Come, gentlemen, come, if you
have any regard for your souls' welfare, and behold the innumerable tricks of your humble servant.   The diversity of which my
neighbour the Leopard boasts, is only on the outside, mine is
within.   Your friend Jacko, son-in-law of Bertrand, the pope's
Monkey, has just arrived in this town, with his suite, in three carriages, on purpose to talk to you,—for you must know that he
speaks; he can dance on the slack-rope, tumble, and perform a
thousand wonderful feats; do you think he would have the face
to charge you sixpence?—no, gentlemen, he asks but one penny;
and if anybody thinks it too dear, the money shall be returned to
him."

The monkey was right· it is not a motley coat that pleases; but a well stored mind. The one always has a fund of agreeable sayings; the other in less than an instant wearies the spectators. Oh! how many of our highest nobility, like the leopard, carry all their talent on their back.

THE MERCHANT AND FORTUNE

A MERCHANT HAD THE GOOD FORTUNE TO ACQUIRE IMMENSE wealth in many a voyage; all his cargoes escaped, without paying toll either to whirlpools, rocks or sandbanks. Fate allowed him to pass free. Neptune never failed of exacting his rights from his fellow traders, whilst Fortune always took care to bring our merchant safely into port. Those he employed, were all faithful to his interests; he had always a market for his sugar, tobacco, cinnamon, in fact for whatever he imported. Luxury and folly swelled his treasure, in a word, wealth was showered upon him. He was not to be spoken with, but through the medium of hard ducats; he possessed dogs, horses, carriages; and throughout the year fared like a prince. A bosom friend observing his splendid repasts, said to him; "How do you manage to fare so sumptuously?"

"How?" replied the merchant, "undoubtedly from my knowledge of business. I am indebted for it to no one but myself; to my prudence, my skill in speculating advantageously, and laying out my money in a proper manner."

Profit appearing to him a very agreeable thing, he again risked the wealth he had acquired; but this time, everything went against him, and chiefly through his own imprudence. A vessel too heavily freighted, perished in the first storm. Another, unprovided with the necessary means of defence, fell into the hands of pirates; a third, arriving safely in port, was unable to dispose of any portion of her merchandise; luxury and folly had no further occasion for the stores wherewith she was laden. In addition to this, his brokers cheated him, and his wealth being vested in different ways, left him unprovided for contingencies, so that he suddenly found himself greatly impoverished.

His friend observing his reduced style of living, enquired the cause. "Alas!" he replied, "it is cruel Fortune who has played me this prank."

In a like case, every one imputes his success to his own industry; but if his imprudence meets with the natural result, he abuses Fate. He is invariably right, Fortune always wrong.

THE FISHES AND THE SHEPHERD WHO PLAYED THE FLUTE

THYRSIS—WHO FOR HIS ANNETTE DEAR
Made music with his flute and voice,
Which might have roused the dead to hear,
And in their silent graves rejoice—
    Sang once the livelong day,
    In the flowery month of May,
Up and down a meadow brook,
While Annette fish'd with line and hook.
    But ne'er a Fish would bite;
    So the Shepherdess's bait
    Drew not a Fish to its Fate,
From morning dawn till night.
The Shepherd, who, by his charming songs
Had drawn savage beasts to him in throngs,
    And done with them as he pleased to,
    Thought that he could serve the Fish so.
"O citizens," he sang, "of this water,
Leave your Naiad in her grot profound;
Come and see the blue sky's lovely daughter,
    Who a thousand times more will charm you;
    Fear not that her prison will harm you,
Though there you should chance to get bound.
'Tis only to us men she is cruel:
    You she will treat kindly;
    A snug little pond she'll find ye,

Clearer than a crystal jewel,
Where you may all live and do well;
   Or, if by chance some few
      Should find their fate
      Conceal'd in the bait,
   The happier still are you;
For envied is the death that's met
At the hands of sweet Annette."
   This eloquence not effecting
   The object of his wishes,
   Since it failed in collecting
      The deaf and dumb Fishes,—
      His sweet preaching wasted,
      His honey'd talk untasted,
A net the Shepherd seized, and, pouncing
   With a fell scoop at the scaly fry,
He caught them; and now, madly flouncing,
   At the feet of his Annette they lie!
O ye shepherds, whose sheep men are,
To trust in reason never dare.
The arts of eloquence sublime
   Are not within your calling;
Your fish were caught, from oldest time,
   By dint of nets and hauling.

THE FEMALE SOOTHSAYERS

OPINIONS ARE OFTEN FORMED BY ACCIDENT; AND IT IS ACCIDENT which always sets the fashion; in support of this assertion, innumerable instances can be adduced.

A woman at Paris set up for a soothsayer and was soon consulted on every occasion; if a dish-clout were lost, if one had a lover, or a faithless husband, a cross-grained mamma, or a jealous wife, a visit was immediately paid to the wise woman. Her stock in trade consisted of a good address, a few scientific terms, considerable effrontery, aided now and then by an accidental fulfilment of one of her predictions; all this concurred to close the eyes of her dupes, and made them often look upon these effects of chance as miracles. In fact, although ignorant as a magpie, she passed for an oracle.

The prophetess was lodged in an attic: and without further resource, this woman managed to fill her purse in such manner, that she bought a title for her husband, purchased a conveniently situated office, and a dwelling-house. The attic was soon filled with a new tenant, to whom the whole town repaired as formerly; wives, daughters, valets, statesmen, in fact, every one who desired to be made acquainted with Fate's intention towards himself. The garret became the Sibyl's temple. The other female had already brought customers enough to the place. The last comer in vain protested that she could not prophesy. "I foretell events," said she, "you are making a jest of me: why, gentlemen, I can't read; and never learnt aught but my pater-noster." These arguments were of no weight, she must of necessity, prophesy, inspired by the chinking of good ducats; and in spite of herself, gained more than any two barristers in full practice. The furniture of her residence was of great assistance: four rickety stools, and a broom-handle, gave clear testimony of her attendance at the nocturnal meetings of the witches.

If this woman had prophesied correctly in a tapestried chamber, she would have been ridiculed; fashion demanded her location in an attic. It looked more genuine. The other woman had no company, and was therefore forced to be contented with dancing attendance upon herself.

THE DOG THAT CARRIED HIS MASTER'S DINNER

OUR EYES ARE NOT PROOF AGAINST BEAUTY, NOR OUR HANDS against gold: few persons can guard a treasure faithfully.

A certain Dog was commissioned to carry his master's dinner, which was hung in a basket round his neck. He was temperate; more so, indeed, than he desired, when he had anything delicate under his nose; we are all tempted when we have charge of wealth. Strange! that a dog should be taught to moderate his appetite, when human beings never can! Our dog, then, being thus employed, a mastiff approached, and wished to rob him of the dinner; but he was not fated to enjoy it so much as he expected; for, the dog putting down his burden, in order to defend it better, a pitched battle took place. Other dogs soon ran to see the fight; they were of that class which lives on the public, and cared little for blows.

Our Dog finding himself too feeble to resist them all, and perceiving his convoy in manifest danger, determined to have his portion, and wisely said to them; "No more blows, gentlemen; I am content with my share of the dinner, make the most of the rest." Without further ceremony, one snatched at a morsel, and was succeeded by the mastiff, and the whole mob, who each devoured whatever he could come at; every one had a finger in the pie, and soon disposed of the banquet.

THE FUNERAL OF THE LIONESS

THE LION HAVING SUDDENLY LOST HIS QUEEN, EVERY ONE HAStened to shew his allegiance to the monarch, by offering consolation. These compliments, alas! served but to increase the widower's affliction. Due notice was given throughout the kingdom, that the funeral would be performed at a certain time and place; his officers were ordered to be in attendance, to regulate the ceremony, and place the company according to their respective rank.

One may well judge no one absented himself. The monarch gave way to his grief, and the whole cave, lions having no other temples, resounded with his cries. After his example, all the courtiers roared in their different tones. A court is a sort of place where every one is either sorrowful, gay, or indifferent to everything, just as the reigning prince may think fit; or if any one is not actually, he at least tries to appear so; each endeavours to mimic the master. It is truly said, that one mind animates a thousand bodies, clearly shewing, that human beings are mere machines.

But let us return to our subject. The Stag alone shed no tears. How could he, forsooth? The death of the queen avenged him; she had formerly strangled his wife and son. A courtier thought fit to inform the bereaved monarch, and even affirmed that he had seen the Stag laugh. The rage of a king, says Solomon, is terrible, and especially that of a lion-king. "Pitiful forester!" he exclaimed, "darest thou laugh when all around are dissolved in tears? We will not soil our royal claws with thy profane blood! Do thou, brave Wolf, avenge our queen, by immolating this traitor to her august manes."

Hereupon the Stag replied; "Sire, the time for weeping is passed; grief is here superfluous. Your revered spouse appeared to me but now, reposing on a bed of roses; I instantly recognized her. 'Friend,' said she to me, 'have done with this funereal pomp, cease these useless tears. I have tasted a thousand delights in the Elysian fields, conversing with those who are saints like myself. Let the king's despair remain for some time unchecked, it gratifies me.'" Scarcely had he spoken, when every one shouted; "A miracle! a miracle!" The Stag, instead of being punished, received a handsome donation.

Do but entertain a king with dreams, flatter, and tell him a few pleasant lies; whatever may be his indignation against you, he will swallow the bait, and make you his dearest friend.

THE DOG WITH THE CROPPED EARS

"WHAT CRIME HAVE I COMMITTED THAT I SHOULD BE THUS mutilated by my own master?" pensively exclaimed Jowler, a young mastiff. "Here's a pretty condition for a dog of my pretensions! How can I shew my face among my friends? Oh! king of beasts, or rather their tyrant, who would dare to treat you thus?" His complaints were not unfounded, for that very morning, his master, despite the piercing shrieks of our young friend, had barbarously cut off his long, pendent ears. Jowler expected nothing less than to give up the ghost.

As he advanced in years, he perceived that he gained more than he had lost by his mutilation; for, being naturally inclined to fight with others, he would often have returned home with this part disfigured in a hundred places. A quarrelsome dog always has his ears lacerated.

The less we leave others to lay hold of the better. When one has but one point to defend, it should be protected for fear of accident. Take for example Master Jowler, who, being armed with a spiked collar, and having about as much ear as a bird, a wolf would be puzzled to know where to tackle him.

THE TREASURE AND THE TWO MEN

A MAN HAVING NEITHER CREDIT NOR RESERVE, NOR A SINGLE farthing in his possession, dreading to die of hunger, resolved to terminate his misery by hanging himself. With this intention, he proceeded to a ruinous house, carrying a cord with him. In attempting to fasten a nail to one of the old walls, it gave way, when, to his great surprise, he discovered a treasure. Our desperado gathered it up; and without waiting to count the whole, returned home with the gold, well pleased with his good fortune, leaving the halter behind.

Soon after, the man to whom the treasure belonged, arrived; and, perceiving it gone, "What," said he, "have I lost my money, and do I still exist? I should make a point of hanging myself, if a rope were not so expensive." Observing at length that a halter had been left there, he immediately put an end to his trouble by suspending himself from it. The miser seemed as much consoled at having the halter provided for him free of expense, as the impoverished man had been by the discovery of the treasure.

It is rare, indeed, that the miser ends his days without sorrow; for the treasure that he conceals, and is so loth to part with, frequently falls into the hands of others. Such are the changes which Fortune delights to make in her capricious moods. It is a peculiar trait in this fickle goddess, that she adopts the most eccentric means of destroying the hopes of the covetous when at the highest pitch, and to shower her golden gifts on the wretched when least expected.

THE RAT IN RETIREMENT

THERE LIV'D A RAT, SAYS EASTERN STORY,
Who made devotion all his glory.
Enamour'd of a quiet life,
And weary of the world,—or wife,
To pass the remnant of his days at ease,
He sought the shelter of a large Dutch cheese:
Seeking therein much more than food,
Retirement, and deep solitude.
He nibbled and scratch'd, and soon work'd himself in,
And he delv'd very deep—for Dutch cheese is not thin;
At the bottom he found it would amply afford—
'Twas all that he wish'd—quiet, lodging, and board.
Settled here at his ease, need I add that the rat,
Having "eaten and worshipp'd," soon grew very "fat"?
It chanced one day, that a legation,
Deputed by the rattish nation,
To sue for succour and supplies
In foreign parts, from their allies,
Demanding alms upon the road,
Sought our secluded saint's abode.
They told the purport of their mission:
Their country's desolate condition;

Invaded by the feline foe,
And want's still wider-wasting woe;
Ratapolis the tabbies leaguer,
They quitted it in haste so eager,
That sudden sent without their pay,
The embassy must beg its way.
Small aid they ask'd, for Heaven be praised,
The siege, they said, would soon be raised.
"My friends," replied the devotee,
"The world and its concerns affect not me:
We long since parted;
Yet let me not be thought hard-hearted;
I give to misery all I have, a prayer—
And hope high Heaven may·make you much its care!
What can a solitary pauper more?"
He spoke—and speaking, closed the door.
Whose is this image, reader? can you guess?
"A monk's, I ween."—What! rich and pitiless?
A monk slight the poor!   Oh, no; 'tis a dervise!
A monk, we all know, would have render'd 'em service.

THE CAT AND THE TWO SPARROWS

A CAT LIVED IN THE GREATEST FRIENDSHIP WITH A YOUNG SPAR-
row, and no wonder, since they were of the same age, and had
from their birth occupied the same apartment.   The bird often
provoked his companion by pecking her with his beak, which she
returned only by fondling him with her paws.   The Cat always
spared her friend, never chastising him save in jest; and even then,
she was very scrupulous not to make use of her talons.   The
sparrow, less circumspect, dealt heavy blows with his beak; but
Puss, like a sage and discreet individual, made allowances for these
familiarities; for one should never seriously give way to anger
among friends.   As they had been intimate from their earliest
youth, the force of habit maintained peace between them, and
their frolics never had an angry ending.

At length a sparrow, residing in their immediate vicinity, came to visit them, and was soon the inseparable companion of petulant Dick and of sage Puss. The two birds shortly fell out, and Puss took part in the quarrel. "This stranger," she exclaimed, "is behaving mighty prettily, to insult my friend! Is the Sparrow of another to be the death of ours? No! by all that is feline!" and joining in the combat, she seized and devoured the intruder.

"Really!" exclaimed Miss Puss, "there is a most exquisite and delicate flavour about these sparrows!" This profound reflection occurred to her often afterwards, till, no longer able to restrain her appetite, she fell upon and made a meal of her friend.

THE COBBLER AND THE BANKER

A COBBLER PASSED HIS TIME IN SINGING FROM MORNING TILL night; it was wonderful to see, wonderful to hear him; he was more contented in making shoes, than was any of the seven sages. His neighbour, on the contrary, who was rolling in wealth, sung but little, and slept less. He was a banker; when by chance he fell into a doze at day-break, the cobbler awoke him with his song. The banker complained sadly that Providence had not made sleep a saleable commodity, like edibles or drinkables. Having at length sent for the songster, he said to him; "How much a year do you earn, Master Gregory?"

"How much a year, sir?" said the merry cobbler laughing; "I never reckon in that way, living as I do from one day to another; somehow I manage to reach the end of the year; each day brings its meal."

"Well then! how much a day do you earn, my friend?"

"Sometimes more, sometimes less; but the worst of it is,—and, without that our earnings would be very tolerable,—a number of days occur in the year on which we are forbidden to work; and the curate, moreover, is constantly adding some new saint to the list."

The banker, laughing at his simplicity, said; "In future I shall place you above want. Take this hundred crowns, preserve them carefully, and make use of them in time of need." The cobbler fancied he beheld all the wealth which the earth had produced in the past century for the use of mankind. Returning home, he buried his money and his happiness at the same time. No more singing; he lost his voice, the moment he acquired that which is the source of so much grief. Sleep quitted his dwelling; and cares, suspicions, and false alarms took its place. All day, his eye wandered in the direction of his treasure; and at night, if some stray cat made a noise, the cat was robbing him. At length the poor man ran to the house of his rich neighbour; "Give me back," said he, "sleep and my voice, and take your hundred crowns."

THE SCULPTOR AND THE STATUE OF JUPITER

A BLOCK OF MARBLE WAS SO FINE,
  To buy it did a Sculptor hasten.
"What shall my chisel, now 'tis mine—
  A god, a table, or a basin?"
"A god," said he, "the thing shall be;
  I'll arm it, too, with thunder.
Let people quake, and bow the knee
  With reverential wonder."
So well the cunning Artist wrought
  All things within a mortal's reach,
That soon the marble wanted nought
  Of being Jupiter, but speech.
Indeed, the Man whose skill did make
  Had scarcely laid his chisel down,
Before himself began to quake,
  And fear his manufacture's frown.
Imagination rules the heart:
  And here we find the fountain head
From whence the pagan error start,
  That o'er the teeming nations spread.
All men, as far as in them lies,
  Create realities of dreams.
To truth our nature proves but ice;
  To falsehood, fire it seems.

THE CAT AND THE RAT

THERE WERE FOUR DIFFERENT ANIMALS, THE CAT, THE OWL, the rat, and the weasel, all of which had various propensities; but all frequented the trunk of a wild and savage-looking old pine-tree. One evening, a man surrounded this tree with a net. Early the next morning, the cat was going to seek her prey; but the shadow of her form prevented her from seeing the net, into which she, therefore, fell. Being in danger of perishing, she cried out piteously. The Rat, hearing her plaint, hastened to her assistance; but was filled with joy, at finding in the captive his mortal enemy.

"My dear friend," said the Cat, "I know that you have a benevolent heart; let me entreat you, therefore, to commiserate my situation, and come and help me out of the snare into which I have fallen through ignorance. It will be doing me a kindness, for which I shall always be grateful; at the same time allow me to assure you of my great personal regard for you, and to inform you that I have always loved you with devoted affection. I was merely going, according to my usual morning custom, to seek my prey, when I was caught in this snare. My life is in your hands; come, therefore, and untie these knots."

"But what recompense shall I have?" asked the Rat. "I promise you my eternal friendship and alliance," said the Cat. "With my claws I will protect you against every enemy. The Weasel and the Screech-owl shall invite you to be of their dinner parties."

"You are an idiot," said the Rat, "to suppose that I will be your deliverer. Learn, however, that I am not quite so foolish."

Wishing Puss a good morning, the rat returned towards his retreat. The weasel hastened after him from his hole; but the rat climbed into a high tree, where he perceived the screech-owl. Though surrounded, however, on every side with danger, he effected his escape; and, returning to the Cat, loosened the knots, and rescued the hypocrite. At this instant, the man who owned the snare appeared, and both these new acquaintances ran away; the Rat keeping at a distance from his companion, and on the alert against any nefarious attempt upon his person.

"Ah! my dear brother," said the Cat, when they had got out of reach of danger, "come and embrace me; your caution and suspicion offend me, and do me injustice. You cannot imagine I have forgotten that I owe to you my life."

"Nor," said the Rat, "can you imagine that I have forgotten your late pretended humanity, concerning the owl and the weasel."

We should never form an alliance with an enemy unless forced by necessity.

THE PASHA AND THE MERCHANT

A GREEK MERCHANT TRADED LARGELY IN A MUSSULMAN COUN-
try. A Pasha protected him, for which the Greek paid him a proportionate amount; protection for a wealthy man is expensive. This cost so much, that our Greek complained universally. Three other Turks, of a less elevated rank, came to offer him their united support, and would be contented with considerably less than he had hitherto paid to one alone. The Greek eagerly listened, and entered into an agreement with them. The Pasha was soon informed of it, and counselled to be even with the interlopers by sending them with a message to the tomb of the Prophet. The three allies, however, knowing that he would have people on the road ready to avenge him, sent the merchant a poison sufficiently powerful to put the Pasha in a fair way of offering his protection to the traders of the other world.

This reaching the Turk's ear, he went straightway to the house of the merchant, and took a seat at his table. In his whole discourse and manner, no one would have imagined that he mistrusted aught.

"Friend," said he, "I am aware that you are about to leave my protection; I am even warned of the consequences; but I will place faith in you, for you have not the appearance of a poisoner, and will therefore drop the subject. With respect to these gentry who offer you their support, listen to me; without wearying you with a host of *pros* and *cons*, I will merely relate the following:

" 'There was formerly a shepherd who lived peaceably with his dog and his flock. Some one asked him what he wanted with so enormous a mastiff which devoured a whole loaf at every meal. A fine animal like that should be given to the squires; while he, the shepherd, for economy's sake, could have two or three terriers, which, costing less, would watch the flock better than this one great beast.   He devoured as much as three; but they forgot that he had also triple jaws when the wolves offered battle.   The shepherd got rid of him; and took three smaller dogs, which cost him less to keep, but avoided the conflict.   The flock suffered for it.'

"And so will you suffer for your choice of this rabble.   If you would be safe, you will return to me."   The merchant took his advice.

THE DRAGONS

AN ENVOY FROM THE SULTAN'S WIDE DOMAIN,
 Who at Vienna's court had long resided,
Observ'd one day: "To me 'tis very plain
 The armies by my master's power provided,
And muster'd underneath the Turkish firman
Are in their structure better than the German."
"Bah!" cried an Austrian, nettled at this praise.
 "You think too highly of your own resources:
My master has dependents, who can raise
 Troops full a match for all your Turkish forces."—
"I know your strength:—but if your ear you'll lend, I
Will tell a strange true story," said th' Effendi.
"Once on a time, on t'other side a hedge,
 With hundred heads a monstrous snake I saw.
I felt some fear, I'll honestly allege,
 The dragon seemed to wish me in his maw:
But 'mongst the pales and briars, and tangled bushes,
His hundred heads the Hydra vainly pushes.
Then came, which struck me with still greater dread,
 A second dragon with a host of tails.
But this vast serpent had a single head,
 Which forced its way with ease thro' briars and pales.—
This, noble Count, I venture to opine,
Marks the great difference 'twixt your Lord and mine."

THE TWO ADVENTURERS

THE PATH OF PLEASURE NEVER LEADS TO GLORY! THE PRODI-
gious achievements of Hercules were the result of high adventure,
and though there is little, either in fable or history, to shew that
he had any rivals, still it is recorded that a knight-errant, in com-

pany with a fellow adventurer, sought his fortune in a romantic
country. He had not travelled far when his companion observed
a post, on which was written the following inscription; "Brave
adventurer, if you have a desire to discover that which has never
been seen by any knight-errant, you have only to pass this tor-
rent, and then taking in your arms an elephant of stone, carry it
in one breath to the summit of this mountain, whose noble head
seems blended with the sky."

"But," said the companion of the knight, "the water may be
deep, as well as rapid, and though notwithstanding, we should pass
it, why should we be encumbered with the elephant? What a
ridiculous undertaking!" and philosophically and with nice calculation, he observed that it might be carried four steps; but for
conveying it to the top of the mountain in one breath, that was
not in the power of mortal; unless it should be the dwarf figure
of an elephant, fit only to be placed on the top of a stick; and
then what honour would there be in such an adventure?

"There is," said he, "some deception in this writing. It is an enigma only fit to amuse a child. I shall therefore leave you and your elephant."

The reasoner then departed; but the adventurous man rushed with his eyes closed across the water; neither depth nor violence prevented him, and according to the inscription he saw the elephant lying on the opposite bank. He took it and carried it to the top of the hill, where he saw a town. A shriek from the elephant alarmed the people of the city, who rose in arms; but the adventurer, nothing daunted, was determined to die a hero. The people were however awed by his presence, and he was astonished to hear them proclaim him successor to their king, who had recently died.

Great enterprises are only achieved by adventurous spirits. They who calculate with too great nicety every difficulty and obstacle which is likely to lie in their way, lose that time in hesitation, which the more daring seize and render available to the loftiest purposes.

THE CAT, THE WEASEL, AND THE YOUNG RABBIT

ONE FINE MORNING, MRS. WEASEL TOOK POSSESSION OF THE fortress of a young rabbit. The master being absent, this was easily effected; and, while he had gone to pay his respects to Aurora, she transferred her household goods to his residence. After he had browsed, trotted, and made several calls, Master Rabbit returned to his subterranean dwelling, and perceived the snout of the Weasel at the window. "Oh! ye gods, what do I behold?" exclaimed the animal, excluded from the home of his fathers. "Hallo! Mrs. Weasel, get out of my house without further ado, or I shall at once give notice of your whereabouts to all the rats in the kingdom."

The sharp-snouted lady replied, that the earth belonged to the first occupier. It was a fine pretence for war, indeed; a dwelling to which he had only gained access by dint of scratching; and even supposing it to be a kingdom, she would be glad to be informed what law constituted it for ever the heir-loom of John, the son or nephew of Peter or William, in preference to that of Paul, or of herself.

Master Rabbit alleged use and custom. "Those who preceded me," said he, "have rendered me lord and master of this fortress, by transmitting it from father to son, from Peter to Simon, and at length to me. Can there be anything more reasonable, than that it should belong to the original possessor?"

"Well! well," cried the weasel, "no more words about it; let us refer to and abide by the decision of Grimalkin." This was a cat, living like a pious hermit; a sanctified tabby, well coated with fur, large and fat; an expert arbitrator in all disputes. Master Rabbit consented that he should be the judge, and they soon appeared before his feline majesty. "Come nearer, my children," said Grimalkin to them, "nearer still; I am very deaf, and borne down by the weight of years." Both approached fearlessly, dreading no harm. As soon as the pious Grimalkin beheld the disputants within his reach, darting his claws on either side at the same moment, he settled their differences by devouring both.

This forcibly resembles the justice sometimes dealt out to petty sovereigns, who refer their disputes to more powerful monarchs.

THE RAT AND THE OYSTER

A RAT WHO LIVED IN A FIELD AND WAS POSSESSED OF VERY FEW brains, one day deserted his hole and set out to view the world. He had not travelled far from his narrow habitation, before he exclaimed; "How large and spacious is the earth, there are the Apennines, and here is the Caucasus." The smallest molehill seemed a mountain in his eyes. After some days our traveller arrived at a place where the sea had washed numerous Oysters ashore; at first he imagined they must be vessels cast away. "Ah!" said he, "my father was a poor stay-at-home; he had never travelled all his life; but as for me, I have passed the deserts and have already seen the maritime empire."

All the Oysters except one were closed, which remained open to gape at the sun, and taste the reviving balm of the dewy zephyr; this one was exceedingly white and plump, and of matchless flavour. "What do I perceive!" said the Rat, "surely this must be fit to eat, and if I am not mistaken in its appearance, I shall fare nobly to-day." Master Rat greedily approached the shell, and stretching out his neck to take it, found himself caught in a trap, for the Oyster, suddenly closing, held him fast.

This fable bears more than one moral; it shews that those who are unacquainted with the world are astonished at every trifle; and we may also learn by it, that he who strives illegally to possess himself of the goods of others, often, like the rat, gets caught in a snare; what can be more true, than that the biter is frequently the first to be bitten?

THE PHYSICIANS

DR. NEVERWELL WENT TO VISIT A PATIENT, WHO WAS ALSO ATtended by his rival Betterall. The latter held out hopes, although his comrade affirmed that the sick man was going to pay a visit to his forefathers. Each of them prescribed differently for the cure, and, as might be expected, their patient paid the tribute of nature, just as Neverwell had predicted. The two congratulated themselves on the case. One said; "He is dead, just as I foresaw."

"If he had followed my directions," said the other, "he would still be among the living."

THE WOLF AND THE HUNTSMAN

A HUNTSMAN, HAVING BROUGHT DOWN A DOE, PERCEIVED A Fawn, and letting fly an arrow, made her keep company with the defunct. Both lay on the turf. The prey was fairly earned; any moderate huntsman would have been content. However, a wild Boar, a superb and enormous monster, again tempts our archer;

the beast falls stunned by the force of the blow. Surely here was enough? But no! nothing can satisfy the vast appetite of a conqueror. While the Boar was coming to himself, the archer perceives a Partridge, and, levelling his cross-bow, prepares to shoot, when the wild Boar, collecting his remaining strength, rushes on the huntsman, transfixes him with his tusks, and dies avenged on his body.

A Wolf, passing that way, beheld the piteous spectacle; "O! Fortune," said he, "I promise to build thee a temple. Four carcases! what a mine of wealth! but I must nevertheless economise them; these windfalls are scarce." (Thus do misers excuse themselves.) "I shall have enough," said the Wolf, "for at least a month; one, two, three, four bodies; just four complete weeks, if I know anything of arithmetic. In two days I shall begin, and in the meantime will eat this bow-string, which is doubtless made of real gut; the odour of it is sufficient." Thus speaking he flies at the bow, which being spanned, goes off, and sends the arrow through the heart of the Wolf.

THE GOUT AND THE SPIDER

DIRE NEMESIS, THE SURE, THOUGH SLOW
Avenger in the realms below,
Has often various schemes designed
In this our world to vex mankind;
And oft from Pluto's dark domains
Sent pestilence and hurricanes;
Earthquakes, which shake the shores of Tagus,
And divers minor ills to plague us.
Of this small fry the dame possest,
In order ranged, an ample chest,
Well furnished with as rich a store as
That box which poets call Pandora's.
    Two at a time once issued out:
The loathsome spider, and the gout.

"Imps!" said the goddess, "leave your den!
Go seek above the abodes of men,
To you shall open every door:
Take one the rich, and one the poor.
Gout! of the two, as you're the worst,
Yours be the right of choosing first."
 When gout on earth's fair surface found him,
Turning his fiery eye-balls round him,
At once proposed himself to niche
In the gay mansions of the rich.
But peering there with curious eye,
Some big-wigged folks he chanced to spy,
(This was ere fashion's power prevailing
Had cropt the solemn sons of Galen)
And canes they bore with amber heads,
Guarding their patrons' downy beds:
Their only business is, they say,
To drive disease and pain away.
"Oh!" cried the gout, "I plainly see
This residence is not for me.
Spider! be yours the palace lot;
Be mine the poor man's humble cot,
For there these perukes enter not.
With peasants let me take my pleasure,
And pinch the hardy rogues at leisure."
 The spider, her rich lot beholding,
Longed to deform each gilded moulding.
"That sculptured frieze and cornice fretted,
By me," said she, "shall soon be netted;
My filth these works of art shall hide,
To mortify the master's pride;
Whilst on the pangs of many a fly
I'll sate my lust of cruelty."
 'Twas fixed:—and in their several stations
They both commenced their operations.
But ere this plan had lasted long,

Each found his hasty choice was wrong.
The spider felt in every room
Her mortal enemy the broom;
She shifts her ground, but soon her toil
Hasten fresh Abigails to spoil.
Gout, in his turn, was sure to meet
With rough impenetrable feet.
Each host his limbs unwildly mocks,
Sets him to dig, hoe, cleave hard blocks.
His engines fail of racking pain,
To light his fires he tries in vain;
No fuel luxury supplies,
They're quenched by constant exercise.
He moves, but finds from every neighbour
He's chased by temperance and labour.

Now having run their utmost range,
At length the fiends agree to change;
Pleased, to a hut the spider rushes,
Nor trembles with the fear of brushes.
Her bloated form collects supplies,
Unchecked from swarms of vulgar flies,
Where dust plebeian long had rested,
She plies her weaving unmolested.

Gout scours the country and the town
For sumptuous feasts, and beds of down.
Experience has his views enlightened;
No more by scare-crow perukes frightened,
The men with canes he shrewdly judges
Spring from the family of Fudges:
And strikes his talons void of fear,
In toes of alderman or peer:
Finding his late rejected quarters
The choicest spot to urge his tortures.

Both pests now thrive, and both content,
Each in his proper element.

THE SCHOOL-BOY, THE PEDANT, AND THE GARDENER

A CERTAIN SCHOOL-BOY RENDERED DOUBLY WILD AND DOUBLY roguish by his extreme youth, and by the privilege which pedants enjoy of turning their wits, was in the habit of robbing a neighbour of fruits and flowers. In the autumn, this neighbour was blessed with Pomona's choicest gifts. Each season brought its tribute; for in the spring he was overwhelmed with the gifts of Flora. One day he espied our school-boy, who, carelessly climbing a fruit-tree, spoilt all his clothes, even to the buttons. He shook and broke the branches of the trees in such a manner, that

the gardener sent to make his complaints to the school-master. The latter came, followed by a troop of children, thus filling the garden with a band of spoilers worse than the first. The pedant had graciously increased the evil by bringing with him his ill-bred rabble, in order, he said, that the chastisement he intended to inflict on the offender might make a salutary impression on the minds of his scholars, which should never be effaced during their lives. Hereupon he commenced quoting Virgil and Cicero, as authorities for the importance of early impressions. His discourse lasted so long, that the little depredators had time to despoil the garden in a hundred places.

I detest pieces of eloquence misplaced, which have no end in view; and I am acquainted with no animal in the world worse than a school-boy, unless it be a pedant. To speak the truth, I should feel very ill at ease with even the better of these two for a neighbour.

EDUCATION

LARIDON AND CÆSAR WERE TWIN BROTHERS, OWING THEIR ORIGIN to a famous sporting dog. They were handsome, well-proportioned, and courageous; these two dogs, however, had different pursuits; the one frequented the woods, the other the kitchen. Each had at first different names, but a certain scullion called the latter Laridon. The diversity of training, which preserved the excellence of the breed in the one, entirely reversed it in the other. Cæsar displayed a disposition for high adventure, and in the chase had brought many a stag and wild-boar to bay; by avoiding unworthy mistresses, he maintained the nobleness of the race whence he sprung; but Laridon, by a vulgar association with every passing object, only multiplied his breed, to produce a race of turnspits, which became common throughout France.

Alas! how many through not following the valuable advice of parents in due time, and neglecting to cultivate the gifts of Nature, sink into a like degeneracy; and from being Cæsars, become Laridons!

THE WOLF TURNED SHEPHERD

A WOLF, WHOSE GETTINGS FROM THE FLOCKS
    Began to be but few,
Bethought himself to play the Fox
    In character quite new.
A Shepherd's hat and coat he took,
    A cudgel for a crook,
    Nor e'en the pipe forgot:

And more to seem what he was not,
Himself upon his hat he wrote,
"I'm Willie, Shepherd of these sheep."
 His person thus complete,
 His crook in upraised feet,
The impostor Willie stole upon the keep.
The real Willie, on the grass asleep,
 Slept there, indeed, profoundly,
His dog and pipe slept, also soundly;
 His drowsy sheep around lay.
 As for the greatest number,
Much bless'd the hypocrite their slumber,
And hoped to drive away the flock,
Could he the Shepherd's voice but mock.
 He thought undoubtedly he could.
He tried: the tone in which he spoke,
 Loud echoing from the wood,
 The plot and slumber broke;
 Sheep, dog, and man awoke.
 The Wolf, in sorry plight,
 In hampering coat bedight,
 Could neither run nor fight.
There's always leakage of deceit
Which makes it never safe to cheat.
 Whoever is a Wolf had better
 Keep clear of hypocritic fetter.

THE ADVANTAGE OF SCIENCE

IN THE OLDEN TIME, IN A CERTAIN TOWN, THERE OCCURRED A difference between two citizens, one of whom was poor but clever, the other rich but ignorant. The latter endeavoured to obtain an advantage over his rival; thinking that every wise man ought to be obliged to honour him. He was foolish enough to suppose that good fortune, whether accompanied with merit or not, deserved to be venerated. "My friend," said he to the sage, "you seem to hold yourself in high estimation; but tell me, do you not associate with those who always lodge on the third floor, and dress in June and December alike? The republic has always most trouble and concern with the poor and dependent. The rich and independent, who think nothing of the mere common necessaries of life, by indulging in luxuries, employ the artificer and the tradesman, while you devote yourself to persons who think they are gentlemen, merely because they read vicious books and trashy plays."

These impertinent observations met with the retort they deserved. The learned man did not rebut the silly insult with hostile or scornful expressions; but achieved a complete victory over his antagonist with the passive indignation of satire. After this encounter they both quitted the town. The rich man, who was conceited and imperious, was shunned and despised wherever he went; but the learned man was admired and respected.

Fools may seek to indemnify themselves by talking; but knowledge alone is universally prized.

THE ASS AND THE DOG

MUTUAL ASSISTANCE IS THE LAW OF NATURE; HOWEVER, AN ASS, one day, defied it, and being naturally a kind-hearted beast, I scarcely know how it came about. He was journeying across the country, accompanied by the Dog, and very gravely thinking of nothing. Their joint master followed; but soon lay down to sleep. The Ass commenced grazing, being at that time in a meadow, the grass of which was very much to his liking. True there were no thistles; but as one must not always be dainty, he overlooked that; and, in the absence of this dish, our donkey knew very well how to make a banquet without it. The Dog, dying with hunger, said to him; "Dear comrade, pray stoop a little, that I may get my dinner from your bread-pannier." No reply; the long-eared beast was fearful of losing a bite if he wasted an instant; and remained a long time deaf to his comrade's petition. At length he replied; "Friend, I advise you to wait till our master has taken his nap; when he awakes, he will not fail to give you your usual portion; he will not be long."

During this conversation, another famished beast, a Wolf, emerging from the forest, approached. The Ass immediately called the Dog to his assistance, who, without stirring, replied; "Friend, I advise you to fly, until your master wakes, he will not be long, set off at once, and run. What if the Wolf overtake you? Break his skull, you have been newly shod; and doubtless you will at once make him measure his length."

During this sage counsel, Master Wolf effectually strangled the selfish Ass.

THE WOLF AND THE LEAN DOG

A HUNGRY WOLF CAUGHT A DOG NAPPING AT SOME DISTANCE from the village; but the latter awaking, begged him to have compassion for a short time only; as he had not yet made his will, and his numerous relations would go to loggerheads about his worldly possessions, if he were to be devoured thus prematurely. "Moreover," said the dog, "it will be for your own benefit to spare me for a few days, seeing how lean I am at present. To-morrow, my master gives away his only daughter in marriage to a rich country-gentleman. The wedding feast will not fail to be protracted for a week; during which time I shall become as plump as you can desire; and will not fail to be prepared, whenever you feel inclined to call upon me."

The Wolf believing the Dog's assertions, let him depart. After some days, he bethought himself of ascertaining whether his property were better worth eating; but the Dog was within the gates, and said to him through the palings; "My friend, I am coming out directly; if you will just wait there an instant, the porter and myself will be with you at once." By the porter, the cunning hound meant an enormous mastiff, famous for despatching wolves. Our Wolf somehow mistrusted the scheme. "My respects to the porter," said he; and set off at full speed. Fortunately for his hide he was very nimble, and escaped; but never again stayed his appetite for a wedding.

JONATHAN
SWIFT

Ireland 1667 -- 1748

THE WASP AND THE MAN

A MAN SEEING A WASP CREEPING INTO A VIAL FILLED WITH honey, that was hung on a fruit tree, said thus; "Why, thou sottish animal, art thou mad to go into the vial, where you see many hundred of your kind dying before you?"

"The reproach is just," answered the Wasp, "but not from you Men, who are so far from taking example by other people's follies, that you will not take warning by your own. If after falling several times into this vial, and escaping by chance, I should fall in again, I should then but resemble you."

THE MISER'S JACKDAW

AN OLD MISER KEPT A TAME JACKDAW, THAT USED TO STEAL pieces of money and hide them in a hole; which the Cat observing asked; "Why he would hoard up those round shining things that he could make no use of?"

"Why," said the Jackdaw, "my master has a whole chest full, and makes no more use of them than I."

Men are contented to be laughed at for their wit, but not their folly.

JOHN
GAY

England 1685 -- 1732

THE SHEPHERD'S DOG AND THE WOLF

A WOLF, WITH HUNGER FIERCE AND BOLD,
Ravag'd the plains, and thinn'd the fold:
Deep in the wood secure he lay,
The thefts of night regal'd the day.
In vain the shepherd's wakeful care
Had spread the toils, and watch'd the snare;
In vain the dog pursu'd his pace.
The fleeter robber mock'd the chase.
    As Lightfoot rang'd the forest round,
By chance his foe's retreat he found.
    "Let us awhile the war suspend,
And reason as from friend to friend."
    "A truce," replies the Wolf. " 'Tis done."
The dog the parley thus begun.
    "How can that strong intrepid mind
Attack a weak defenceless kind?
Those jaws should prey on nobler food,
And drink the boar's and lion's blood.
Great souls with generous pity melt,
Which coward tyrants never felt.
How harmless is our fleecy care!
Be brave, and let thy mercy spare."

"Friend," says the Wolf, "the matter weigh;
Nature design'd us beasts of prey;
As such, when hunger finds a treat
'Tis necessary Wolves should eat.
If mindful of the bleating weal,
Thy bosom burns with real zeal:
Hence, and thy tyrant lord beseech;
To him repeat the moving speech;
A wolf eats sheep but now and then,
Ten thousands are devour'd by men.
An open foe may prove a curse,
But a pretended friend is worse."

THE JUGGLERS

A JUGGLER LONG THROUGH ALL THE TOWN
Had raised his fortune and renown;
You'd think (so far his art transcends)
The devil at his finger ends.

Vice heard his fame, she read his bill;
Convinced of his inferior skill,
She sought his booth, and from the crowd
Defied the man of art aloud:

"Is this then he so famed for sleight?
Can this slow bungler cheat your sight?
Dares he with me dispute the prize?
I leave it to impartial eyes."

Provoked, the juggler cried: " 'Tis done;
In science I submit to none."

Thus said, the cups and balls he played;
By turns this here, that there conveyed,
The cards, obedient to his words,
Are by a fillip turned to birds.
His little boxes change the grain:
Trick after trick deludes the train.

He shakes his bag, he shews all fair;
His fingers spread, and nothing there;
Then bids it rain with showers of gold:
And now his iv'ry eggs are told;
But when from thence the hen he draws,
Amazed spectators hum applause.

Vice now stept forth, and took the place,
With all the forms of his grimace.

"This magic looking-glass," she cries,
" (There, hand it round,) will charm your eyes."
Each eager eye the sight desired,
And every man himself admired.

Next, to a senator addressing:
"See this bank-note; observe the blessing,
Breathe on the bill.   Heigh, pass! 'tis gone."
Upon his lips a padlock shone.
A second puff the magic broke;
The padlock vanished, and he spoke.

Twelve bottles ranged upon the board,
All full, with heady liquor stored,
By clean conveyance disappear,
And now, two bloody swords are there.

A purse she to a thief exposed;
At once his ready fingers closed.
He opes his fist, the treasure's fled:
He sees a halter in its stead.

She bids ambition hold a wand;
He grasps a hatchet in his hand.

A box of charity she shews:
"Blow here"; and a churchwarden blows.
'Tis vanished with conveyance neat,
And on the table smokes a treat.

She shakes the dice, the board she knocks,
And from all pockets fills her box.

She next a meagre rake addressed:
"This picture see; her shape, her breast!
What youth, and what inviting eyes!

Hold her, and have her." With surprise
His hand exposed a box of pills,
And a lough laugh proclaimed his ills.

A counter in a miser's hand,
Grew twenty guineas at command.
She bids his heir the sum retain,
And 'tis a counter now again.
A guinea with her touch you see
Take every shape but charity,
And not one thing you saw, or drew,
But changed from what was first in view.

The juggler now, in grief of heart,
With this submission owned her art:
"Can I such matchless sleight withstand!
How practice hath improved your hand!
But now and then, I cheat the throng;
You every day, and all day long."

THE MONKEY WHO HAD SEEN THE WORLD

A MONKEY, TO REFORM THE TIMES,
Resolv'd to visit foreign climes:
For men in distant regions roam
To bring politer manners home.
So forth he fares, all toil defies;
Misfortune serves to make us wise.

At length the treach'rous snare was laid;
Poor Pug was caught, to town convey'd,
There sold. How envied was his doom,
Made captive in a lady's room!
Proud as a lover of his chains,
He day by day her favour gains.
Whene'er the duty of the day
The toilet calls, with mimic play
He twirls her knots, he cracks her fan,
Like any other gentleman.

In visits too his parts and wit,
When jests grew dull, were sure to hit.
Proud with applause, the thought his mind
In ev'ry courtly art refin'd;
Like Orpheus burnt with public zeal,
To civilize the monkey weal:
So watch'd occasion, broke his chain,
And sought his native woods again.

    The hairy sylvans round him press,
Astonish'd at his strut and dress.
Some praise his sleeve; and others gloat
Upon his rich embroider'd coat;
His dapper periwig commending,
With the black tail behind depending;
His powder'd back, above, below,
Like hoary frost, or fleecy snow:
But all with envy and desire
His flutt'ring shoulder-knot admire.

    "Hear and improve," he pertly cries;
"I come to make a nation wise.
Weigh your own worth, support your place,
The next in rank to human race.
In cities long I pass'd my days,
Convers'd with men, and learn'd their ways.
Their dress, their courtly manners see;
Reform your state, and copy me.
Seek ye to thrive! in flatt'ry deal;
Your scorn, your hate, with that conceal,
Seem only to regard your friends,
But use them for your private ends.
Stint not to truth the flow of wit;
Be prompt to lie whene'er 'tis fit.
Bend all your force to spatter merit:
Scandal is conversation's spirit.
Boldly to everything attend,
And men your talents shall commend.
I knew the great.   Observe me right;
So shall you grow like man polite."

He spoke, and bow'd.   With mutt'ring jaws
The wond'ring circle grinn'd applause.
Now warm with malice, envy, spite,
Their most obliging friends they bite;
And, fond to copy human ways,
Practise new mischiefs all their days.
 Thus the dull lad, too tall for school,
With travel finishes the fool;
Studious of every coxcomb's airs,
He drinks, games, dresses, lies, and swears;
O'erlooks with scorn all virtuous arts;
For vice is fitted to his parts.

THE UNIVERSAL APPARITION

A RAKE BY EV'RY PASSION RUL'D,
With ev'ry vice his youth had cool'd;
Disease his tainted blood assails;
His spirits droop, his vigour fails:
With secret ills at home he pines,
And like infirm old age declines.
 As twing'd with pain he pensive sits;
And raves, and prays, and swears by fits;
A ghastly phantom, lean and wan,
Before him rose, and thus began:
 "My name, perhaps, hath reach'd your ear;
Attend, and be advis'd by Care.
Nor love, nor honour, wealth nor pow'r,
Can give the heart a cheerful hour
When health is lost.   Be timely wise:
With health all taste of pleasure flies."
 Thus said, the phantom disappears;
The wary counsel wak'd his fears;
He now from all excess abstains;
With physic purifies his veins;
And, to procure a sober life,

Resolves to venture on a wife.

But now again the sprite ascends;
Where'er he walks his ear attends:
Insinuates that beauty's frail;
That perseverance must prevail;
With jealousies his brain inflames,
And whispers all her lovers' names,
In other hours she represents
His household charge, his annual rents,
Increasing debts, perplexing duns,
And nothing for his younger sons.

Straight all his thought to gain he turns,
And with the thirst of lucre burns.
But, when possest of fortune's store,
The spectre haunts him more and more:
Sets want and misery in view,
Bold thieves and all the murd'ring crew;
Alarms him with eternal frights,
Infests his dream, or wakes his nights.
How shall he chase this hideous guest?
Pow'r may perhaps protect the rest.
To pow'r he rose: again the sprite
Besets him morning, noon, and night;
Talks of ambition's tottering seat,
How envy persecutes the great;
Of rival hate, of treach'rous friends,
And what disgrace his fall attends.

The court he quits, to fly from Care,
And seeks the peace of rural air:
His groves, his fields, amus'd his hours;
He prun'd his trees, he rais'd his flow'rs.
But Care again his steps pursues;
Warns him of blasts of blighting dews,
Of plund'ring insects, snails and rains,
And droughts that starv'd the labour'd plains.
Abroad, at home, the spectre's there:
In vain we seek to fly from Care.

At length he thus the ghost address'd:
"Since thou must be my constant guest,
Be kind, and follow me no more;
For Care by right should go before."

THE BUTTERFLY AND THE SNAIL

ALL UPSTARTS INSOLENT IN PLACE
Remind us of their vulgar race.
As, in the sunshine of the morn,
A butterfly but newly born
Sat proudly perking on a rose,
With pert conceit his bosom glows;
His wings, all glorious to behold,
Bedropt with azure, jet and gold,
Wide he displays; the spangled dew
Reflects his eyes, and various hue.

His now-forgotten friend, a snail,
Beneath his house, with slimy trail,
Crawls o'er the grass; whom when he spies
In wrath he to the gard'ner cries:
"What means yon peasant's daily toil,
From choking weed to rid the soil?
Why wake you to the morning's care?
Why with new arts correct the year?
Why glows the peach with crimson hue?
And why the plum's inviting blue?
Were they to feast his taste designed,
That vermin of voracious kind?
Crush then the slow, the pilfering race;
So purge thy garden from disgrace."—

"What arrogance!" the snail replied:
"How insolent is upstart pride!
Hadst thou not thus, with insult vain,
Provoked my patience to complain,
I had concealed thy meaner birth,

Nor traced thee to the scum of earth.
For scarce nine suns have waked the hours,
To swell the fruit and paint the flowers,
Since I thy humbler life surveyed,
In base and sordid guise arrayed;
A hideous insect, vile, unclean,
You dragged a slow and noisome train,
And from your spider-bowels drew
Foul film and spun the dirty clue.
I own my humble life, good friend;
Snail was I born, and snail shall end.
And what's a butterfly?   At best
He's but a caterpillar drest;
And all thy race (a num'rous seed)
Shall prove of caterpillar breed."

THE RABBITS

HARD BY THE MARGIN OF A WOOD,
By several savage hounds pursued,
A rabbit, sinking with affright,
Strove to elude their scent and sight.
Away he fled in full career;
When, starting from a thicket near,
His comrade cried across the mead:
"Whence all this bustle, all this speed?"—
"Oh, fatal speed, and source of pain,
Two greyhounds chased me o'er the plain;
And down yon hill without remorse,

Behold they wind their rapid course!"—
"I view them, friend, but by their yell
They beagles are, I know them well."—
"Beagles or greyhounds, this I know,
They will effect my overthrow:—
Mark how they bound with luckless strength,
I'm sure they're greyhounds by their length."—
"Poh! poh! they beagles are, I swear,
Their very voices so declare!"—
"No, no—they're greyhounds."—"You mistake,
They beagles are—I know their make!"
　　At length, so warm the matter rose,
From words they almost came to blows;
When straight the dogs, then running mute,
Killed both, and ended the dispute.

*THE OWL, THE SWAN, THE COCK, THE SPIDER, THE
ASS, AND THE FARMER*

AN OWL OF MAGISTERIAL AIR,
Of solemn voice, of brow austere,
Assum'd the pride of human race,
And bore his wisdom in his face.
Not to depreciate learned eyes,
I've seen a pedant look as wise.
　　Within a barn from noise retir'd,
He scorn'd the world, himself admir'd;
And, like an ancient sage, conceal'd
The follies public life reveal'd.
　　Philosophers of old he read,
Their country's youth, to science bred,
Their manners form'd for every station,
And destin'd each his occupation.
When Xenophon, by numbers brav'd,
Retreated, and a people sav'd,
That laurel was not all his own;

The plant by Socrates was sown.
To Aristotle's greater name
The Macedonian ow'd his fame.
  Th' Athenian bird, with pride replete,
Their talents equall'd in conceit;
And, copying the Socratic rule,
Set up for master of a school.
Dogmatic jargon, learn'd by heart,
Trite sentences, hard terms of art,
To vulgar ears seem'd so profound,
They fancy'd learning in the sound.
  The school had fame: the crowded place
With pupils swarm'd of every race.
With these the Swan's maternal care
Had sent her scarce-fledg'd cygnet heir:
The Hen, tho' fond and loth to part,
Here lodg'd the darling of her heart:
The Spider, of mechanic kind,
Aspir'd to science more refin'd:
The Ass learn'd metaphors and tropes,
But most on music fix'd his hopes.
  The pupils now, advanc'd in age,
  Were call'd to tread life's busy stage;
And to the master 'twas submitted,
That each might to his part be fitted.
  "The Swan," says he, "in arms shall shine:
The soldier's glorious toil be thine."
  "The Cock shall mighty wealth attain:
Go seek it on the stormy main."
  "The court shall be the Spider's sphere:
Pow'r, fortune, shall reward him there."
  "In music's art the Ass's fame
Shall emulate Corelli's name."
  Each took the part that he advis'd,
And all were equally despis'd.
A Farmer, at his folly mov'd,

The dull preceptor thus reprov'd:
"Blockhead," says he, "by what you've done,
One would have thought 'em each your son;
For parents, to their offspring blind,
Consult nor parts, nor turn of mind;
But ev'n in infancy decree
What this, what t'other son shall be.
Had you with judgment weigh'd the case,
Their genius thus had fix'd their place;
The Swan had learnt the sailor's art:
The Cock had play'd the soldier's part;
The Spider in the weaver's trade
With credit had a fortune made;
But for the fool in evr'y class
The blockhead had appeared an Ass."

THE MASTIFF

THOSE WHO IN QUARRELS INTERPOSE,
Must often wipe a bleeding nose.
A Mastiff of true English blood,
Lov'd fighting better than his food.
When dogs were snarling for a bone,
He long'd to make the war his own:
And often found when two contend,
To interpose obtain'd his end;
He glory'd in his limping pace;
The scars of honour seam'd his face;
In ev'ry limb a gash appears,
And frequent fights retrench'd his ears.
    As, on a time, he heard from far
Two dogs engag'd in noisy war,
Away he scours and lays about him,
Resolv'd no fray should be without him.
    Forth from his yard a tanner flies,

And to the bold intruder cries,
"A cudgel shall correct your manners:
Whence sprung this cursed hate to tanners?
While on my dog you vent your spite,
Sirrah! 'tis me you dare not fight."
To see the battle thus perplex'd,
With equal rage a butcher vex'd,
Hoarse-screaming from the circled crowd,
To the curs'd Mastiff cries aloud:
"Both Hockley-Hole and Marybone,
The combats of my dog have known.
He ne'er like bullies, coward-hearted,
Attacks in public to be parted.
Think not, rash fool, to share his fame;
Be his the honour or the shame."
Thus said, they swore, and rav'd like thunder,
Then dragg'd their fasten'd dogs asunder;
While clubs and kicks from ev'ry side
Rebounded from the Mastiff's hide.
All reeking now with sweat and blood,
A while the parted warriors stood,
Then pour'd upon the meddling foe;
Who, worried, howl'd and sprawl'd below.
He rose and limping from the fray
By both sides mangled, sneak'd away.

THE CUR, THE HORSE, AND THE SHEPHERD'S DOG

A VILLAGE-CUR, OF SNAPPISH RACE,
The pertest puppy of the place,
Imagin'd that his treble throat
Was bless'd with music's sweetest note;
In the mid-road he basking lay,
The yelping nuisance of the way;
For not a creature pass'd along,

But had a sample of his song.
  Soon as the trotting steed he hears,
He starts, he cocks his dapper ears;
Away he scours, assaults his hoof:
Now near him snarls, now barks aloof;
With shrill impertinence attends;
Nor leaves him till the village ends.
  It chanc'd, upon his evil day,
A Pad came pacing down the way;
The cur, with never-ceasing tongue,
Upon the passing trav'ller sprung.
The horse, from scorn provok'd to ire,
Flung backward; rolling in the mire
The Puppy howl'd and bleeding lay:
The Pad in peace pursu'd his way.
  A Shepherd's Dog, who saw the deed,
Detesting the vexatious breed,
Bespoke him thus: "When coxcombs prate,
They kindle wrath, contempt, or hate;
If thy vile tongue had judgment ty'd,
Thou had'st not like a puppy dy'd."

THE OWL AND THE FARMER

AN OWL OF GRAVE DEPORT AND MIEN,
Who (like the Turk) was seldom seen,
Within a barn had chose his station,
As fit for prey and contemplation.
Upon a beam aloft he sits,
And nods, and seems to think, by fits.
So have I seen a man of news,
Or Postboy, or Gazette peruse;
Smoke, nod, and talk with voice profound,
And fix the fate of Europe round.
Sheaves pil'd on sheaves hid all the floor.

At dawn of morn, to view his store
The Farmer came.   The hooting guest
His self-importance thus express'd:
  "Reason in man is mere pretence:
How weak, how shallow is his sense!
To treat with scorn the Bird of Night,
Declare his folly or his spite.
Then too, how partial is his praise!
The lark's, the linnet's chirping lays
To his ill judging ears are fine;
And nightingales are all divine.
But the more knowing feather'd race
See wisdom stamp'd upon my face.
Whene'er to visit light I deign,
What flocks of fowls compose my train!
Like slaves, they crowd my flight behind,
And own me of superior kind."
  The Farmer laugh'd, and thus reply'd:
"Thou dull important lump of pride,
Dar'st thou, with that harsh grating tongue
Depreciate birds of warbling song?
Indulge thy spleen.   Know, men and fowl
Regard thee, as thou art, an Owl.
Besides, proud blockhead, be not vain
Of what thou call'st thy slaves and train.
Few follow wisdom or her rules;
Fools in derision follow fools."

THE MAN AND THE FLEA

WHETHER IN EARTH, IN AIR, OR MAIN,
Sure every thing alive is vain!
Does not the hawk all fowls survey
As destined only for his prey?
And do not tyrants, prouder things,
Think men were born for slaves to kings?
  When the crab views the pearly strands,

Or Tagus, bright with golden sands;
Or crawls beside the coral grove,
And hears the ocean roll above:
"Nature is too profuse," says he,
"Who gave all these to pleasure me!"
  When bord'ring pinks and roses bloom,
And every garden breathes perfume;
When peaches glow with sunny dyes,
Like Laura's cheeks when blushes rise;
When with huge figs the branches bend,
When clusters from the vine depend;
The snail looks round on flower and tree,
And cries: "All these were made for me!"
  "What dignity's in human nature!"
Says Man, the most conceited creature,
As from a cliff he cast his eyes,
And viewed the sea and arched skies:
The sun was sunk beneath the main;
The moon, and all the starry train,
Hung the vast vault of Heaven. The man
His contemplation thus began:
  "When I behold this glorious show,
And the wide wat'ry world below,
The scaly people of the main,
The beasts that range the wood or plain,
The winged inhabitants of air,
The day, the night, the various year,
And know all these by Heaven designed
As gifts to pleasure human-kind:
I cannot raise my worth too high;
Of what vast consequence am I!"
  "Not of th' importance you suppose,"
Replies a flea upon his nose:
"Be humble, learn thyself to scan;
Know, pride was never made for Man.
'Tis vanity that swells thy mind.
What, Heaven and earth for thee designed!
For thee! made only for our need,
That more important fleas might feed."

ROBERT

DODSLEY

England 1703 -- 1764

THE SNIPE SHOOTER

AS A SPORTSMAN RANGED THE FIELDS WITH HIS GUN, ATTENDED by an experienced old Spaniel, he happened to spring a snipe, and almost at the same instant, a covey of partridges. Surprised at the accident, and divided in his aim, he let fly too indeterminately, and by this means missed them *both*. "Ah! my good master," said the Spaniel, "you should never have two aims at once. Had you not been dazzled and seduced by the luxurious hope of partridge, you would most probably have secured your snipe."

PROMETHEUS

PROMETHEUS FORMED MAN OF THE FINEST CLAY, AND ANImated his work with fire stolen from Heaven. He endowed him with all the faculties to be found among the animal creation, gave him the courage of the lion, the subtlety of the fox, the providence of the ant, and the industry of the bee, and enabled him, by the superiority of his understanding, to subdue them all, and to make them subservient to his use and pleasure. He discovered to him the metals hidden in the bowels of the earth, and shewed him their several uses. He instructed him in everything that might tend to cultivate and civilize human life; taught him to till the ground to improve the fertility of nature; to build houses, to cover himself with garments, and to defend himself against the inclemencies of the air and the seasons; to compound medicines of salutary herbs, to heal wounds, and to cure diseases; to construct ships, to cross the seas, and to communicate to every country the riches of all. In a word, he endowed him with sense and memory, with sagacity and invention, with art and science; and to crown all, gave him an insight into futurity.

But, alas! this latter gift, instead of improving, wholly destroyed the proper effect of all the former. Furnished with all the means and instruments of happiness, man nevertheless was miserable; through the knowledge and dread of future evil, he was incapable of enjoying present good. Prometheus saw, and resolved to remedy this inconvenience; he effectually restored man to a capacity for happiness by depriving him of prescience, and giving him hope in its stead.

THE FIGHTING-COCKS AND THE TURKEY

TWO COCKS OF THE GENUINE GAME-BREED MET BY CHANCE upon the confines of their respective walks. To such great and heroic souls, the smallest matter imaginable affords occasion for dispute. They approach each other with pride and indignation, they look defiance; they crow a challenge, and immediately commence a bloody battle. It was fought on both sides with so much courage and dexterity; they gave and received such desperate wounds, that they both lay down upon the turf utterly spent, blinded, and disabled.

While this was their situation, a turkey, that had been a spectator of all that passed between them, drew near to the field of battle, and reproved them in this manner; "How foolish and absurd has been your quarrel, my good neighbours! A more ridiculous one could scarcely have happened among the most contentious of all creatures, men. Because you have crowed perhaps in each other's hearing, or one of you has picked up a grain of corn upon the territories of his rival, you have both rendered yourselves miserable for the remainder of your days."

THE REDBREAST AND THE SPARROW

AS A REDBREAST WAS SINGING ON A TREE, BY THE SIDE OF A RURAL cottage, a Sparrow, perched upon the thatch, took occasion thus to reprimand him. "And dost thou," said he, "with thy dull autumnal note, presume to emulate the birds of spring? Can thy weak warblings pretend to vie with the sprightly accents of the thrush and the blackbird? with the various melody of the lark and the nightingale, whom other birds, far thy superiors, have been long content to admire in silence?"

"Judge with candour, at least," replied the Robin; "nor impute those efforts to ambition solely, which may sometimes flow from love of the art. I reverence, indeed, but by no means envy the birds whose fame has stood the test of ages. Their songs have charmed both hill and dale; but their season has past, and their throats are silent. I feel not, however, the ambition to surpass or equal them; my efforts are of a much humbler nature, and I may surely hope for pardon, while I endeavour to cheer these forsaken valleys, by an attempt to imitate the strains I love."

THE ELM-TREE AND THE VINE

AN EXTRAVAGANT YOUNG VINE, VAINLY AMBITIOUS OF INDE-pendence, and fond of rambling at large, despised the alliance of a stately elm that grew near, and courted her embraces. Having risen to some small height without any kind of support, she shot forth her flimsy branches to a very uncommon and superfluous length; calling on her neighbour to take notice how little she wanted his assistance. "Poor infatuated shrub," replied the elm, "how inconsistent is thy conduct! Wouldst thou be truly independent, thou shouldst carefully apply those juices to the enlargement of thy stem, which thou lavishest in vain upon unnecessary foliage. I shortly shall behold thee grovelling on the ground; yet countenanced, indeed, by many of the human race, who, intoxicated with vanity, have despised economy; and who, to support for a moment their empty boast of independence, have exhausted the very source of it in frivolous expenses."

THE OAK AND THE SYCAMORE

A SYCAMORE GREW BESIDE AN OAK; AND BEING NOT A LITTLE elevated by the first warm days in spring, began to shoot forth his leaves apace, and to despise the naked oak for insensibility and want of spirit. The Oak, conscious of the superiority of his nature, made this philosophical reply; "Be not, my friend, so much delighted with the first precarious address of every fickle zephyr. Consider, the frosts may yet return; and if thou covetest an equal share with me in all the glories of the rising year, do not afford an opportunity to nip thy beauties in their bud. For myself, I only wait to see this genial warmth a little confirmed: and whenever that is the case, I shall perhaps display

a majesty that will not easily be shaken. But the tree which appears too forward to exult in the first favourable glance of spring, will ever be the readiest to droop beneath the frowns of winter."

THE ECLIPSE

ONE DAY WHEN THE MOON WAS UNDER AN ECLIPSE, SHE COMplained thus to the sun of the discontinuance of his favours: "My dearest friend, why do you not shine upon me as you used to do?"

"Do I not shine upon thee?" said the sun. "I am very sure that I intend it."

"O no," replied the moon, "but I now perceive the reason. I see that dirty planet the earth has got between us."

THE TOAD AND THE EPHEMERON

AS SOME WORKMEN WERE DIGGING MARBLE IN A MOUNTAIN OF Scythia, they discerned a toad of an enormous size in the midst of a solid rock. They were very much surprised at so uncommon an appearance, and the more they considered the circumstances of it, the more their wonder increased. It was hard to conceive by what means this creature had preserved life, and received nourishment in so narrow a prison; and still more difficult to account for his birth and existence in a place so totally inaccessible to all of his species. . . . They could conclude no otherwise, than that he was formed together with the rock in which he had been bred, and was coeval with the mountain itself.

While they were pursuing these speculations, the toad sat swelling and bloating, till he was ready to burst with pride and self-importance; to which at last he thus gave vent; "Yes," said he, "you behold in me a specimen of the antediluvian race of animals. I was begotten before the flood. And who is there among the present upstart race of mortals, that shall dare to contend with me in nobility of birth, or dignity of character?"

An ephemeron, sprung that morning from the river Hypanis, as he was flying about from place to place, chanced to be present, and observed all that passed with great attention and curiosity. "Vain boaster," said he, "what foundation hast thou for pride, either in thy descent, merely because it is ancient, or thy life because it has been long? What good qualities hast thou received from thy ancestors? Insignificant even to thyself as well as useless to others, thou art almost as insensible as the block in which thou wast bred. Even I, that had my birth only from the scum of the neighbouring river, at the rising of this day's sun, and who shall die at its setting, have more reason to applaud my condition, than thou hast to be proud of thine. I have enjoyed the warmth of the sun, the light of the day, and the purity of the air. I have flown from stream to stream, from tree to tree, and from the plain to the mountain. I have provided for posterity, and shall leave behind me a numerous offspring, to people the next age of tomorrow. In short, I have fulfilled all the ends of my being, and am happy. My whole life, 'tis true, is but of twelve hours; but even one hour of it is to be preferred to a thousand years of mere existence, which have been spent, like thine, in sloth, ignorance and stupidity."

THE BOY AND THE BUTTERFLY

A BOY, GREATLY SMITTEN WITH THE COLOURS OF A BUTTERFLY, pursued it from flower to flower with indefatigable pains. First he aimed to surprise it among the leaves of a rose; then to cover it with his hat as it was feeding on a daisy. Now he hoped to secure it as it rested on a sprig of myrtle; and now grew sure of his prize, when he perceived it loitering on a bed of violets. But the fickle fly, continually changing one blossom for another, still eluded his attempts. At length, observing it half buried in the cup of a tulip, he rushed forward, and, snatching it with violence,

crushed it to pieces.   The dying insect, seeing the poor boy somewhat chagrined, addressed him with all the calmness of a stoic, in
the following manner; "Behold now the end of thy unprofitable
solicitude! and learn that all pleasure is but a painted butterfly,
which, although it may serve to amuse thee in the pursuit, if em-
braced with too much ardour, will perish in thy grasp."

THE WATER-FALL

FROM THE HEAD OF A NARROW VALLEY THAT IS WHOLLY OVER-
shaded by the growth of trees, a large cascade bursts forth with a
luxuriance unexpected.   First the current rushes down a preci-
pice with head-long impetuosity; then, dashed from rock to
rock, and divided as it rolls along by fragments of stone or trunks
of trees, it assumes a milk-white appearance, and sparkles through
the gloom.   All is intricacy; all is profusion: and the tide, however ample, appears yet more considerable by the fantastic growth
of roots that hide the limits of its channel.   Thus, bounding
down from one descent to another, it no sooner gains the level
than it sinks beneath the earth and buries all its glory at our feet.
A spectator, privy to the scanty source which furnished out

this grand appearance, stood one day in a musing posture, and began to moralise on its prodigality. "Ah, silly stream!" said he, "why wilt thou hasten to exahust thy source, and thus wilfully incur the contempt that waits on poverty? Art thou ignorant that thy funds are by no means equal to this expense?"—"Fear not, my kind adviser," replied the generous cascade; "the gratitude I owe my master, who collected my rills into a stream, induces me to entertain his friends in the best manner I am able; when alone, I act with more economy."

THE FLY IN SAINT PAUL'S CUPOLA

AS A FLY WAS CRAWLING LEISURELY UP ONE OF THE COLUMNS of Saint Paul's cupola, she often stopped, surveyed, examined, and at last broke forth into the following exclamation; "Strange! that anyone who pretends to be an artist, should ever leave so superb a structure with so many roughnesses unfinished!"

"Ah! my friend," said a very learned architect, who hung in his web under one of the capitals, "you should never decide of things beyond the extent of your capacity. This lofty building was not erected for such diminutive animals as you or I, but for a certain sort of creatures, who are at least ten thousand times as large. To their eyes, it is very possible, these columns may seem as smooth as to you appear the wings of your favourite mistress."

THE SPIDER AND THE BEE

ON THE LEAVES AND FLOWERS OF THE SAME SHRUB, A SPIDER AND a bee pursued their several occupations; the one covering thighs with honey; the other distending his bag with poison. The spider, as he glanced his eye obliquely at the Bee, was ruminating with spleen on the superiority of her productions. "And how happens it," said he, in a peevish tone, "that I am able to collect nothing but poison from the self-same plant that supplies thee with honey? My pains and industry are no less than thine; in those respects we are each indefatigable."

"It proceeds only," replied the Bee, "from the different disposition of our nature; mine gives a pleasing flavour to everything I touch, whereas, thine converts to poison, what by a different process had been the purest honey."

THE MUSHROOM AND THE ACORN

AN ACORN FELL FROM THE TOP OF AN OLD, VENERABLE OAK, full on the head of a Mushroom that unhappily sprung up beneath it. Wounded by the blow, the Mushroom complained of the incivility. "Impertinent upstart," replied the Acorn, "why didst thou, with familiar boldness, approach so near to thy superiors? Shall the wretched offspring of a dunghill, presume to raise its head on a spot ennobled by my ancestors for so many generations?"

"I do not mean," returned the Mushroom, "to dispute the honour of thy birth, or to put my own in competition with it. On the contrary, I must acknowledge that I hardly know whence I sprung. But sure it is merit, and not mere ancestry, that obtains the regard of those whose approbation is truly valuable. I have

little, perhaps, to boast, but surely thou, who hast thus insulted me, canst have no pretence to boast any. I please the palates of mankind, and give a poignant flavour to their most elegant entertainments; whilst thou, with all the pride of thy ancestry, art fit only to fatten hogs."

THE MISER AND THE MAGPIE

AS A MISER SAT AT HIS DESK, COUNTING OVER HIS HEAPS OF gold, a Magpie eloping from his cage, picked up a guinea, and hopped away with it. The miser, who never failed to count his money a second time, immediately missed a piece, and rising up from his seat in the utmost consternation, observed the felon hiding it in a crevice of the floor. "And art thou," cried he, "that worst of thieves, who hast robbed me of my gold, without the plea of necessity, and without regard to its proper use? But thy life shall atone for so preposterous a villainy."

"Soft words, good master," quoth the Magpie. "Have I then injured you in any other sense than you defraud the public? and am I not using your money in the same manner you do yourself? If I must lose my life for hiding a single guinea, what do you, I pray, deserve, who secrete so many thousands?"

THE DIAMOND AND THE GLOW-WORM

A DIAMOND HAPPENED TO FALL FROM THE RING OF A YOUNG lady as she was walking one evening on a terrace in the garden. A Glow-worm, who had beheld it sparkle in its descent, as soon as the gloom of night had eclipsed its lustre, began to mock and to insult it. "Art thou that wondrous thing, that vauntest of thy prodigious brightness? Where now is all thy boasted brilliancy? Alas! in evil hour has fortune thrown thee within the reach of my superior blaze."

"Conceited insect!" replied the gem, "that owest thy feeble glimmer to the darkness that surrounds thee. Know, my lustre bears the test of day, and even derives its chief advantage from that distinguishing light, which discovers thee to be no more than a dark and paltry worm!"

THE WOLF AND THE SHEPHERD'S DOG

A WOLF, RANGING OVER THE FOREST, CAME WITHIN THE BORDERS of a sheep-walk; when meeting with a shepherd's Dog, that with a surly sort of growl demanded his business there, he thought proper to put on as innocent an appearance as he could, and protested upon his honour that he meant not the least offence. "I am afraid," said the Dog, "the pledge of your honour is but a poor deposit for your honesty; you must not take it amiss if I object to the security." "No slur upon my reputation," replied the Wolf, "I beg of you. My sense of honour is as delicate, as my great achievements are renowned. I would not leave a stain upon my memory for the world."

"The fame of what are generally called great achievements is very precious, to be sure," returned the Dog; "almost equal to the character of an excellent butcher, a gallant highwayman, or an expert assassin." While the dog was yet speaking, a lamb happened to stray within reach of our hero. The temptation was stronger than he was able to resist; he sprung upon his prey, and was scouring hastily away with it. However, the dog seized and held him till the arrival of the shepherd, who took measures for his execution.

Just as he was going to despatch him, "I observed," said the Dog, "that one of your noble achievements is the destruction of the innocent. You are welcome to the renown, as you are also to the reward of it. As for me, I shall prefer the credit of having honestly defended my master's property, to any fame you have acquired by thus heroically invading it."

THE SUN AND THE VAPOUR

IN THE EVENING OF A SUMMER'S DAY, THE SUN, AS HE DE-scended behind the western hills, beheld a thick and unwholesome vapour extending itself over the whole face of the valleys. Every shrub, and every flower immediately folded up its leaves, and shrunk from the touch of this detested enemy. "Well hast thou chosen," said the god of day, "this the hour of my departure, to spread thy pestilential influence, and taint the beauties of the creation. Enjoy for a short space the notable triumphs of thy malignity. I shall return again with the morning, repair thy mischiefs, and put an end to thy existence. May the slanderer in thy fate discern his own, and be warned to dread the return of truth!"

THE POET AND THE DEATH-WATCH

AS A POET SATE IN HIS CLOSET FEASTING HIS IMAGINATION WITH the hopes of fame and immortality, he was startled on a sudden with the ominous sound of a death-watch. However, immediately recollecting himself, "Vain insect," said he, "cease thy impertinent forebodings, sufficient indeed to frighten the weakness of women or of children, but far beneath the notice of a Poet and Philosopher. As for me, whatever accident may threaten my life; my fame, spite of thy prognostics, shall live to future ages."

"It may be so," replied the insect; "I find at least thou had'st rather listen to the maggot in thy head, than to the worm beneath thy table; but know, that the suggestions of vanity are altogether as deceitful as those of superstition."

THE TROUTS AND THE GUDGEON

A FISHERMAN IN THE MONTH OF MAY STOOD ANGLING ON THE bank of the Thames with an artificial fly. He threw his bait with so much art, that a young trout was rushing towards it, when she was prevented by her mother. "Never," said she, "my child, be too precipitate, where there is a possibility of danger. Take due time to consider, before you risk an action that may be fatal. How know you whether yon appearance be indeed a fly, or the snare of an enemy? Let some one else make the experiment before you. If it be a fly, he will very probably elude the first attack: and the second may be made, if not with success, at least with safety."

She had no sooner spoken, than a gudgeon seized the pretended fly, and became an example to the giddy daughter of the importance of her mother's counsel.

THE NIGHTINGALE AND THE BULLFINCH

A NIGHTINGALE AND A BULLFINCH OCCUPIED TWO CAGES IN THE same apartment. The Nightingale perpetually varied her song, and every effort she made afforded fresh entertainment. The Bullfinch always whistled the same dull tune that he had learnt, till all the family grew weary of the disgustful repetition. "What is the reason," said the Bullfinch one day to his neighbour, "that your songs are always heard with peculiar attention, while mine, I observe, are almost as wholly disregarded?"

"The reason," replied the Nightingale, "is obvious; your audience are sufficiently acquainted with every tone you have been taught, and they know your natural abilities too well to expect anything new from that quarter. How then can you suppose they will listen to a songster, from whom nothing native or original is to be expected?"

BENJAMIN

FRANKLIN

America 1706 -- 1790

APOLOGUE

LION, KING OF A CERTAIN FOREST, HAD AMONG HIS SUBJECTS A body of faithful dogs, in principle and affection strongly attached to his person and government, but through whose assistance he had extended his dominions, and had become the terror of his enemies.

Lion, however, influenced by evil counsellors, took an aversion to the dogs, condemned them unheard, and ordered his tigers, leopards, and panthers to attack and destroy them.

The dogs petitioned humbly, but their petitions were rejected haughtily; and they were forced to defend themselves, which they did with bravery.

A few among them, of a mongrel race, derived from a mixture with wolves and foxes, corrupted by royal promises of great rewards, deserted the honest dogs and joined their enemies.

The dogs were finally victorious: a treaty of peace was made, in which Lion acknowledged them to be free, and disclaimed all future authority over them.

The mongrels not being permitted to return among them, claimed of the royalists the reward that had been promised.

A council of the beasts was held to consider their demand.

The wolves and the foxes agreed unanimously that the demand was just, that royal promises ought to be kept, and that every loyal subject should contribute freely to enable his majesty to fulfil them.

The horse alone, with a boldness and freedom that became the nobleness of his nature, delivered a contrary opinion.

"The King," said he, "has been misled, by bad ministers, to war unjustly upon his faithful subjects. Royal promises, when made to encourage us to act for the public good, should indeed be honourably acquitted; but if to encourage us to betray and destroy each other, they are wicked and void from the beginning. The advisers of such promises, and those who murdered in consequence of them, instead of being recompensed, should be severely punished. Consider how greatly our common strength is already diminished by our loss of the dogs. If you enable the King to reward those fratricides, you will establish a precedent that may justify a future tyrant to make like promises; and every example of such an unnatural brute rewarded will give them additional weight. Horses and bulls, as well as dogs, may thus be divided against their own kind, and civil wars produced at pleasure, till we are so weakened that neither liberty nor safety is any longer to be found in the forest, and nothing remains but abject submission to the will of a despot, who may devour us as he pleases."

The council had sense enough to resolve—that the demand be rejected.

THE EPHEMERA

An Emblem of Human Life

YOU MAY REMEMBER, MY DEAR FRIEND, THAT WHEN WE LATELY spent that happy day in the delightful garden and sweet society of the Moulin Joly, I stopped a little in one of our walks, and stayed some time behind the company. We had been shown numberless skeletons of a kind of little fly, called an ephemera, whose successive generations, we were told, were bred and expired within the day. I happened to see a living company of them on a leaf, who appeared to be engaged in conversation. You know

I understand all the inferior animal tongues: my too great application to the study of them is the best excuse I can give for the little progress I have made in your charming language. I listened through curiosity to the discourse of these little creatures; but as they, in their national vivacity, spoke three or four together, I could make but little of their conversation. I found, however, by some broken expressions that I heard now and then, they were disputing warmly on the merit of two foreign musicians, one a *cousin*, the other a *moscheto;* in which dispute they

spent their time, seemingly as regardless of the shortness of life as if they had been sure of living a month.

Happy people! thought I, you live certainly under a wise, just, and mild government, since you have no public grievances to complain of, nor any subject of contention but the perfections and imperfections of foreign music. I turned my head from them to an old grey-headed one, who was single on another leaf, and talking to himself. Being amused with his soliloquy, I put it down in writing, in hopes it will likewise amuse her to whom I am so much indebted for the most pleasing of all amusements, her delicious company and heavenly harmony.

"It was," said he, "the opinion of learned philosophers of our race, who lived and flourished long before my time, that this vast world, the Moulin Joly, could not itself subsist more than eighteen hours; and I think there was some foundation for that opinion, since, by the apparent motion of the great luminary that gives life to all nature, and which in my time has evidently declined considerably towards the ocean at the end of our earth, it must then finish its course, be extinguished in the waters that surround us, and leave the world in cold and darkness, necessarily producing universal death and destruction. I have lived seven of those hours, a great age, being no less than four hundred and twenty minutes of time. How very few of us continue so long! I have seen generations born, flourish, and expire. My present friends are the children and grandchildren of the friends of my youth, who are now, alas, no more! And I must soon follow them; for, by the course of nature, though still in health, I cannot expect to live above seven or eight minutes longer. What now avails all my toil and labor, in amassing honey-dew on this leaf, which I cannot live to enjoy! What the political struggles I have been engaged in, for the good of my compatriot inhabitants of this bush, or my philosophical studies for the benefit of our race in general! for, in politics, what can laws do without morals? Our present race of ephemeræ will in a course of minutes become corrupt, like those of other and older bushes, and consequently as wretched. And in philosophy how small our progress! Alas! art is long, and life is short! My friends would comfort me with the idea of a name, they say, I shall leave behind me; and they tell me I have lived long enough to nature and to glory. But what will fame be to an ephemera who no longer exists? And what will become of all history in the eighteenth hour, when the world itself, even the whole Moulin Joly, shall come to its end, and be buried in universal ruin?"

To me, after all my eager pursuits, no solid pleasures now remain, but the reflection of a long life spent in meaning well, the sensible conversation of a few good lady ephemeræ, and now and then a kind smile and a tune from the ever amiable *Brillante*.

AN ARABIAN TALE

ALBUMAZAR, THE GOOD MAGICIAN, RETIRED IN HIS OLD AGE TO the top of the lofty mountain Calabut; avoided the society of men, but was visited nightly by genii and spirits of the first rank, who loved him, and amused him with their instructive conversation.

Belubel, the strong, came one evening to see Albumazar; his height was seven leagues, and his wings when spread might overshadow a kingdom. He laid himself gently down between the long ridges of Elluem; the tops of the trees in the valley were his couch; his head rested on Calabut as on a pillow, and his face shone on the tent of Albumazar.

The magician spoke to him with rapturous piety of the wisdom and goodness of the Most High; but expressed his wonder at the existence of evil in the world, which he said he could not account for by all the efforts of his reason.

"Value not thyself, my friend," said Belubel, "on that quality which thou callest reason. If thou knewest its origin and its weakness, it would rather be matter of humiliation."

"Tell me then," said Albumazar, "what I do not know; inform my ignorance, and enlighten my understanding."

"Contemplate," said Belubel, "the scale of beings, from an elephant down to an oyster. Thou seest a gradual diminution of faculties and powers, so small in each step that the difference is scarce perceptible. There is no gap, but the gradation is complete. Men in general do not know, but thou knowest, that in ascending from an elephant to the infinitely Great, Good, and Wise, there is also a long gradation of beings, who possess powers and faculties of which thou canst yet have no conception."

CHRISTIAN FÜRCHTEGOTT

GELLERT

Germany 1715 -- 1769

THE LAND OF THE HALT

MANY YEARS SINCE IN A SMALL TERRITORY, THERE WAS NOT one of the inhabitants who did not stutter when he spoke, and halt in walking; both these defects, moreover, were considered accomplishments. A stranger saw the evil, and thinking how they would admire his walking, went about without halting, after the usual manner of our race. Every one stopped to look at him, and all those who looked, laughed, and holding their sides to repress their merriment, shouted; "Teach the stranger how to walk properly!"

The stranger considered it his duty to cast the reproach from himself. "You halt," he cried, "it is not I, you must accustom yourselves to leave off so awkward a habit!" This only increased the uproar, when they heard him speak; he did not even stammer; this was sufficient to disgrace him, and he was laughed at throughout the country.

Habit will render faults which we have been accustomed to regard from youth, beautiful; in vain will a stranger attempt to convince us, that we are in error.

THE FOAL

A FOAL, THAT HAD NEVER FELT THE RIDER'S WEIGHT, LOOKED upon the bridle and saddle as marks of great distinction. Under this impression, it ran after every horse, upon which it saw a man astride, and sighed inwardly for the same honour. How rarely do those who strive for fame, know what they long for.

At length the envied trappings were placed upon our Foal; and it was gently led here and there, in order that it might accustom itself to the curb. The Foal strutted proudly up and down, and was in excellent humour with itself.

Elate with its new honours, it returned to its stall, and neighing, made all the horses acquainted with its good fortune. "I was praised by all who saw me," it said to the nearest horse, "a red bridle came out of my mouth, hanging gracefully over my black mane."

But how was it the next day? The Foal came sorrowfully back, covered with perspiration, and said; "What a plague is this fancied happiness. True, the bridle serves to decorate me, but it was not made for that; it was invented for my rider's convenience, and to ensure my submission to slavery."

THE DANCING BEAR

A BEAR, WHO HAD FOR A LONG TIME GAINED HIS LIVING BY dancing, at length escaped from his master, and returned to his former companions in the woods. His brethren welcomed him with the most friendly growls. The traveller now related what he had seen in foreign countries, told a long history of his adventures, and, to exhibit his feats of agility, began, in an erect position, to dance the Polonaise. His brethren, who were spectators of the performance, were astonished at his grace, and endeavoured to imitate his ballet steps. It was in vain; no sooner were they raised on two legs, than they fell again upon all fours.

Seeing their awkwardness, Bruin proceeded to exhibit some higher displays of his art, which, at length, rendered the others so envious of his extraordinary feats, that they drove him from their society.

THE DOG

PHYLAX WHO BY NIGHT AND DAY HAD SO FAITHFULLY WATCHED the house, and by his barking resisted whole troops of robbers, was suddenly attacked by a fever.

All the neighbours offered their advice. The dog must make up his mind to swallow pine-oil and blue pills; but with little apparent benefit; even the skill of the landlord of the neighbouring public-house, who had formerly practised abroad as a physician, was of no avail with the beast.

Scarcely was the news made public, when all his brethren and acquaintance leaving their dinners, hastened to visit the afflicted Phylax. Pantaloon, his best friend, licked his parched lips. "O wretched hour," he sighed, "who could be prepared for so great a calamity?"—"Alas! my dear Pantaloon," said Phylax, "I am dying, is it not so? Had I taken none of their vile drugs, I might perhaps have escaped. Should I expire, you may safely attribute the cause of my decease to the physic I have been compelled to swallow. I should meet my fate with resignation, if I could only enjoy the numerous bones I have buried! It is this makes me regret life; that I should forget this treasure; neither eat it before my end, nor take it with me. Do you love and are you still faithful to me? if so, fetch me them here; you will find one of them under the linden by the garden gate; another, dear Pantaloon, did I hide but yesterday in the barn; but restrain your appetite, and bring them to me untouched."

Pantaloon departed, and faithfully conveyed what he found to his dying friend. Phylax feebly smelt his property; at length, as his sight began to fail, he said; "Let it all lie here; if I die it shall be your own, but not till then, brother. Should I be so fortunate as to be able to enjoy the beautiful ham-bone that I —no, I'll not reveal where it is hidden; but if I recover, I promise you the best half of it; yes, you shall—" Here Phylax gave up the ghost.

LICHTWER

Germany 1719 -- 1783

THE WEASEL AND THE HEN

A WEASEL WAS QUITE JUSTLY EXECUTED AFTER SHE HAD RECEIVED a great beating before a farmyard of chickens. They all cackled with joy. Only one of the chickens took no part in the demonstration, but remained quiet. "Alas!" she said, "they are breaking the bones of the thief, but the wrong done me is beyond repair. Who will give me back my children?"

THE CAPON AND THE HEN

A CAPON AND A HEN MET ONE HOT DAY NEAR A FOUNTAIN where they came to drink. The Capon had the weakness of Narcissus, he liked to go to the edge of the water so that he might see his reflection. A mirror is a precious thing as our fine young men and young ladies know. The water was very clear and everything on the bank reflected in its flat surface. So the proud Capon could see himself in all his glory and he saw and admired even his defects.

"My dear young lady, look here," he said to the Hen, "tell me if I don't look pretty fine?"

"Sir," said the Hen, "I grant you that you are well turned out and very handsome. Your feathers are very becoming. All you need is a comb, then I should be very glad to take you for my bridegroom. As it is you have too much of the lady about you."

THE SNAKE

THERE WAS A SNAKE IN AFRICA THAT FOR NO GOOD REASON BIT all animals it met. And those it bit did not survive very long. The wound swelled and the animal died. This went on for a long time until once while the snake was playing in the grass, it saw its own shadow which it took for another snake. So it bit itself unwittingly with such force that it died. See yourself, slanderer.

THE TWO OLD WOMEN

THE CLOCK STRUCK ELEVEN IN THE NIGHT. AN OLD WOMAN walked in a narrow, lonely street. Another old woman came along from the other direction. The fools each took the other for a ghost and stood staring. They remained there until morning, then angrily left each other. In the world we hold one another back with absurd fancies.

THE MOOR AND THE WHITE MAN

A MOOR AND A WHITE MAN HELD A DISPUTE. THE WHITE MAN said to the Bengal; "If I were you I should never allow myself to be painted so dark. Just look at your pitch-black face, and tell us, black man, didn't Nature choose you to be an object of horror to us?"

The Moor replied; "Your pale face is like a canvas which the painter has not yet touched. The world in which we live, is like a great tree of which, my dear child, you are the unripe plums."

They argued for a long time, and since neither wanted to give in, they decided to submit the case to a wise judge. When the white man was declared in the right, the Moor said; "You win. I lose, but in Tunis you would have lost."

All depends upon the country. What is good, depends upon where we live.

THE FOX

THE FOX FOUND A BOOK IN THE GRASS. IN THE GRASS YOU ASK? How did the book get in the grass? My friend, don't bother me. I say he found it there and he found it with his nose. So runs my chronicle. And if he didn't find it in the grass, where else should he have found it? The leather-bound book that Master Fox found in the grass was, alas, the world-famous *Vulpiade*, otherwise known as *Reinecke Fuchs*.

The Fox stuck his nose deep into the pages. It seemed as

though he wished to read. But how could he do it all alone? He had never been to school. The poor devil was only looking for something to fill his empty stomach with. He looked for meat and found paper. He even wanted to eat the cover. He noticed his picture in the book and fearfully turned over the leaves, and there to his astonishment he saw his picture everywhere. Many happenings, lucky and unlucky, were shown in these pictures. Above all he was struck by one that seemed quite natural, in which he was brought to the gallows as a condemned criminal. Sentence was pronounced over him. The white staff lay in front of his feet. The gallows stood before him and seemed to greet him as a welcome guest. The tom-cat Hinz held the gallows' rope and invited him to walk up the steps. The Bear as father confessor came up to pray with him,—so near did his last moment seem.

Here the chicken thief got angry and complained; "Either my memory has as many holes as a sieve, or the man who painted all that so industriously is a lying fool. Here are recorded many deeds of mine, of which I have not the slightest memory."

What the Fox said we should hear from a hundred old heroes if they knew what our books tell about them.

GOTTHOLD EPHRAIM

LESSING

Germany 1729 -- 1781

THE FOX AND THE MASK

IN ANCIENT TIMES, A FOX FOUND THE MASK OF A PLAYER, formed so as to cover the whole head, with a large distorted mouth. "What a strange-looking head," exclaimed the observing fox. "No brains, and the mouth open! Surely this must be the head of a chatter-box!"

Everlasting talkers! perverters of our most innocent thoughts! The fox knew you.

THE FAIRIES' GIFT

TWO BENEVOLENT FAIRIES ATTENDED AT THE BIRTH OF A PRINCE, who afterwards became one of the greatest Monarchs his country had ever boasted.

"I bestow on my *protégé*," said the one, "the piercing eye of the Eagle, from whose view not the smallest Fly can escape in this extensive kingdom."

"The gift is noble," interrupted the second Fairy. "The Prince will become a discerning Monarch. But the Eagle is not blessed with his keen sight merely to discover the smallest Fly; he possesses also a supreme contempt for chasing them. And this gift do I bestow on the Prince."

"Thanks, dearest sister, for this wise restriction," resumed the first Fairy. "Nothing is more true than that many would have been much greater kings, if, with their extreme penetration, they had less often made use thereof on the most trifling occasions."

THE MOUSE

A PHILOSOPHICAL MOUSE SPOKE LOUDLY IN PRAISE OF NATURE'S goodness for having made the mice such particular objects of her regard and preservation. "For," she said, "one half of us is provided by her with wings; so that if all here below were extirpated by Grimalkin, she could easily restore our extinguished race by means of the bats."

The good little mouse knew not that there were also flying cats. And thus does our pride chiefly rest on ignorance.

THE WILD APPLE-TREE

A SWARM OF BEES SETTLED AND BUILT THEIR HIVE IN THE HOLLOW trunk of a wild apple-tree. They soon filled it with the treasures of honey, and the tree became so proud in consequence, that it despised all its neighbours.

Hereupon a rose-bush thus addressed it; "Miserable pride on account of borrowed sweetness! Is your fruit, therefore, the less bitter? Sweeten it with your honey if you can; for only then will you be prized by mankind!"

THE WOLF AND THE SHEPHERD

A SHEPHERD LOST THE WHOLE OF HIS FLOCK BY A DREADFUL illness. The wolf, hearing of it, came to console with him.

"Shepherd," said he, "is it true that thou hast met with so severe a misfortune, and art deprived of thy whole flock? So amiable, pious a flock! I feel for thee, and could shed tears of blood."

"Many thanks, master Wolf," said the shepherd. "I see thou hast a heart brimful of compassion."

"Indeed, he has," added the shepherd's dog, "whenever he suffers in person by his neighbour's misfortune."

THE OWL AND THE TREASURE-SEEKER

A CERTAIN TREASURE-SEEKER WHO WAS A VERY UNREASONABLE man, ventured among the ruins of an old castle, and perceived there an Owl which had caught a half-starved mouse and was about to devour it. "Is that fitting," said he, "for the philosophical favourite of Minerva?"

"Why not?" replied the Owl; "because I am fond of quiet meditation, can I therefore live upon air? though I am well aware that mankind frequently condemn the learned to such diet."

THE SPARROW AND THE OSTRICH

"YOU MAY BOAST AS MUCH AS YOU PLEASE OF YOUR STRENGTH and size," said the Sparrow to the Ostrich, "but you will never be so good a bird as I am; I don't fly far, 'tis true, and that only by starts; yet I do fly, and you cannot do any such thing."

THE CRICKET AND THE NIGHTINGALE

"I ASSURE YOU," SAID THE CRICKET TO THE NIGHTINGALE, "THAT my singing does not lack admirers."—"Pray name them," said the nightingale.

"The industrious reapers," replied the cricket, "are very fond of listening to me; and you cannot deny that they form the most useful body of men in the whole community!"

"In the latter remark I agree with you," said the nightingale; "but you must nevertheless not pride yourself upon their opinion. Honest people, whose thoughts are occupied solely by their daily labour, cannot be possessed of very keen perception. Think nothing of your singing, therefore, until the careless shepherd, who himself plays so sweetly on his flute, listens to you with silent rapture."

THE WATER-SNAKE

JOVE HAD AT LENGTH GRANTED THE FROGS ANOTHER KING; instead of a peaceable log, a greedy water-snake.

"If you wish to be our king," said the frogs, "why do you devour us?" "Because," replied the snake, "you petitioned for me."

"I never petitioned for you!" cried one of the frogs, which the snake had already swallowed in imagination. "No?" said the water-snake, "so much the worse. Then I must make a point of devouring you for not having done so."

THE EAGLE

"WHY DO YOU REAR YOUR EAGLETS IN SUCH ELEVATED SITUA-tions?" said Man to the Eagle. The latter replied, "Would they venture so near the sun when arrived at the years of maturity, if I built my nest on the ground?"

THE THORN

"JUST INFORM ME," SAID THE WILLOW TO THE THORN, "WHY you are so anxious to seize the clothes of mankind as they pass by you. Of what use can they be to you?"

"None," said the Thorn. "Neither do I wish to take them from him; I only want to tear them."

THE SPARROWS

AN OLD CHURCH, IN THE CHINKS OF WHICH THE SPARROWS had built innumerable nests, was repaired. As it stood in its new lustre, the Sparrows returned to look for their old dwellings; but they found them all bricked up. "Of what earthly use," cried they, "can so large a building now be? Come, let us leave the useless heap of stones to its fate!"

THE GOOSE

THE FEATHERS OF A GOOSE PUT THE NEWLY-FALLEN SNOW TO the blush. Proud of this dazzling gift of Nature, she considered herself intended for a Swan, rather than for that which she was. Accordingly, separating herself from her companions, she swam, solitary and majestically, round the pond. She now stretched her neck, the treacherous shortness of which she endeavoured to obviate with all her might. Now she tried to give it the graceful bend, which designates the beautiful Swan the bird of Apollo. But in vain, it was too stiff, and with all her pains, she remained a ridiculous Goose, without inspiring a single beholder with the least idea of her resemblance to a Swan.

How many geese are there, without wings, who, for similar assumption, become laughing-stocks to their neighbours!

THE ASS AND THE WOLF

AN ASS HAD THE MISFORTUNE TO BE MET BY A HUNGRY WOLF. "Have mercy on me," said the trembling animal; "I am a poor sick beast; look what a great thorn I have run into my foot!"

"Really, you quite grieve me," replied the Wolf. "Conscientiously speaking, I feel myself compelled to put you out of your misery."

He had scarcely spoken, when he tore the supplicating Donkey to pieces.

THE BOY AND THE SNAKE

A BOY WAS PLAYING WITH A TAME SNAKE. "MY DEAR LITTLE creature," said he, "I should not be so familiar with you, had you not been deprived of your venom. You snakes are the most malignant, unthankful reptiles! I well remember reading what happened to a poor countryman, who picked up a snake, perhaps one of your ancestors, from beneath a hedge, where it lay almost frozen to death, and compassionately put it into his bosom, that it might be restored by the warmth. Scarcely had the wicked creature recovered, than she bit her benefactor; and the good, kind-hearted man gave up the ghost."

"I am astonished," said the snake. "How partial your historians must be! Ours relate this story quite differently. Your kind-hearted countryman thought the snake was really frozen to death; and it being a handsome specimen, he picked it up in order to skin it when he arrived home. Was that correct?"

"Be silent," replied the boy, "what ungrateful wretch ever lacked an excuse?"

"True, my son," interrupted the boy's father, who had been listening to this conversation. "At the same time, whenever you hear of any remarkable instance of ingratitude, examine strictly every circumstance, before branding a person with so ignominious a blemish. True benefactors have seldom conferred favours on the ungrateful; for the honour of mankind I will hope never. But those benefactors possessed with narrow-minded selfish views, deserve, my son, to meet with ingratitude instead of thankful acknowledgment."

THE FOX

A FOX, CLOSELY FOLLOWED BY THE HOUNDS, SAVED HIMSELF BY springing on to a wall. In order to get down with ease on the other side, he caught hold of a Thorn-bush, and arrived safely at the bottom. He was, however, severely scratched by the Thorns. "Wretched help," cried the Fox, "why could you not render assistance, without injuring those who relied upon you?"

SOLOMON'S GHOST

A VENERABLE OLD MAN, DESPITE HIS YEARS AND THE HEAT OF the day, was ploughing his fields with his own hand, and sowing the grain in the willing earth, in anticipation of the harvest it would produce.

Suddenly, beneath the deep shadow of a spreading oak, a divine apparition stood before him! The old Man was seized with affright.

"I am Solomon," said the Phantom encouragingly. "What dost thou here, old friend?"

"If thou art Solomon," said the owner of the field, "how canst thou ask?   In my youth I learnt from the Ant to be industrious and to accumulate wealth.   That which I then learnt I now practise."

"Thou hast learnt but the half of thy lesson," pursued the Spirit.   "Go once more to the Ant, and she will teach thee to rest in the winter of thy existence, and enjoy what thou hast earned."

THE BLIND HEN

A HEN WHO HAD LOST HER SIGHT, AND WAS ACCUSTOMED TO scratching up the earth in search of food, although blind, still continued to scratch away most diligently.   Of what use was it to the industrious fool?   Another sharp-sighted Hen who spared her tender feet, never moved from her side, and enjoyed, without scratching, the fruit of the other's labour.   For as often as the blind Hen scratched up a barley-corn, her watchful companion devoured it.

THE RAVEN

THE RAVEN OBSERVED THAT THE EAGLE BROODED THIRTY DAYS over her eggs.   "Doubtless," said she, "that is the reason why the eaglets are so sharp-sighted and strong.   Good!   I'll try the same method."

Since that period she has always brooded thirty days over her eggs; but, hitherto, has only succeeded in hatching miserable ravens.

THE STATUE OF BRASS

A STATUE OF BRASS, THE MASTERPIECE OF AN EXCELLENT ARTIST, happened to be melted down by a terrible fire, and in that condition, fell into the hands of another Statuary. His happy chisel produced another, the subject whereof was different from the former, but the workmanship was fully as exquisite, and the expression equally noble. Envy saw it, and gnashed her teeth. At last she endeavoured to console herself by saying; "This Statue is passable; but the workman would not have made it, if he had not found the metal of the old one."

THE OX AND THE CALF

A POWERFUL OX TORE AWAY THE UPPER PART OF THE DOOR-WAY with his horns, in pushing himself through the low entrance to his stall. "Look, master!" shouted a young calf; "*I* do not injure you in this manner."—"How gladly do I wish," said the latter, "that you were able to do so."

THE KNIGHT IN CHESS

TWO BOYS PLAYING AT CHESS, HAVING LOST A KNIGHT, PUT A mark on a spare Pawn, and agreed it should pass for one. "A word with you," cried the old Knights to the new one: "whence come you, Mr. Upstart?" "Silence!" said the Boys; "does he not give us the same service as you do?"

THE WOLF, A HERO

"MY FATHER, OF GLORIOUS MEMORY," SAID A YOUNG WOLF TO a fox, "was a true hero! He made himself dreaded by the whole neighbourhood! At various periods he triumphed over more than two hundred enemies, and sent their polluted souls to the Kingdom of Death. How can it be wondered at that he was at length compelled to yield to one?"

"Thus would the writer of epitaphs express himself," said the fox: "the impartial historian, however, would add; 'the two hundred enemies he triumphed over at various periods, were sheep and asses; and the one enemy to whom he succumbed, was the first ox he ever dared to attack.'"

THE RAVEN

THE FOX SAW THAT THE RAVEN ROBBED THE ALTARS OF THE gods, and lived on the sacrifices offered to them. "I should like to know," thought he, "if the raven partakes of the sacrifice because he is a bird of prophecy; or whether he be esteemed such, because he has the boldness to share in the offerings made to the gods."

THE FOX AND THE TIGER

"WOULD THAT I POSSESSED THY SPEED AND STRENGTH!" SAID a fox to a tiger.

"Is there nothing else about me which would suit you?" enquired the latter.

"Not that I perceive."

"Not even my beautiful skin?" said the tiger. "Its colors are as manifold as your imagination, and the outside would thus be well matched with the interior."

"For that precise reason would I decline it," replied the fox. "I must not appear that which I am. But I would to Heaven I could change my hair for plumes!"

THE LION WITH THE ASS

AS AESOP'S LION WAS GOING TO THE FOREST IN COMPANY WITH the Ass, who was to assist him with his terrible voice, an impertinent Crow called to him from a tree; "A pretty companion! Are you not ashamed of yourself to be walking with an Ass?"— "Whomsoever I can make use of," replied the Lion, "I may very well allow to walk by my side."

Thus think the great, when they honour a common man with their company.

THE OSTRICH

"NOW, I AM GOING TO FLY!" CRIED THE GIGANTIC OSTRICH, AND the whole concourse of the birds assembled round him in grave expectation. "Now I am going to fly," he again exclaimed, and expanding his mighty wings, darted, like a ship in full sail, along the ground, without losing a single step.

Thus it is those poetical geniuses, who, at the commencement of an enormous ode, boast of being about to soar above both clouds and stars, and remain faithful to their parent dust!

THE WOLF ON HIS DEATH-BED

A WOLF LAY AT THE LAST GASP, AND GLANCED AT THE EVENTS of his past life. "True, I am a sinner," said he; "but let me still hope, none of the greatest. I have done harm; but also much good. Once, I remember, a bleating Lamb, which had wandered from the flock, came so near me, that I could easily have throttled it; and yet I did nothing to it. At the same time I listened to the jeers and jibes of a Sheep with the most surprising indifference, although I had no watchful Dogs to fear."

"I can explain all that," interrupted his friend the Fox, who was assisting in preparing him for death. "I have a distinct recollection of all the attendant circumstances. It was precisely the time that you almost choked with the bone, which the kind-hearted Crane afterwards drew out of your throat."

HISTORY OF THE OLD WOLF

I

THE CRUEL WOLF GROWING OLD, FORMED THE GENTLE RESOLUTION of living on good terms with the shepherds. He immediately set out, and came to the swain whose flocks were nearest to his cave.

"Shepherd," said he, "you call me a blood-thirsty robber, although I am not such in reality. True I am compelled to attack your sheep when I am famished; for hunger is painful. Only save me from famine, give me enough to eat, and you shall have nothing to complain of, with respect to me; for I am really the tamest and most amiable beast when my hunger is satisfied."

"When your hunger is satisfied? I have no doubt of it," replied the shepherd. But when is your ravenous mouth ever satisfied? You and avarice never yet had enough. Go your way!"

II

The rejected wolf came to a second swain.

"You must be aware," he commenced, "that I could throttle a good many sheep for you during the year. Now if you like to give me annually, six sheep, I will be satisfied. You may then sleep in safety and fearlessly dismiss your dogs."

"Six sheep?" said the shepherd. "Why, that is a whole flock of itself!"

"Well, since I know you, I'll let you off with five," said the wolf.

"You're joking; five sheep! I scarcely sacrifice five to Pan during the year."

"Shall we say four?" pursued the wolf; the shepherd shook his head in derision.

"Three? Two?"

"Not a single one," was at length the reply. "It would be madness, indeed, to render myself tributary to a foe, against whom I can protect myself, by keeping a sharp lookout."

III

"Misfortunes never come alone," thought the wolf, and repaired to a third shepherd.

"I am very near being decried among you shepherds," said he, "as the most cruel, unreasonable animal in existence. I will convince you, Montano, how unjustly I am dealt with. Give me annually, one sheep, and your flock shall pasture uninjured in yonder forest, which is rendered unsafe by none but me. One sheep! What a trifle! Could I behave more generously, more disinterestedly?—You laugh, shepherd? What excites your humor?"

"Oh! nothing, nothing! But how old are you, friend?" said the shepherd.

"What does my age concern you? Old enough to carry off your most cherished lambs."

"Don't put yourself in a passion, old Grizzly! I regret that you are some years too late with your proposition. Your toothless jaws betray you. You would now pretend to play a disinterested part, in order that you may be fed more easily, without exposing yourself to the least danger."

IV

The wolf became snappish; but restraining himself, went to the fourth shepherd. The faithful dog of the latter had just expired, and the wolf took advantage of this circumstance.

"Shepherd," said he, "I have fallen out with my brethren in the forest, and in such wise, that I will never be reconciled to them. You know how much you have to dread from them! If, however, you take me into your service, in the place of your deceased dog, I will pledge myself that they shall never even cast an irreverent glance on your sheep."

"You mean, then, to protect them against your brethren in the forest?" said the shepherd.

"What else should I mean? Certainly."

"That were not so bad! But if I admitted you among my flock, tell me, who would then protect my poor sheep against yourself? To take a thief into the house, as a safeguard against those without, is considered by us men—"

"I understand," said the wolf: "you are beginning to moralize. Farewell!"

V

"Were I not so old!" snarled the wolf. "But I must bend to circumstances." So saying he came to the fifth shepherd.

"Do you know me, friend?" questioned the wolf.

"I know at least your equal," replied the shepherd.

"My equal? I doubt that considerably. I am so remarkable a wolf, that I well merit your friendship, and that of every shepherd."

"And pray what makes you so remarkable?"

"This; if my life depended upon it, I could not possibly make up my mind to strangle and devour a living sheep. I eat nothing but dead sheep. Is not that praiseworthy? Allow me, therefore, occasionally to visit your flock, and ask whether you have not—"

"Spare your breath!" said the shepherd. "You must never eat sheep, not even dead ones, unless you wish me to become your enemy. A beast who makes no bones of devouring dead sheep, is easily taught by hunger to consider sick sheep, dead, and healthy ones, sick. Therefore don't reckon on my friendship; but be off!"

VI

"I must now bring my forlorn hope into action, in order to carry my point!" thought the wolf, wending his way to the sixth shepherd.

"Good morning to you, friend, how do you like my skin?" asked the wolf.

"Your skin?" said the shepherd. "Let me look at it! It is in good condition; the dogs can scarcely have tackled you often."

"Well, then, listen, my friend; I am old, and cannot carry on my game much longer. Cherish and feed me till death, and I will make my skin over to you."

"Mighty fine!" said the shepherd. "A pretty old miser you are. No, no; your skin would in the end cost me seven times as much as its value. If, however, you really mean to make me a present, why, give it me at once." Hereupon the shepherd grasped his club, and the wolf fled.

VII

"Oh! the heartless brutes!" shouted the wolf, flying into the most furious rage. "I will die then as I have lived, their implacable foe, rather than perish with hunger; for so they will have it!"

Rushing into the dwellings of the shepherds, he bit and lacerated their children, committing incredible mischief, before he could be slain.

Then spake the wisest of the shepherds; "We were in the wrong thus to bring the old robber to extremities, and to deprive him of all chance of improvement; even though he might have been driven to it from necessity alone!"

THE ASS WITH THE LION

AS THE ASS WAS GOING TO THE FOREST WITH AESOP'S LION, WHO made use of him instead of a hunting-bugle, he was met by another Ass of his acquaintance, who called to him; "Good morning, brother!" "Impertinent scoundrel!" was the reply.

"And wherefore?" said the former. "Because you are walking with a Lion, are you any better than I? Anything more than an Ass?"

THE NIGHTINGALE AND THE HAWK

AS A NIGHTINGALE WAS CHANTING HIS ACCUSTOMED NOTES, A Hawk pounced upon him. "Since thou singest so charmingly," said he, "thou must be a delicious morsel!" Did the Hawk say this out of spite, out of scorn, or out of simplicity? I can't tell. But I heard a person say, yesterday; "That lady, who is so fine a poet, must undoubtedly be extremely handsome"; and certainly he said it through simplicity.

THE MISER

"OH! MISERABLE WRETCH THAT I AM!" SAID A MISER TO HIS neighbour. "Some heartless thief has stolen from me, last night, the treasure which I had buried in my garden, and deposited a cursed stone in its place."

"You would have made no use of your gold," replied his neighbour. "Just fancy that the stone is the treasure; and you will be no poorer."

"Even though I were not any poorer," returned the miser, "is not another just so much richer? Another so much richer! O! I shall go mad."

THE LION AND THE HARE

A LION ONCE HONOURED A HARE WITH HIS FRIENDSHIP. "IS IT really a fact," demanded the Hare, "that the crowing of a miserable Cock is sufficient to compel you Lions to take to flight?"

"Such is undoubtedly the case," replied the Lion; "and it is a general remark, that we large animals are usually possessed by some trivial weakness. You must have heard for example that the grunt of a Pig causes astonishment and fright in the Elephant."

"Indeed!" interrupted the Hare. "Ha! now I can understand why we Hares are so terribly afraid of the Dogs."

THE NIGHTINGALE AND THE PEACOCK

A SOCIABLE NIGHTINGALE FOUND AMONGST THE SONGSTERS OF the grove plenty who envied her, but no friend. "Perhaps," thought she, "I may find one in another species," and flew confidingly to the Peacock.

"Beautiful Peacock! I admire thee."—"And I thee, lovely Nightingale!"—"Then let us be friends," continued the Nightingale; "we shall not be envious of each other; thou art as pleasing to the eye as I to the ear." The Nightingale and the Peacock became friends.

THE PELICAN

PARENTS CANNOT DO TOO MUCH FOR WELL-BRED CHILDREN; but when a weak-minded father draws the blood from his heart for a degenerate son, then love becomes madness.

A pious pelican, seeing his young ones languishing, tore open his breast with his sharp beak and revived them with his blood. "I am surprised at your tenderness," said the eagle to him, "and pity your blindness. See how many worthless cuckoos you have hatched with your young ones!"

It was even as he said; the frigid cuckoo had deposited his eggs in the pelican's nest. "Was it wise to purchase the lives of such worthless creatures so dearly?"

HERCULES

WHEN HERCULES WAS ADMITTED INTO HEAVEN, HE MADE HIS bow to Juno before any other deity. All Olympus and Juno were struck with amazement. "What," cried every one, "do you give precedence to your enemy?"—"Yes, even to her," replied Hercules. "It was mainly her precautions which gave me the opportunities of achieving those deeds by which I have rendered Heaven so much service."

Olympus approved of the answer of the new god, and Juno became reconciled to him.

THE STAG AND THE FOX

"WHAT IS NOW TO BECOME OF US POOR CREATURES?" SAID A stag to a fox, "the lion has entered into an alliance with the wolf!"

"With the wolf?" said the fox. "That may well pass! The lion roars, the wolf howls; and so you will be able to save yourself betimes by flight. But should the mighty lion join company with the skulking lynx, then indeed there would be no hope for us."

THE LION AND THE TIGER

THE LION AND THE HARE BOTH SLEEP WITH THEIR EYES OPEN. While the former was one day reposing thus, before the entrance of his terrible cave, fatigued with the mighty chase, a tiger leaped near him and laughed at the light slumber. "The fearless lion," he exclaimed, "sleeps there with open eyes like the timid hare!"

"Like the timid hare?" roared the lion, springing up, and seizing the mocker by the throat. The tiger weltered in his blood, and the appeased victor again lay down to sleep.

THE BEASTS STRIVING FOR PRECEDENCE

I

A SERIOUS DISPUTE AROSE AMONG THE BEASTS, AS TO WHO should take precedence of his neighbour. "I propose," said the Horse, "that we call in Man to adjust the difference; he is not one of the disputants, and can therefore be more impartial."

"But has he sufficient understanding for it?" asked the Mole. "It appears to me that it must be very acute to detect all our deeply-hidden perfections."

"That was well thought of!" said the Marmot.

"Undoubtedly!" exclaimed also the Hedge-hog. "I can never believe that Man possesses sufficient penetration for the task."

"Silence!" commanded the Horse. "We know well enough, that he who can place least reliance on the merits of his cause, is always the readiest to doubt the wisdom of his judge."

II

Man, therefore, was constituted arbitrator. "Another word with thee," said the majestic Lion to him, "before thou pronouncest judgment! By what standard dost thou intend fixing our relative worth?"

"By what standard? Doubtless," replied the Man, "according as you are more or less useful to me."

"Excellent!" returned the offended Lion. "How much lower in the scale should I rank than the ass! Man! thou canst not judge for us. Quit the assembly!"

III

The Man retired. "Now," said the sneering Mole, and the Marmot and Hedge-hog again chimed in with their friend, "dost thou perceive, friend Dobbin? the Lion also thinks that Man is not fit to be our judge.   The Lion thinks like us."

"But from weightier reasons than ye!" said the Lion, glancing contemptuously at the speaker.

IV

The Lion continued; "The struggle for precedency, now I consider all the circumstances, is but a sheer waste of time!   Whether you regard me as the highest or the least, is perfectly immaterial. Enough, I know my power!"   Thus speaking, he rose, and left the assembly.

He was followed by the sage Elephant, the fearless Tiger, the grave Bear, the cunning Fox, the noble Horse; in short, all who felt their own worth, or thought they felt it.

Those who went away last, and murmured most at the breaking up of the assembly, were—the Ape and the Donkey.

JUPITER AND APOLLO

JUPITER AND APOLLO WERE DISPUTING TOGETHER AS TO WHICH was the best archer.   "Let us try," said Apollo.   Drawing his bow, he shot so exactly in the centre of the object aimed at, that Jupiter saw no possibility of excelling him.   "I see," said he, "that you really shoot very well.   I shall have some trouble in doing better.   However, I'll try some other time."   The cautious Jove has still to make the trial.

THE RAVEN AND THE FOX

A RAVEN BORE AWAY A BIT OF POISONED MEAT IN HIS CLAWS, which an enraged gardener had intended for his neighbours' cats.

He was just preparing to devour it on an old oak, when Renard approaching said to him; "Heaven be praised, bird of Jove!" "What do you take me for?" asked the raven.   "What do I take you for?" replied the fox; "are you not the soaring eagle, who daily descends from the right hand of Jupiter to alight on this oak, and feed a poor wretch like me? Why do you deny yourself? Do I not see in your victorious talons the supplicated gift, which your god continues to send me through you?"

The raven was astonished, and inwardly rejoiced at being taken for an eagle. "I must not," thought he, "enlighten the fox on his mistake." Stupidly generous, he let fall his prey; and flew proudly on.

The fox seized the flesh laughing, and devoured it with malicious joy. But this soon gave way to dreadful pangs; the poison commenced taking effect, and he expired.

Accursed flatterers, may your praises never procure aught for you but poison!

MEROPS

"I WISH TO ASK YOU A QUESTION," SAID A YOUNG EAGLE TO A thoughtful and very studious Owl.

"It is said there is a bird called Merops, which, when it rises into the air, flies with its tail first, and the head looking down to the earth. Is it a fact?"

"By no means," said the Owl; "it is only a silly fiction of mankind. Man is himself a sort of Merops; for he would most willingly soar towards Heaven without losing sight of the world for a single instant."

THE PHŒNIX

MANY AGES HAD NOW PASSED AWAY SINCE THE PHŒNIX HAD been seen in the world. At last he again appeared. Immediately all the different kinds of animals, both birds and beasts, flocked around him.

Astonished at his beauty, they stared and admired, and broke out into great praise. But in a short time, the wisest and most prudent amongst them began to look upon him with an eye of compassion, and they sighed; "O unhappy Phœnix! Fate has been hard to him. He has neither mate nor friend. He will never know the pleasure of loving, or of being loved."

JUPITER AND THE SHEEP

A SHEEP WAS ONCE FORCED TO SUBMIT TO MUCH HARM FROM the other animals. He therefore appeared before Jupiter, and begged him to lessen his misery. Jove appeared willing, and said to the sheep; "I see plainly, my pious creature, that I have created you too defenceless. Now choose how I had best remedy this fault. Shall I arm your jaws with terrible fangs, and your feet with claws?"

"O, no!" exclaimed the sheep, "I will have nothing in common with the beasts of prey."

"Or," said Jupiter, "shall I make your bite poisonous?"

"Alas!" replied the sheep: "the poisonous snakes are so sadly detested."

"Well, what shall I do? Shall I plant horns on your forehead, and give strength to your neck?"

"Nor that, gracious father; I should then butt like the goat."

"At the same time you would be able to injure others, if I gave you the means of defending yourself."

"Should I, indeed?" sighed the sheep. "Oh! then leave me, merciful father, as I am. For the power of injuring, would, I am fearful, awake the desire of doing so; and it is better to suffer harm, than to inflict it."

Jove blessed the pious sheep, who ceased from that moment his complaints.

THE NIGHTINGALE AND THE LARK

WHAT SHOULD WE SAY TO THE POETS WHO TAKE FLIGHTS BEYOND the understanding of their readers?

Nothing but what the Nightingale said one day to the Lark. "Do you soar so very high, my friend, in order that you may not be heard?"

THE DONKEYS

THE DONKEYS COMPLAINED BEFORE JUPITER THAT THEY WERE treated too cruelly by mankind. "Our strong backs," said they, "carry their burdens, which would overwhelm them, and every weaker animal. And still, by unmerciful blows, they would compel us to go at a speed which is rendered impossible by our great burdens, even if it had not been denied us by Nature. Forbid them, Jove, to be so unreasonable, if mankind will allow itself to be forbidden aught wicked. We will serve them, since it seems you have created us for that purpose; but we will not submit to be beaten without cause."

"My creatures," replied Jupiter, addressing their spokesman, "your petition is just; but I see no possibility of convincing mankind that your natural slowness does not arise from idleness. And as long as they believe this, you will be thrashed. But I have thought of a means of lightening your griefs. From the present moment I will diminish your sense of feeling; your hide shall be hardened to resist the blows, and to fatigue the arm of the driver."

"Jove," shouted the donkeys, "you are ever wise and merciful!" They went rejoicing from his throne, as from the seat of universal love.

THE ASS AND THE RACE-HORSE

AN ASS UNDERTOOK TO RUN A RACE WITH THE HORSE. THE result was as might have been expected, and the Ass got laughed at. "I now see what was the matter with me," said the Donkey; "I ran a thorn into my foot some months ago, and it still pains me."

THE SHEEP

AS JUPITER WAS CELEBRATING HIS MARRIAGE FESTIVAL, AND ALL the animals had made offerings to him, Juno missed the Sheep.

"Where is the Sheep?" enquired the goddess. "Why delays the pious Sheep to bring us its humble offering?"

The Dog stepped forward and said; "Do not be angry, goddess! This morning have I seen the Sheep. It seemed very sorrowful, and wept bitterly."

"What may have caused its grief?" asked the goddess, already moved with compassion.

" 'Wretched creature that I am!' it said; 'I have neither milk nor wool; what shall I offer the great Jupiter? Must I alone appear empty-handed before him? Rather will I go to the Shepherd and beg him to sacrifice me on Jove's altar!' "

At this moment the Shepherd's prayer accompanying the scent from the sacrifice of the devoted Sheep, arose through the clouds. Could tears have bedewed celestial eyes, Juno would have wept for the first time.

THE BENEFACTORS

"HAVE YOU IN THE CREATION ANY GREATER BENEFACTOR THAN me?" asked the Bee of a Man.

"Most undoubtedly," replied the Man.

"Name him!"

"The Sheep! For his wool is necessary to me, and your honey is only a luxury. And I will give you another reason, Mrs. Bee, why I consider the Sheep a greater benefactor than you. The Sheep gives me his wool without the least trouble or danger; but when I take your honey, you keep me in constant apprehension of your sting."

THE FOX AND THE APE

"TELL ME ANY BEAST, HOWEVER TALENTED, WHICH I CANNOT imitate!" boasted the ape to the fox.

The fox replied; "And thou, name me ever so worthless a beast which would trouble itself to imitate thee!"

JUPITER AND THE HORSE

"FATHER OF MAN AND BEAST," SAID THE HORSE, APPROACHING the throne of Jupiter, "it is said that I am one of the noblest of the creations with which you have adorned the world, and my vanity bids me believe it. But do you not think my form still capable of improvement?"

"And what dost thou suppose would improve thee? Speak; I am open to instruction," said the gracious deity, smiling.

"Perhaps," continued the Horse, "I should have more speed if my legs were longer and more slender; a long swan-like neck would add to my beauty; a broader chest would increase my strength; and, once for all, since you have destined me to carry your favourite, man, it might be well if the saddle, which the benevolent horseman supplies me with, were a part of my being."

"Good!" pursued Jupiter; "have patience a moment!" and, with a solemn air, the god spake the word of creation. The dust became animated, organised matter was combined; and suddenly stood before the throne, the frightful Camel.

The Horse saw, shuddered, and trembled from excessive disgust.

"Here are longer and more slender legs," said Jove; "here is a long swan-like neck; a broader chest; a ready created saddle! Dost thou desire to be endowed with a similar form?"

The Horse still trembled.

"Go," continued the deity, "and this time the admonition shall suffice without the addition of punishment. To remind thee occasionally, however, of thy audacity, this new creation shall continue to exist!"—Then, casting a sustaining glance upon the Camel, Jove continued; "And the Horse shall never perceive thee without fear and trembling."

THE ARCHER

AN ARCHER HAD AN EXCELLENT BOW MADE OF EBONY, WHICH would carry an arrow true to the mark from a great distance. Consequently he held it in great estimation. Once, however, as he considered it attentively, he soliloquised; "You are still a little too thick; and possess no decorations save your polish. What a pity! But that may be remedied," he pursued. "I will go to the cleverest Artist, and let him carve it ornamentally." Without losing a moment, he set out; the Artist carved a complete hunt on the Bow; and what could be more appropriate on a weapon of the chase?

The Man was rejoiced. "Ah! my dear Bow," said he, "you deserve these embellishments!" Wishing again to essay its powers, he spans the Bow and snaps it in two.

THE TWO DOGS

"HOW GREATLY OUR RACE HAS DEGENERATED!" SAID A TRAVELLED Poodle. "In a remote quarter of the globe which men call India, Dogs are still found of the right sort; Dogs, my friend, you will scarcely credit me, and yet I have seen it with my own eyes, which are not afraid of a Lion, and will even attack him in the boldest manner possible!"

"But," said a sedate Pointer to the Poodle, "do they overcome the Lion?"

"Overcome him?" was the answer, "why, I can't exactly pretend to say. Nevertheless, only think, to attack a Lion!"

"Oh!" pursued the Pointer, "if they don't overcome him, your boasted Dogs in India are no better than we: though undoubtedly they are infinitely more stupid."

THE GRAPES

A GREAT POET IS MORE INJURED BY THE SCREAMING ADMIRATION of his petty imitators, than by the envious contempt of his critics.

"They are most undoubtedly sour!" said the fox speaking of the grapes which he had vainly endeavoured to reach. A sparrow, who overheard him, said; "What! can these grapes be sour? They have anything but the appearance of being so!" Flying to taste them, he found they were uncommonly sweet, and invited a hundred of his sweet-toothed brothers to share the spoil. "Taste them!" he shouted. "Taste them! The fox calls these exquisite grapes sour."

All followed his advice, and in a few seconds, they had handled the grapes in such wise, that not a fox in the world would have ever tried to reach them again.

THE FURIES

"MY FURIES ARE GETTING OLD AND DULL," SAID PLATO TO THE messenger of the Gods. "Go, therefore, Mercury, and seek out in the upper world three females well qualified for the office." Mercury departed.

Shortly after, Juno said to her attendant: "Believest thou, Iris, thou couldst find among mortals three perfectly strict, modest women? But perfectly strict! Do you understand me? I would thus shame Cytherea, who boasts of having overcome the chaste sentiments of the whole female sex. Go, and see where they are located." Iris took her departure.

In what corner of the earth did not the good Iris seek? But all in vain. She returned quite alone, when Juno cried with astonishment: "Is it possible? Oh, chastity! oh, virtue!"

"Goddess," said Iris; "I could indeed have brought you three maidens, who were all perfectly strict and chaste; who had all three never bestowed a look upon man; who had all three stifled every spark of love in their bosoms; but unhappily I came too late."

"Too late," said Juno. "How so?"

"Mercury had just fetched them away for Pluto."

"For Pluto? And how will he make use of these virtuous ones?"

"As the Furies."

THE MARMOT AND THE ANT

"MISERABLE INSECT," EXCLAIMED A MARMOT TO AN ANT, "WHAT avails it, that you toil throughout the summer, to collect such insignificant stores? Could you but see my stock of provisions!"

"Listen," replied the ant. "Since it is so much larger than you require, nothing can be more just than that mankind should dig after you, empty your barns, and make you pay the forfeit of your life for your thievish avarice."

THE HORSE AND THE OX

A BRAVE LAD FLEW PROUDLY ALONG ON A HIGH-METTLED Courser. A wild Ox called out to the Horse; "Shame on thee! never would I be governed by a Boy!"

"I would," said the Horse; "for what honour should I acquire by throwing him off?"

AESOP AND THE ASS

"THE NEXT TIME YOU WRITE A FABLE ABOUT ME," SAID THE Donkey to Aesop, "make me say something wise and sensible."

"Something sensible from you!" exclaimed Aesop; "what would the world think? People would call you the Moralist, and me the Donkey!"

THE SHEPHERD AND THE NIGHTINGALE

"SING TO ME, DEAREST NIGHTINGALE," SAID A SHEPHERD TO THE silent songstress one beautiful spring evening.

"Alas!" said the nightingale, "the frogs make so much noise, that I have no inclination to sing. Do you not hear them?"

"Undoubtedly I hear them," replied the shepherd, "but it is owing to your silence."

THE TWO DOGS AND THE LAMB

HYLAX, OF THE RACE OF WOLFHOUNDS, GUARDED A GENTLE Lamb. Lycodes, who also in hair, muzzle and ears more resembled a Wolf than a Dog, espied him and rushed upon him. "Wolf," said he, "what are you doing with this Lamb?"

"You are a Wolf yourself," returned the latter (the Dogs both mistook each other). "Depart, or you shall find that I know how to take care of it."

Lycodes, however, would take the Lamb by force from Hylax. Hylax was equally determined to keep it, and between these excellent protectors the poor Lamb was torn in pieces.

THE CROW AND THE PEACOCKS

A CONCEITED CROW DECKED HERSELF WITH THE MOULTED feathers of the handsome peacock, and thinking herself sufficiently adorned, boldly ventured into the midst of Juno's superb protégés. She was recognized; and quickly did the peacocks fall upon her with their sharp beaks to tear off the deceitful trappings.

"Give over!" at length screamed the crow, "you have now got back your own." The peacocks, however, who had observed some black plumage about the crow, exclaimed; "Silence, miserable fool; neither can these feathers be yours!"—and continued their attacks.

LORENZO
PIGNOTTI

Italy 1739 -- 1812

THE BOY AND THE WASP

A VERY LIVELY CHILD WAS ONCE SPORTING ABOUT THE SHRUBS
and flowers in a garden, when a golden Wasp buzzed near. The
innocent Boy did not know that the golden Wasp had in itself
concealed a poisonous sting, but attracted by the glittering splen-
dor of the Wasp tried to catch it. The Wasp however escaped
and at length lighted upon the bosom of a Rose. The Boy now
approached cautiously and on tip-toe. At last he grasped the
flower together with the Wasp. But the Wasp grew angry at
this sudden assault and quickly drew his dart and stung the little
hand of the Boy. The Boy shrieked with pain and never again
has chased a Wasp.

Now the moral of this fable is that often a secret poison lies
buried under the glittering cloak of pleasure.

THE PUMPKIN

A PUMPKIN WAS GRIEVING ONE DAY AT BEING CONDEMNED BY
nature, for he was required to creep on the humble earth.
"Trampled upon as I am, I believe myself the most vile of all
animals. I am covered with mire and always buried in ugly

vapors that lie dense on the humid earth. I never breathe the sweet serene high air." To change its undesired lot, it turned and turned its winding stalks, now backwards, now forwards. It slid along the ground with great effort until it reached a tall old tree. Its winding stalks wrapped themselves around the trunk of the tree. Crawling quietly night and day it found itself after a little while at the very top of the tree. It glanced proudly at the humble shoots lying in the grass. The shoots were filled with wonder and asked how the despised plant was able to climb so high. To which it answered explaining the art that enabled it to rise so high after first crawling along the ground.

The pumpkin has shown the way; he who prizes honor will not disdain it.

THE ASS AND THE HORSE

IN AN EQUESTRIAN FIELD STOOD A NOBLE CHARGER, ADORNED with rich trappings, inviting his rider to his accustomed play. His hair waved over his proud neck, and the white foam covered his gilded bit. He held his ears outstretched and shook his bridle and stamped the ground with his feet.

The horseman jumped upon him and spoke to him with the bit and with his voice; and the horse raised high his two fore feet, made ferocious leaps with his hind legs and whirled about and feigned an assault. Then with prancing steps he ran off. He was surrounded by spectators and the field resounded with festive applause.

In the midst of the spectators, there came an ass with a heavy pack saddle on his back. On top of the pack was seated a rude little peasant, with a stick in his large, rugged hands. The ass saw the beautiful spectacle and felt his heart moved by the desire for glory. Not only men of letters and heroes, but also asses and oxen are inspired by the desire for glory.

And wishing to imitate the swift horse, he gave so quick a

jump that the peasant was thrown to the ground and he was also brought to the ground by his heavy pack. Hisses came from all sides but by braying the ass applauded himself.

The peasant got up, grasped his heavy stick and in great anger beat the stupid and arrogant ass. The ass fled in vain, the peasant followed him, beating him first on one side and then on the other. Between blows and hisses he was made to return to his stable. There are many asses in the world who aspire to glory. But they very often receive the reward of this ass.

THE MOUSE AND THE ELEPHANT

A YOUNG MOUSE HAD JUST ARRIVED FROM ATHENS WHERE HE had acquired a smattering of learning. He was very proud of this little wisdom that he learnt from the books he had studied. Puffed up with pride and conceit and anxious to display his wit he thus one day addressed an Elephant; "Because Nature made you so large you need not be so pompous in your gait. It is true that you are big in size but this has no value; because to my way of thinking it is a great disadvantage. You are too big for nimble motion. Your feet are slow and sluggish. But look at me! I am made to fly. I can skip about from place to place. But

you are lazy and must stop to breathe at each creeping step. Poor beast you are.   And each time I examine your bulk I really pity—"

The proud Mouse did not finish his speech to the Elephant, because just as he was about to conclude his oration, a Cat who grew tired of listening to his words of wisdom, pounced upon him and ate him up.   This experiment that the Cat performed proved that there is a great difference between Mice and Elephants.

DR. JOHN

AIKIN

England 1747 -- 1822

THE HUMMING-BIRD AND THE TRAVELLER

A TRAVELLER WHO HAD VISITED ASIA, AFRICA, AND EUROPE, WAS at length, in making his tour through America, overcome with heat, and lay to repose under a tree. He had scarcely begun to doze, when he was roused by a loud noise, of which he could not discover the cause. Looking about him, he perceived a small bird issuing forth from the hollow of a tree, whose beautiful plumage was variegated like the rainbow, and whose bulk scarcely exceeded that of the cockchafer. "Is it you, little insect, that makes this loud humming noise?" exclaimed the traveller. "Yes," replied the bird, "you need not be surprised at that, for with men, as well as animals, the least often makes the greatest noise."

THE FLY

"THERE IS NOTHING MORE CRUEL THAN THE SWALLOW," SAID the fly; "for no sooner do they behold us than we fall a prey to their voracity." As the fly uttered this complaint she flew into an adjoining stable. "Here," said she, "I am safe from such destroyers!"—But on looking about, she found she was everywhere surrounded with cobwebs and spiders.

"Stupid that I am," exclaimed she, "why do I not visit palaces?

—no such guests are permitted there." She immediately winged her way to court, and exclaimed, "How delightful is everything! here I shall live undisturbed by swallow or spider." Behold, at the approach of evening, innumerable tapers were lighted.— "Ah!" exclaimed the fly, "how enchanting this is!—now I can enjoy the night as well as the day!" Scarcely had she pronounced this, when she approached too near the flame of a candle, and her wings being singed, she fell and was trodden to death.

THE HART AND THE FOX

AN ENVIOUS FOX, AFTER HAVING FOR A CONSIDERABLE TIME admired the symmetry of a fine hart, began to censure the thinness of his legs. "Indeed!" replied the hart, to him who brought this intelligence, "now am I more particularly sensible of the indulgent kindness of Nature in forming me, since envy can find but one fault in my shape!"

THE GOOSE AND THE HORSE

A GOOSE, WHO WAS PLUCKING GRASS UPON A COMMON, THOUGHT herself affronted by a horse who fed near her; and, in hissing accents, thus addressed him; "I am certainly a more noble and perfect animal than you, for the whole range and extent of your faculties is confined to one element. I can walk upon the ground as well as you; I have besides, wings, with which I can raise myself in the air; and when I please, I can sport on ponds and lakes, and refresh myself in the cool waters. I enjoy the different powers of a bird, a fish, and a quadruped."

The horse, snorting somewhat disdainfully, replied; "It is true you inhabit three elements, but you make no very distinguished figure in any one of them. You fly, indeed; but your flight is so heavy and clumsy, that you have no right to put yourself on a level with the lark or the swallow. You can swim on the surface of the waters, but you cannot live in them as fishes do; you cannot find your food in that element, nor glide smoothly along the bottom of the waves. And when you walk, or rather waddle upon the ground, with your broad feet and your long neck stretched out, hissing at every one who passes by, you bring upon yourself the derision of all beholders. I confess that I am only formed to move upon the ground; but how graceful is my make! how well turned my limbs! how highly finished my whole body! how great my strength! how astonishing my speed! I had much rather be confined to one element, and be admired in that, than be a goose in all."

NATURE AND EDUCATION

NATURE AND EDUCATION WERE ONE DAY WALKING TOGETHER through a nursery of trees. "See," said Nature, "how straight and fine those firs grow; that is my doing! But as to those oaks, they are all crooked and stunted: that, my good sister, is your fault. You have planted them too close, and not pruned them properly."—"Nay, sister," said Education, "I am sure I have taken all possible pains about them; but you gave me bad acorns, so how should they ever make fine trees?"

The dispute grew warm; and at length, instead of blaming one another for negligence, they began to boast of their own powers, and to challenge each other to a contest for the superiority. It was agreed that each should adopt a favourite, and rear it up in spite of the ill-offices of her opponent. Nature fixed upon a vigorous young Weymouth Pine, the parent of which had grown to be the mainmast of a man of war. "Do what you will to this plant," said she to her sister, "I am resolved to push it up as straight as an arrow." Education took under her care a crab-tree. "This," said she, "I will rear to be at least as valuable as your pine."

Both went to work. While Nature was feeding her pine with plenty of wholesome juices, Education passed a strong rope round its top, and pulling it downwards with all her force, fastened it to the trunk of a neighbouring oak. The pine laboured to ascend, but not being able to surmount the obstacle, it pushed out to one side, and presently became bent like a bow. Still, such was its vigour, that its top, after descending as low as its branches, made a new shoot upward; but its beauty and usefulness were quite destroyed.

The crab-tree cost Education a world of pains. She pruned and pruned and endeavoured to bring it into shape, but in vain. Nature thrust out a bow this way, and a knot that way, and would not push a single leading shoot upwards. The trunk was, indeed, kept tolerably straight by constant efforts; but the head grew awry and ill-fashioned, and made a scrubby figure. At length Education, despairing of making a sightly plant of it, engrafted the stock with an apple, and brought it to bear tolerable fruit.

At the end of the experiment, the sisters met to compare their respective success. "Ah, sister!" said Nature, "I see it is in your power to spoil the best of my works."—"Ah, sister!" said Education, "it is a hard matter to contend against you; however, something may be done by taking pains enough."

THE LITTLE DOG

"WHAT SHALL I DO," SAID A VERY LITTLE DOG ONE DAY TO HIS mother, "to shew my gratitude to our good master, and make myself of some value to him? I cannot draw or carry burdens like the horse; nor give him milk like the cow; nor lend him my covering for his clothing like the sheep; nor produce him eggs like the poultry; nor catch mice and rats so well as the cat. I cannot divert him with singing like the canaries and linnets; nor can I defend him against robbers like our relation, Towzer; I should not be of use to him even if I were dead, as the hogs are. I am a poor insignificant creature, not worth the cost of keeping; and I don't see that I can do a single thing to entitle me to his regard." So saying, the poor little dog hung down his head in silent despondency.

"My dear child," replied his mother, "though your abilities are but small, yet a hearty good-will is sufficient to supply all defects. Do but love him dearly, and prove your love by all the means in your power, and you will not fail to please him."

The little dog was comforted by this assurance; and, on his master's approach, ran to him, licked his feet, gambolled before him, and every now and then stopped, wagging his tail, and looking up to his master with expressions of the most humble and affectionate attachment. The master observed him. "Ah! little Fido," said he, "you are an honest, good-natured little fellow!" and stooped down to pat his head. Poor Fido was ready to go out of his wits for joy.

Fido was now his master's constant companion in his walks, playing and skipping round him, and amusing him by a thousand sportive tricks. He took care, however, not to be troublesome by leaping on him with dirty paws, nor would he follow him into the parlour, unless invited. He also attempted to make himself useful by a number of little services. He would drive away the sparrows as they were stealing the chickens' meat; and would run

and bark with the utmost fury at any strange pigs or other animals that offered to come into the yard. He kept the poultry, geese, and pigs from straying beyond their bounds and particularly from doing mischief in the garden. He was always ready to alarm Towzer if there was any suspicious noise about the house, day or night. If his master pulled off his coat in the field to help his workman, as he would sometimes do, Fido always sat by it, and would not suffer either man or beast to touch it. By this means he came to be considered as a very trusty protector of his master's property.

His master was once confined to his bed with a dangerous illness. Fido planted himself at the chamber-door, and could not be persuaded to leave it even to take food; and as soon as his master was so far recovered as to sit up, Fido, being admitted into the room, ran up to him with such marks of excessive joy and affection, as would have melted any heart to behold. This circumstance wonderfully endeared him to his master; and some time after, he had an opportunity of doing him a very important service. One hot day, after dinner, his master was sleeping in a summer-house, with Fido by his side. The building was old and crazy; and the dog, who was faithfully watching his master, perceived the walls shake, and pieces of mortar fall from the ceiling. He comprehended the danger, and began barking to awaken his master; and this not sufficing, he jumped up, and gently bit his finger. The master upon this started up, and had just time to get out of the door before the whole building fell down. Fido, who was behind, got hurt by some rubbish which fell upon him: on which his master had him taken care of with the utmost tenderness, and ever afterwards acknowledged his obligation to this little animal as the preserver of his life. Thus his love and fidelity had their full reward.

THE YOUNG MOUSE

A YOUNG MOUSE LIVED IN A CUPBOARD WHERE SWEETMEATS were kept; she dined every day upon biscuit, marmalade, or fine sugar. Never had any little mouse lived so well. She had often ventured to peep at the family while they sat at supper; nay, she had sometimes stolen down on the carpet, and picked up the crumbs, and nobody had ever hurt her. She would have been quite happy, but that she was sometimes frightened by the cat, and then she ran trembling to the hole behind the wainscot.

One day she came running to her mother in great joy.

"Mother!" said she, "the good people of this family have built me a house to live in; it is in the cupboard: I am sure it is for me, for it is just big enough: the bottom is of wood, and it is covered all over with wires; and I dare say they have made it on purpose to screen me from that terrible cat, which ran after me so often; there is an entrance just big enough for me, but Puss cannot follow; and they have been so good as to put in some toasted cheese, which smells so deliciously, that I should have run in directly and taken possession of my new house, but I thought I would tell you first, that we might go in together, and both lodge there tonight, for it will hold us both."

"My dear child," said the old mouse, "it is most happy that you did not go in; for this house is called a trap, and you would never have come out again, except to have been devoured, or put to death in some way or other. Though man has not so fierce a look as a cat, he is as much our enemy, and has still more cunning."

THE HORSE AND THE WASP

A WASP HAVING SEVERELY STUNG A HORSE, THE LATTER KICKED and pranced about, with an intention of destroying its tormentor. "Your exertion is in vain," said the wasp; "for I am in such a secure place on your flank, that you cannot hurt me." The horse now tried the effect of mild treatment, and begged the wasp to desist; which drew the following reply from the little insect; "Mild words will often effect what rude and violent treatment cannot;—as a proof of which, I will sting you no more."

THE HOG AND OTHER ANIMALS

A DEBATE ONCE AROSE AMONG THE ANIMALS IN A FARM-YARD, which of them was most valued by their common master. After the horse, the ox, the cow, the sheep, and the dog, had stated their several pretensions, the hog took up the discourse.

"It is plain," said he, "that the greatest value must be set upon that animal which is kept most for his own sake, without expecting from him any return of use and service. Now which of you can boast so much in that respect as I can?

"As for you, horse, though you are very well fed and lodged, and have servants to attend upon you, and make you sleek and clean, yet all this is for the sake of your labour. Do not I see you taken out early every morning, put in chains, or fastened to the shafts of a heavy cart, and not brought back till noon; when, after a short respite, you are taken to work again till late in the evening? I may say just the same to the ox, except that he works for poorer fare.

"For you, Mrs. Cow, who are so dainty over your chopped straw and grains, you are thought worth keeping only for your milk, which is drained from you twice a day, while your young ones are taken from you, and sent I know not whither.

"You, poor innocent sheep, who are turned out to shift for yourselves upon the bare hills, or penned upon the fallows, with now and then a withered turnip, or some musty hay—you pay dearly enough for your keep, by resigning your warm coat every year, for want of which you are liable to be frozen to death on some of the cold nights before summer.

"As for the dog, who prides himself so much on being admitted to our master's table, and made his companion, that he will scarcely condescend to reckon himself one of us, he is obliged to do all the offices of a domestic servant by day, and to keep watch all the night, while we are quietly asleep.

"In short, you are all of you creatures maintained for use; poor, subservient things, made to be enslaved or pillaged. I, on the contrary, have a warm sty, and plenty of provisions, all at free cost. I have nothing to do but to grow fat, and follow my amusement; and my master is best pleased when he sees me lying at ease in the sun, or filling my belly."

Thus argued the hog, and put the rest to silence by so much logic and rhetoric. This was not long before winter set in. It proved a very scarce season for fodder of all kinds; so that the farmer began to consider how he was to maintain all his livestock till spring. "It will be impossible for me," thought he, "to keep them all; I must therefore part with those I can best spare. As for my horses and working oxen, I shall have business enough to employ them; they must be kept, cost what it will. My cows will not give much milk in the winter, but they will calve in the spring, and be ready for the new grass. I must not lose the profit of my dairy. The sheep, poor things, will take care of themselves as long as there is a bite upon the hills; and if deep snow comes, we must do with them as well as we can, by the help of a few turnips and some hay, for I must have their wool at shearing time, to make out my rent with. But my hogs will eat me out of house and home, without doing me any good. They must go to pot, that's certain; and the sooner I get rid of the fat ones, the better."

So saying, he singled out the *orator* as one of the prime among them, and sent him to the butcher the very next day.

TOMAS DE
YRIARTE

Spain 1750 -- 1791

THE TRAVELLER AND THE HIRED MULE

STUFFED WITH HAY AND BARLEY, A HIRED MULE CAME OUT OF
the inn,
And began to run so fast that the Traveller could scarcely hold
her.
He did not doubt that in an instant he would accomplish half
his journey; but somewhat farther
The false riding beast began to slow down her pace. Suppose
she should play a trick?
Get up! You are stopping? Perhaps a touch of the spur?
Nothing. I greatly fear a calamity.
This whip so slender? Even less. Then this goad? But per-
haps she is already tired?
She kicks . . . and bites: she turns against the horseman. O
what a leap, what a plunge!
Although he presses his legs . . . Not even with these . . .
Curses!
Finally he falls to the ground. Very well! And you are the
one who was running. May the evil glanders kill you, amen!
I will never in all my days rely upon a mule that begins by ac-
complishing similar great feats.

329

After this accident, on seeing an author begin with high sounding noise,

I say at once; Take care! Hold back, man; or you will be found in the shameful state of the hired mule.

THE TWO GUESTS

PASSING THROUGH A MOUNTAIN VILLAGE, TWO YOUTHS ON horseback seek a lodging.

From two neighbors the two friends receive a thousand offers.

Because they do not wish to affront either, they go to lodge in the houses of both.

Of the two houses each guest chooses according to his taste.

That which one prefers has a great court with a splendid façade like a palace:

Over the door it has its coat of arms made of stone.

That of the other did not appear so great; but within there was not wanting space for lodging;

For it had rooms of good temperature, light and clean.

But the other palace with the façade was, in addition to being cramped, dark and cold:

Much portal, and within garrets with a shed roof.

The one who passed a day there, badly lodged, told his companion of the great disappointment:

But the latter said to him: Many books offer disappointments like this.

THE BEAR, THE MONKEY, AND THE PIG

A BEAR WITH WHICH A PIEDMONTESE EARNED HIS LIVING WAS trying out on two feet a dance which he had not learned very well.

Wishing to act like a man, he said to a Monkey, "How is

it?" The Monkey, who was a connoisseur, answered, "Very bad."

"I believe," replied the Bear, "that you are not very kind to me. What, my appearance is not graceful? I do not do the step accurately?"

The Pig was present and said, "Bravo! you are doing well. A more excellent dancer has never been seen, nor will be seen."

The Bear, on hearing this, thereupon took stock of himself, and with a modest manner, exclaimed thus:

"When the Monkey disapproved of me, I began to doubt; but since the Pig praises me, I must dance very badly."

Let an author keep this maxim as his gift: If the wise man does not approve, bad! If the fool applauds, worse!

THE BUSTARD

THE DULL BUSTARD REALIZED HOW HEAVY WAS THE FLIGHT OF her children, and wished to raise a lighter brood, although it be bastard.

For this purpose she took many eggs stolen from Falcon, Linnet, Pigeon, Partridge and Turtle Dove, and kept them mixed together in her nest.

For a long time she sat on them, and although plenty of them turned out to be addled, the rest finally produced various sorts of beautiful birds.

The Bustard invites a thousand birds in order to show off such

an unusual brood: each bird takes away her chicks, and behold
the splendid Bustard!

You who hatch out the works of others, take your brood then
out to fly. Each author will say; "This is mine"; and we shall
see what is left to you.

THE SWORD AND THE SPIT

IN MANY COMBATS SERVED A SWORD,
Polished, fine, sharp, well tempered,
The most famous that came from the workmanship
Of a noted manufacturer of Toledo.
It passed into the power of various owners,
And skilfully brought them out of a thousand engagements.
It was sold in different auctions
Until by strange accidents
It finally came to rest (who would have thought it!)
In an obscure corner of a tavern,
Where this useless furniture, stowed away,
Was falling to pieces with rust. A serving maid
At the command of her master, the innkeeper,
Who must have been a great dolt,
Took it once to the kitchen,
Pierced with it a chicken,
And behold a perfect spit,
That which was a sword of honor and service.

While this occurred in the tavern,
In Madrid, a recently arrived foreigner
Wished to buy a sword,
Having been transformed from clown to knight.
The armorer, seeing that at present
A sword is only an ornament,
And that any blade passes for good,
Since it is the hilt that is chosen,
Told him to come back another day.
Immediately he polished, sharpened and burnished
A spit that he had in his kitchen,

And for a sword of Tomas de Ayala
He sold it to the poor stranger, who did not understand similar
      purchases;
The armorer being as dishonest
As the innkeeper was ignorant.

But of equal ignorance or dishonesty
Could not our nation complain
Against the translators of two classes
Who have infested her with their phrases?
Some translate celebrated works,
And turn swords into spits:
There are others who translate the worst
And sell spits for swords.

THE MANUFACTURER OF GOLD BRAID AND
THE LACEMAKER

NEAR A LACEMAKER
Lived a manufacturer of gold braid.
"Neighbor, who would believe,"
He said to her, "that three yards
Of your lace are worth more doubloons
Than ten of braid gold on both sides?"

"That your merchandise"
(This is what she answered her neighbor)
"Is so much exceeded by mine,
Although you work in gold and I in linen,
Should not astonish you;
Since the art is worth more than the material."

Whoever scorns style
And says that he heeds the matter alone,
Let him be warned that if thread
Sells for more than the noble metal,
Elegance also gives
Its principal value to the substance.

THE LINNET AND THE SWAN

"BE STILL, CHATTERING BIRD," SAID THE SWAN TO THE LINNET. "Are you provoking me to sing, when you know that the sweet melody of my voice has never had its equal among the birds?"

The Linnet repeated his trills; and the Swan continued, "What insolence! Look how the little music-maker is insulting me! If I do not humiliate him by letting out my song, it is thanks to my great prudence."

"Would that you would sing!" the little bird finally answered. "How much would you not be admired with the rare cadences that no one asserts having heard from you, although they attain greater fame than mine!" The Swan wished to sing, and uttered a croak.

A great thing to win repute without knowledge and lose it on arriving at the trial!

JEAN PIERRE CLARIS DE
FLORIAN

France 1755 -- 1794

THE HOUSE OF CARDS

A KIND HUSBAND, HIS WIFE, AND TWO PRETTY CHILDREN, LIVED peacefully in the village where their parents had resided before them. This couple sharing the care of the little household, cultivated their garden, and gathered in their harvests; on summer evenings, supping beneath the green foliage, and in winter before their hearth, they talked to their sons of virtue, wisdom, and of the happiness which these would always procure. The father enlivened his discourse by a story, the mother by a kiss.

The elder of these children, naturally grave and studious, read and reflected incessantly; the younger, merry and active, was always jumping and laughing, and never happy but at play. One evening, according to custom, seated at a table beside their parents, the elder was reading Rollin, the younger, careless about being acquainted with the grand achievements of the Romans and Parthians, was employing all his ingenuity, all his skill, in erecting a fragile House of Cards; he scarcely breathed for fear of demolishing it.

The student leaving off for a moment, said, "Father, be so good as to inform me, why certain warriors are called conquerors, and others founders of empires; have these two names a different meaning?" The father was thinking of a proper answer, when his younger son, transported with pleasure at having, after so much trouble, succeeded in building a second story, cried out; "I have done it!" His brother, angry at the noise, with a single blow, destroyed that which it had taken him so long to erect, and made him burst into tears.

"My son," then replied the father, "the founder is your brother, and you are the conqueror."

THE ASS AND THE FLUTE

AS AN ASS WAS QUIETLY DINING ON THISTLES, HE BEHELD A shepherd seated beneath a tree, awakening sweet echoes on his flute, and charming the ears of all within hearing: excepting our discontented lop-eared brute, who thus soliloquized; "The world is going mad! Behold all the people admiring, with open mouths, a fool who is straining and puffing himself into a perspiration with blowing into a little hollow tube. So easily are mankind pleased, while I—but no matter. Let me hasten out of the fool's hearing. I shall go mad."

As our scandalized ass was moving off at a brisk canter, he presently almost kicked against a flute, which chanced to have been left on the turf by an amorous shepherd. The ass stopped, gazed knowingly round, and contemplated the flute as it lay; slowly he lowered his head, and placing his under lip on the mouth-hole, he blew into the despised instrument, when, *mirabile dictu*, it yielded an agreeable sound. Our ass thought himself a clever fellow, and cried aloud, as he kicked his hind legs in the air with joy, "Bravo! I too can play on the flute!"

THE TWO PEASANTS AND THE CLOUD

TWO PEASANTS WALKING TOGETHER, ONE OF THEM REMARKED to the other, in a piteous tone, that he was sure yonder black Cloud would be the harbinger of misfortune. "How so?" replied William, pleasantly. "How so?" retorted John: "I will wager that it is charged with hailstones; the harvest will be destroyed; not an ear of wheat will be left standing, and famine must ensue."

"What is the man dreaming of?" said William, good-humouredly; "I see nothing in that leaden Cloud but an abundance of rain, which has been so long ardently prayed for. Instead of injury, the rain will enrich us, and ensure a plentiful year; let us, therefore, rejoice, and take a cup of ale upon the strength of it."

"How can you talk at this rate?" exclaimed John, angrily; to which William retorted; "Your eyes serve you to but little purpose." In this manner the quarrel proceeded to such a height, that they were about to proceed to blows; when a brisk wind arose, the Cloud was dispersed, and both were deceived.

THE OLD TREE AND THE GARDENER

A MAN HAD AN OLD, BARREN TREE IN HIS GARDEN; IT WAS A large pear-tree, which had formerly been very fruitful, but had grown old; such is the fate of all. The ungrateful Gardener resolved to remove it; and one morning took his axe for the purpose. At the first blow, the Tree said to him; "Have some regard for my great age, and recollect the fruit that I have borne for you every year. My death is at hand, I have but a moment to live; do not assassinate a dying Tree, which has so often been your benefactor."

"I regret being compelled to cut you down," replied the Gardener, "but I have need of wood." All at once, a hundred nightingales exclaimed; "Oh! spare it! we have but this one left; when your wife seats herself beneath its shade, we rejoice her with our merry songs; she is often alone, we beguile her solitude."

The Gardener drives them away, laughing at their request, and makes a second stroke. A swarm of bees immediately issued from the trunk, saying to him; "Stay your hand, inhuman man, and listen to us; if you leave us this asylum, we will give you every day a delicious honey-comb, which you can carry to the market for sale." Does this appeal affect him?

"I weep with tenderness," replied the avaricious Gardener; "what am I not indebted to this unhappy pear-tree, which has nourished me in its youth? My wife often comes to listen to these birds; it is enough for me: let them continue their songs unmolested; and for you, who condescend to augment my wealth, I will sow the whole province with flowers." Thus speaking, he departed, and left the old trunk to repose in peace.

THE TWO GARDENERS

TWO BROTHERS WHO WERE GARDENERS, HAD A PIECE OF LAND for their inheritance, of which each cultivated the half; united by a strict friendship they had everything in common. One of them, named John, of an inquisitive mind, and some oratorical powers, thought himself a great philosopher; therefore Mr. John passed his time in reading the almanac, in observing the weather, the weathercock, and the wind. Presently, giving the rein to his sublime genius, he wished to discover how such millions of peas could be so quickly produced from a single one; and wherefore the seed of the linden, which produces a large tree, should be smaller than the bean, which attains but two feet in height; and again, by what mysterious secret this bean, which is heedlessly sown in the earth, contrives to attain a proper position in its bosom, so as to shoot out a root below, while it elevates its stem above the surface.

While he is thus meditating and afflicting himself at not being able to penetrate these important secrets, he forgets to water his garden; his spinach and lettuces die for want of moisture; the north-wind kills his fig-trees, which he neglects to cover up. No fruit is sent to market, no money comes to his purse; and the poor philosopher, with his almanacs, has no resource but his brother.

The latter was at work from the first dawn of day, singing at the top of his lungs; he grafted, and watered everything, from the peach-tree to the currant-bush; without caring to discover that which he could not comprehend, he continued to sow, in order that he might reap. Consequently his garden thrived to a miracle; he had money, fruit and pleasure. It was he who supported his brother; and when Mr. John, in astonishment, came to ask him how he was so successful, "Brother," said he, "here is the whole secret; I work, and you reflect; which is the more profitable? You are racking your mind, while I am enjoying myself; which of us is the wiser?"

THE MOLE AND THE RABBITS

MOST OF US ARE AWARE OF SOME OF OUR DEFECTS, BUT TO AVOW them is quite another matter; we prefer the endurance of real evils, rather than confess that we are afflicted with them. I recollect to have been witness to a fact very difficult of belief, but not the less applicable to what has just been asserted.

One fine moonlight evening, several Rabbits were amusing themselves on the turf with playing at blindman's buff. Rabbits! you exclaim, the thing is impossible. Nothing, however, is more true; a pliant leaf was placed over the eyes of one, like a bandage, and then tied under the neck; it was done in an instant. He whom the riband deprived of light placed himself in the centre; the others leapt and danced round him, performing miracles; now running away, then coming close, and pulling his ears or his tail. The poor blind Rabbit, turning suddenly round, throws out his paws hap-hazard; but the flock quickly get out of his reach, and he seizes nothing but air; in vain does he torment himself, he would remain there till to-morrow. A stupid Mole, who had heard the noise in her earthly dwelling, coming out of her hole, joined the party. You may imagine that being blind she was immediately caught.

"Gentlemen," said the Rabbit, "it would not be fair play to blindfold our sister; we must let her off, she has no eyes and cannot help herself."—"By no means," sharply replied the Mole, "I am caught fairly; put on the bandage."—"Willingly, my dear, here it is; but I think it will be unnecessary to tie the knot tightly."

"Excuse me, sir," replied the Mole angrily, "tie it very tightly, I can see.—That is not tight enough, I can still see."

JUPITER AND MINOS

"MY SON," SAID JUPITER ONE DAY TO MINOS, "EXPOUND TO ME, you who are the judge of the human race, why hell scarcely suffices to contain the numerous souls sent to you by Atropos. What fatal adversary of Virtue corrupts feeble humanity to such a degree? Is it not selfishness?"

"Selfishness? no, father."

"What then?"

"Idleness."

THE SQUIRREL AND THE LION

A SQUIRREL, MERRILY LEAPING ON THE BRANCHES OF AN OAK tree, accidentally missed its hold and fell upon a Lion who lay at the trunk, basking in the shade. His Majesty awoke in anger, and, raising his shaggy mane, displayed his terrific teeth to the trembling Squirrel, who, in the most abject manner, begged forgiveness for the intrusion. "I grant you your life," said the Lion; "but on condition that you tell me the reason why you little beings are always so lively and happy, while my time passes so irksomely."

"Yes, sire," replied the Squirrel, "I will, in return for your mercy, comply with your request: but he who speaks the truth ought to stand higher than he who hears it; permit me, therefore, to ascend the tree."

The Lion consented to this; and when the Squirrel was out of his reach he thus addressed him: "You seek to know how I am always merry. Conscience gives me a joyous mind, and learn, sire, that the infallible recipe for happiness—a good conscience— you are in want of. You are day and night oppressed with the sting of iniquity for the crimes and wanton cruelties you have committed. How many animals have you devoured, while I have been employed in carrying nuts to alleviate the distresses of my poor brethren! You hate, and I love! Believe me, there is great meaning and truth in these words, and often have I heard my father observe when young: 'Son, let your happiness be founded in virtue, and hilarity will be the constant inmate of your bosom.'"

THE HUSBANDMAN AND THE RATS

A HUSBANDMAN HAD A BARN FULL OF CORN, WHICH HE CAREfully kept locked up; not far from this lived a rat, who laboured long on every side of it, endeavouring to make a hole somewhere to creep in at. After great trouble, he at length found his way into the barn, and when he had thoroughly filled his belly, amazed at the vast treasures which he saw himself master of, away he ran, full of joy, and gave notice of it to a multitude of other rats, his neighbours; telling them of his immense riches, but carefully concealing the place where they lay.

On the news of his good fortune, all the rats of the neighbouring villages presently flocked about him, and made him a thousand offers of their service, scraping and cringing to him, and soothing him in all the excursions of his fantastic humour. The fool, taking all this for reality, grew very proud and stately, as believing himself to be some extraordinary person; and never considering that this magazine was not to last always, began most extravagantly to play the prodigal at the poor husbandman's cost, treating his companions and flatterers every day with as much as they could cram.

At this juncture, there happened in the same country so terrible a famine, that the poor cried out for bread, while the rats lay wallowing in plenty. The husbandman now believing it time to make the best of his corn, opened his barn-door; but finding a most unexpected consumption of his store, he fell into a passion, and presently removed what he had to another place. The rat, who looked upon himself to be sole master in the barn, was then asleep, but his parasites were awake, and seeing the husbandman go and come, soon began to fear there was something the matter, and that they should by-and-by be murdered for their monstrous robberies: upon this they betook themselves every one to flight, leaving the poor cullied rat fast asleep, not one of them having gratitude enough to give him the least hint of the danger that threatened him.

This is the practice of your smell-feast friends: while you keep a plentiful table they are your most humble and obedient servants, but when the accommodation fails, like Tartars they seek for other pastures, and leave you to destruction.

THE CAT AND THE LOOKING-GLASS

ARDENT PHILOSOPHERS, WHO PASS YOUR DAYS ENDEAVOURING to explain that which is inexplicable, deign to listen to an anecdote of the sagest Grimalkin the world ever produced!

A cat, perceiving a looking-glass on a lady's toilette-table, jumped up to examine it; but was struck with astonishment at perceiving, as he thought, one of his brethren, in a threatening attitude! Our Puss, wishing to join company, finds himself stopped. Surprised, he concludes the glass to be transparent, and goes to the other side, finds nothing, returns, and again the intruder is before him. After a little reflection, lest the other should escape while he walks round the glass, he perches himself astride on the top, with one paw on either side, so that he can seize in any direction. Making sure of his prey, he inclines his head gently towards the glass, and catches sight of an ear, then of two. Instantly darting his claws to the right and left, he loses his equilibrium, falls, and has caught nothing. Without waiting any longer to find out that which he cannot comprehend, he forsakes the looking-glass, saying: "What do I care about penetrating this mystery? I had better return to the kitchen, and catch a mouse for dinner."

THE DOG AND THE CAT

A DOG THAT HAD BEEN SOLD BY HIS MASTER, BROKE HIS CHAIN, and returned to the house where he had been born. Judge his surprise, when, as a reward for his zeal, he was soundly beaten, and taken back to his new residence. An old cat of his acquaintance, observing his extreme surprise, said to him; "Poor fool! did you imagine that we were prized for our own sakes?"

THE HORSE AND THE COLT

UNACQUAINTED WITH THE IRON SWAY OF TYRANT MAN, LIVED A venerable Horse, who had been left a widower, with an only son; he reared him in a meadow, where the streams, the flowers, and the inviting shade offered at once all that was requisite for happiness. Abusing these enjoyments, as is customary with youth, the Colt stuffed himself every day with clover, fooled away the time on the flowery plain, galloped about without an object, bathed without requiring it, or rested himself without being fatigued. Lazy and fat, the young hermit grew weary, and became tired of wanting for nothing; disgust soon followed; and, seeking his father, he said to him; "For some time I have been unwell; this grass is unwholesome, and kills me; this clover is without smell; this water is muddy; the air we breathe here attacks my lungs; in short, I shall die unless we leave it."

"Since it concerns your life, my dear son," replied his parent, "we will instantly take our departure." No sooner said than done—the two immediately set off in search of a new home.

The young traveller neighed for joy; the old one, less merry, went at a sedate pace, taking the lead, and made his child clamber up steep and arid mountains without a tuft of herbage, and where there was nothing which could afford them the least nourishment.

Evening came, but there was no pasturage; and our travellers were fain to go to bed supperless. The next day, when nearly exhausted by hunger, they were glad of a few stunted briars. This time there was no galloping on the part of the Colt; and after two days, he could scarcely drag one leg after the other.

Considering the lesson sufficient, the father returned by a road unknown to his son, and reconducted him to his meadow in the middle of the night. As soon as our Colt discovered a little fresh grass, he attacked it with avidity. "Oh! what a delicious banquet! What beautiful grass!" he exclaimed: "was there ever anything so sweet and tender? My father, we will seek no further, let us take up our abode for ever in this lovely spot. What country can equal this rural asylum!"

As he thus spoke, day began to break; and the Colt recognising the meadow he had so lately quitted, cast down his eyes in the greatest confusion.

His father mildly said to him; "My dear child, in future remember this maxim; 'he who enjoys too much, is soon disgusted with pleasure; to be happy, one must be moderate.'"

THE YOUTH AND THE OLD MAN

"MY DEAR FATHER," SAID AN AMBITIOUS YOUTH, "HAVE THE goodness to tell me how to make a fortune." "It is," said the Old Man, "a glorious pursuit; in order to acquire a fortune, one must labour in the common cause, devote his days, his nights, his talents to the service of his country."

"Ah! that would be too wearisome a life; I wish for some less brilliant means."

"There is a more certain method, intrigue."

"That were disgraceful; I would enrich myself without vice and without labour."

"Well, then, be a fool, I have known many a one succeed."

THE HUSBANDMAN OF CASTILE

THE GRANDSON OF A KING, RENDERED GREAT BY HIS VERY MIS-fortunes, Philip of Spain, without money, troops, or credit, being driven by the English from Madrid, fancied his diadem was lost. He fled almost alone, deploring his misery. Suddenly an old Husbandman presents himself to his view, a frank, simple, straightforward man, loving his children and his king, his wife and his country, better than his life; speaking little of virtue, but extensively practising it; rich but beloved: held up as an example for every family in Castile. His coat, made by his daughters, was girded by the skin of a wolf. Under a large hat, his intelligent head displayed a pair of sparkling eyes, and comely features, and his mustachios depended from his upper lip, reaching down to his ruff. A dozen sons followed him, all tall, handsome and vigorous; a mule laden with gold was in the midst of them.

This Man with his strange equipage stopped before the King, and said; "Where art thou going? Art thou cast down with a single reverse? Of what use is the advantage the arch-duke has gained over thee? it is thou who wilt reign, for thou art cherished by us. What matters it that Madrid has been retaken from thee? Our love still remains, our bodies shall be thy bucklers; we will perish for thee in the field of honour. Battles are gained by chance; but virtue is necessary to gain our hearts. Thou art in possession of it, and wilt reign. Our money, our lives are thine, take all; thanks to forty years of labour and economy, I am enabled to offer thee this gold. Here are my twelve children, behold in them twelve soldiers; despite my grey hairs I will make the thirteenth; and the war being finished, when thy generals, officers, and great men come to demand of thee, wealth, honour, riband, as the price of their services, we will ask but for repose and justice; it is all that we require. We poor people furnish the King with blood and treasure, but, far from revelling in his bounty, the less he gives, the more we love him. When thou shalt be happy, we will fly thy presence, we will bless thee in silence; thou art conquered and we seek thee."

Having so said, he fell on his knees; with a paternal hand, Philip raised him, sobbing audibly; he presses this faithful subject in his arms, wishes to speak, but tears interrupt his words.

Soon, according to the prophecy of the good old Man, Philip became the conqueror; and, seated on the throne of Iberia, did not forget the Husbandman.

The Monarch most beloved is always the most powerful. Fortune in vain endeavours to overwhelm him; in vain do a thousand enemies, leagued against him, seem to presage his destruction as inevitable; the love of his subjects renders their efforts useless.

THE KING AND THE TWO SHEPHERDS

A CERTAIN MONARCH WAS ONE DAY REGRETTING THE MISFORtune of being king: "What a wearisome occupation!" said he; "is there any mortal on the earth more annoyed than I am? I wish to live in peace, and am forced to go to war; I cherish my subjects and impose few taxes on them; I am a lover of truth, and yet am incessantly deceived; my people is oppressed with ills, and I am consumed with grief. I seek advice everywhere, use all means; but my trouble is only thrown away; the more I exert myself, the less do I succeed."

At this moment a flock of lean sheep caught his eye in the plain. They were almost without fleece; ewes without lambs, lambs without their mothers; dispersed, bleating, scattered; and the powerless rams wandering among the bushes. Their pastor Lubin was running here and there, now after this sheep, which was at the entrance of the forest, now after yonder, which was lagging behind, then after his pet lambs. While he is in one quarter, a wolf seizes one of the flock and makes off with it. Away posts the Shepherd, and another wolf carries off the lamb he has just quitted. Lubin stops quite out of breath, and tears his hair, not knowing which way to run, and frantically beating his breast, calls on death for relief.

"Here is a faithful representation of me," cried the Monarch; "these poor Shepherds endure a slavery no milder than we Kings, constantly surrounded by danger. That's some consolation."

As he uttered these words, he perceived in a meadow another flock of sheep, all fat and scarcely able to walk from the weight of their fleece; the rams strutted proudly about, and the ewes with their dugs full, made the bounding lambs hasten to share the sweet nourishment. Their Shepherd luxuriously stretched beneath a hedge was composing verses in praise of his mistress, sweetly singing them to the listening echoes; and then repeating the plaintive air on his flute.

The King was astonished, and said; "This beautiful flock will soon be destroyed; the wolves will scarcely be afraid of amorous swains, singing to their shepherdesses; a flute is a sorry weapon wherewith to repel them. Oh! how I should laugh!—"

At that moment, as if to please him, a wolf came in sight; but scarcely had he appeared, when a watchful dog sprang upon and throttled him. Two sheep, frightened at the noise of the combat, quitted the flock and ran about the plain. Another dog sets off, brings them back, and order is restored in an instant. The Shepherd views all, seated on the turf, without ceasing to play.

Hereupon the King said to him half angrily; "How do you

manage? The woods are filled with wolves; your sheep, fat and beautiful, are almost countless; and with the utmost tranquillity you take care of the whole flock yourself!"

"Sire," replied the Shepherd, "the thing is perfectly easy; my whole secret consists in making choice of good dogs."

IVAN ANDREYEVICH

KRILOFF

Russia 1768 -- 1844

THE HORSE AND THE DOG

A DOG AND A HORSE, WHICH SERVED THE SAME PEASANT, BEGAN to discuss each other's merits, one day.

"How grand we are, to be sure!" says Barbos. "I shouldn't be sorry if they were to turn you out of the farmyard. A noble service, indeed, to plough or to draw a cart! And I've never heard of any other proof of your merit. How can you possibly compare yourself with me? I rest neither by day nor by night. In the daytime I watch the cattle in the meadows; by night I guard the house."

"Quite true," replied the Horse. "What you say is perfectly correct. Only remember that, if it weren't for my ploughing, you wouldn't have anything at all to guard here."

THE TWO PEASANTS

"GOOD DAY, GOSSIP THADDEUS!"

"Good day, gossip Egor!"

"Well, friend, how are you getting on?"

"Oh, gossip, I see you don't know about my misfortune. God has afflicted me: I have burnt myself out of house and home, and have been obliged to go about begging ever since."

"How ever did you manage that? That was a poor joke, my friend."

349

"Just so. On Christmas Day we had a feast. I went out to give the horses their food, candle in hand. I must confess there was buzzing in my head. Well, I don't know how it was, but I must have let a spark fall. I just managed to save myself; but my homestead was burnt, and all I had in it. Now for your story."

"Ah, Thaddeus, a sad piece of work! With me, also, it seems, God has been angry. You see, I have no feet left. I think it's a perfect miracle that I escaped with my life. I went to the cellar for beer. It was Christmas Day in my case too, and I, too, must confess that I had swallowed a little too much brandy along with my friends. Well, that I mightn't set the house on fire in my drunkenness, I blew the candle right out. But the devil gave me such a fall downstairs in the dark, that he made me a mere wreck of a man; and here I've been a cripple ever since."

"Blame yourselves, friends," said their kinsman Stefan. "To tell the truth, I don't think it a miracle that one of you has burnt his house down, and the other is on crutches. Things go ill with a drunken man, when he has a candle in his hand; but he is even worse off when he is in the dark."

THE THREE MOUJIKS

THREE MOUJIKS [PEASANTS] STOPPED AT A VILLAGE TO PASS THE night. They had done their business at Petersburg as drivers; had sometimes worked, and sometimes amused themselves; and were now going back to their native place. As a Moujik does not like to go to bed empty, our visitors asked for supper. But villagers have no variety of dishes. They set on the table before the hungry travellers a basin of cabbage soup, some bread, and the remains of a bowl of porridge. It wasn't like Petersburg fare, but there was no use in talking about that; at all events, it was better than going to bed hungry. So the Moujiks crossed themselves, and sat down to table. Then the one who was the sharpest of them, seeing that there was altogether but little for three, perceived how the business might be mended. When force can't win the day, a little cunning must be tried.

"Comrades," he cries, "you know Thomas; well, he's likely to have his hair cropped and enlisted as a soldier, during this levy."

"What levy?"

"Why, there's news of a war with China. Our father the Czar has ordered the Chinese to pay a tribute of tea."

On that the two others took to weighing the matter, and deliberating upon it; unfortunately they could read, and had studied newspapers and reports, as to how the war would be carried on, and who should have the command. Our friends began a regular discussion, surmised, explained, wrangled.

That was just what our trickster wanted. While they were giving their advice, and settling affairs, and arranging the forces, he didn't say a word, but ate up the whole of the soup and the porridge.

THE MONKEY IN THE MIRROR

A MONKEY, WHICH SAW ITS IMAGE ONE DAY IN A MIRROR, GAVE a Bear a slight push with its foot, and said; "Only look, my dear gossip, what a hideous creature that is! What grimaces it makes! How it skips about! I should hang myself from vexation if I were at all like that. But, if we must tell the truth, are there not in the number of our friends five or six such grimacers?"

"Why take the trouble to count up your friends? Would it not be better to take a look at yourself?" answered the Bear.

But Mishka's advice was only thrown away uselessly.

THE RAZORS

AS I WAS TRAVELLING, ONE DAY, I FELL IN WITH AN ACQUAINT-ance, and we spent the night in the same bed-room. As soon as I awake next morning, what do I hear? My friend is evidently in trouble. The night before, we had both gone to bed merry and free from care; but now my friend is entirely changed. He groans, he sighs, he mutters words of complaining.

"What is the matter, my friend?" I cry. "You're not ill, I hope."

"Oh, no," he replies; "but I'm shaving."

"What! is that all?" I exclaim; and thereupon I get up and look at him. The strange fellow is making faces at himself in the looking-glass, with tears in his eyes, and looking as agonized all the time as if he were expecting to be flayed alive.

When I had at last discovered the cause of such sufferings, I say to him; "It's no wonder, and it's entirely your own fault that you are so much hurt. Just look at those things of yours. They are more like carving-knives than razors; as to shaving with them, that is impossible. All you can do is to scrape yourself painfully with them."

"I must allow, brother," he replies, "that the razors are excessively blunt; how can I help knowing that? I'm not such a fool as all that. But I never use sharp ones, for fear of cutting myself."

"But I venture to assure you, my friend, that you will cut yourself much sooner with a blunt razor. With a sharp one you will shave yourself twice as safely; only you must know how to use it properly."

Are there not many, though they would be ashamed to own it, who are afraid of clever people, and are more ready to have fools about them?

THE TRIGAMIST

A CERTAIN SINNER, WHILE HIS WIFE WAS STILL ALIVE, MARRIED two other women. As soon as the news of this reached the King, who was a severe king, and disinclined to permit such scandals, he immediately ordered the polygamist to be tried for the offence, and ordained that such a punishment should be discovered for him as would terrify the whole people, so that no one should in future be capable of attempting so great a crime. "But if I see that his punishment is a light one," he added, "then I will hang all the judges around the judgment-seat."

This pleasantry is disagreeable to the judges. Fear bathes them in a cold sweat. For three whole days they deliberate as to what punishment can be contrived for the culprit. Punishments are plentiful; but experience has proved that none of them will deter people from sinning. However, at last Heaven inspired them. The criminal was brought into court for the announcement of the judicial decision, by which they unanimously decreed: That he should live with all his three wives at once!

At such a decision the people were lost in astonishment, and expected that the King would hang all the judges. But, before the fifth day arrived, the Trigamist had hanged himself. And the sentence produced such alarm that since that time no man has committed trigamy in that country.

THE CAT AND THE NIGHTINGALE

A CAT, WHICH HAD CAUGHT A NIGHTINGALE, STUCK ITS CLAWS into the poor bird, and, pressing it lovingly, said; "Dear Nightingale, my soul! I hear that you are everywhere renowned for song, and that you are considered equal to the finest singers. My gossip, the Fox, tells me that your voice is so sonorous and wonderful that, at the sound of your entrancing songs, all the shepherds and shepherdesses go out of their wits. I have greatly desired to hear you—don't tremble so, and don't be obstinate, my dear; never fear; I haven't the least wish to eat you. Only sing me something; then I will give you your liberty, and release you to wander through the woods and forests. I don't yield to you in love for music, and I often purr myself to sleep."

Meanwhile our poor Nightingale scarcely breathed under the Cat's claws.

"Well, why don't you begin?" continued the Cat. "Sing away, dear, however little it may be."

But our songster didn't sing; only uttered a shrill cry.

"What! is it with that you have entranced the forest?" mockingly asked the Cat. "Where is the clearness, the strength, of which every one talks incessantly? Such a squeaking I'm tired of hearing from my kittens. No; I see that you haven't the least skill in song. Let's see how you will taste between my teeth."

And it ate up the poor singer, bones and all.

THE GNAT AND THE SHEPHERD

HAVING CONFIDED HIS SHEEP TO THE CARE OF HIS DOGS, A SHEP-herd went to sleep in the shade. Remarking that, a snake glided towards him from under the bushes, brandishing its forked tongue. The Shepherd would have passed away from the world, had not a Gnat taken pity on him, and stung him with all its might. Roused from his slumber, the Shepherd killed the snake. But first, while half awake, and half asleep, he hit the Gnat such a slap that the poor thing was utterly done for.

THE WOLF AND THE CAT

A WOLF RAN OUT OF THE FOREST INTO A VILLAGE—NOT FOR A visit, but to save its life; for it trembled for its skin. The huntsmen and a pack of hounds were after it. It would fain have rushed in through the first gateway; but there was this unfortunate circumstance in its way, that all the gateways were closed.

Our Wolf sees a Cat on a partition fence, and says, pleadingly; "Vaska, my friend, tell me quickly which of the moujiks here is the kindest, so that I may hide myself from my evil foes? Listen to the cry of the dogs and the terrible sound of the horns! All that noise is actually made in chase of me!"

"Go quickly, and ask Stefan," says Vaska the Cat; "he is a very kind moujik."

"Quite true; only I have torn the skin off one of his sheep."

"Well, then, you can try Demian."

"I'm afraid he's angry with me, too. I carried off one of his kids."

"Run over there, then. Trofim lives there."

"Trofim! I should be afraid of even meeting him. Ever since the spring, he has been threatening me about a lamb."

"Dear me, that's bad! But perhaps Klim will protect you."

"Oh, Vaska, I have killed one of his calves."

"What do I hear, gossip? You've quarrelled with all the village," said Vaska to the Wolf. "What sort of protection can you hope for here? No; our moujiks are not so destitute of sense as to be willing to save you to their own hurt. And, really, you have only yourself to blame. What you have sown, that you must now reap."

THE TWO DOGS

BARBOS, THE FAITHFUL YARD-DOG, WHO SERVES HIS MASTER zealously, happens to see his old acquaintance Joujou, the curly lap-dog, seated at the window on a soft down cushion. Sidling fondly up to her, like a child to a parent, he all but weeps with emotion; and there, under the window, he whines, wags his tail, and bounds about.

"What sort of a life do you lead now, Joujoutka, ever since the master took you into his mansion? You remember, no doubt, we used often to suffer hunger out in the yard. What is your present service like?"

"It would be a sin in me to murmur against my good fortune," answers Joujoutka. "My master cannot make enough of me. I live amidst riches and plenty, and I eat and drink off silver. I frolic with the master, and, if I get tired, I take my ease on carpets or on a soft couch. And how do you get on?"

"I?" replied Barbos, letting his tail dangle like a whip, and hanging his head. "I live as I used to do. I suffer from cold and hunger; and here, while guarding my master's house, I have to sleep at the foot of the wall, and I get drenched in the rain. And if I bark at the wrong time, I am whipped. But how did you, Joujou, who were so small and weak, get taken into favour, while I jump out of my skin to no purpose? What is it you do?"

" 'What is it you do?' A pretty question to ask!" replied Joujou, mockingly. "I walk upon my hind legs."

THE SQUIRREL AND THE THRUSH

A CROWD COLLECTED IN A VILLAGE, ONE HOLIDAY, UNDER THE windows of the seignorial mansion, looking, with open-mouthed wonder, at a Squirrel in a revolving cage. A Thrush also was wondering at it, perched on a neighbouring birch tree. The Squirrel ran so fast that his feet seemed to twinkle, and his bushy tail spread itself straight out.

"Dear old compatriot," asked the Thrush, "can you tell me what you are doing there?"

"Oh, dear friend, I have to work hard all day. I am, in fact, the courier of a great noble. So that I can never stop to eat, nor to drink, nor even to take breath"; and the Squirrel betook itself anew to running round in its wheel.

"Yes," said the Thrush, as it flew away, "I can see plainly enough that you are running; but, for all that, you are always there at the same window."

Look at some busybody or other. He worries himself; he rushes to and fro; every one wonders at him. It seems as if he were going to jump out of his skin; only, in spite of all that, he does not make any more progress than the Squirrel in the wheel.

THE ANT

A CERTAIN ANT HAD EXTRAORDINARY STRENGTH, SUCH AS HAD never been heard of even in the days of old. It could even, as its trustworthy historian states, lift up two large grains of barley at once! Besides this, it was also remarkable for wonderful courage. Whenever it saw a worm, it immediately stuck its claws into it, and it would even go alone against a spider. And so it acquired such a reputation on its ant-hill, that it became the sole subject of conversation.

Extravagant praise I consider poison; but our ant was not of the same opinion; it delighted in it, measured it by its own conceit, and believed the whole of it. At length its head became so turned that it determined to exhibit itself to the neighbouring city, that it might acquire fame by showing off its strength there.

Perched on the top of a lofty cart-load of hay, having proudly made its way to the side of the moujik in charge, it enters the city in great state. But, alas! what a blow to its pride! It had imagined that the whole bazaar would run together to see it, as to a fire. But not a word is said about it, every one being absorbed in his own business. Our Ant seizes a leaf, and jerks it about,

tumbles down, leaps up again.   Still not a soul pays it any attention.   At last, wearied with exerting itself, and holding itself
proudly erect, it says, with vexation, to Barbos, the mastiff, lying
beside its master's cart; "It must be confessed, mustn't it, that
the people of your city have neither eyes nor brains?   Can it
really be true that no one remarks me, although I have been straining myself here for a whole hour?   And yet I'm sure that at home
I am well known to the whole of the ant-hill."

And so it went back again, utterly crestfallen.

FORTUNE AND THE BEGGAR

A WRETCHED BEGGAR, CARRYING A RAGGED OLD WALLET, WAS
creeping along from house to house; and, as he grumbled at his
lot, he kept wondering that folks who lived in rich apartments,
and were up to their throats in money and in the sweets of indulgence, should be always unsatisfied, however full their pockets
might be, and that they should go so far as often to lose all they
have, while unreasonably craving for, and laying their hands on,
new riches.

"Here, for instance," he says, "the former master of this house
succeeded in trading prosperously, and made himself enormously
rich by commerce.   But then, instead of stopping, and handing
over his business to another, and spending the rest of his years in
peace, he took to equipping ships for the sea in the spring.   He
expected to get mountains of gold; but the ships were smashed,
and his treasures were swallowed up by the waves.   Now they all
lie at the bottom of the sea, and he has found his riches melt away
like those in dreams.   Another man became one of the farmers of
the spirit-tax, and so gained a million.   That was a trifle: he
wanted to double it.   So he plunged up to his ears in speculations,
and was utterly ruined.   In short, instances of this are countless.
And quite right too: a man should use discretion."

At this moment Fortune suddenly appeared to the Beggar, and
said; "Listen!   I have long wished to help you.   Here is a lot of

ducats I have found. Hold out your wallet, and I will fill it with them; but only on this condition:—All shall be gold that falls into the wallet; but if any of it falls out of the wallet to the ground, it shall all become dust. Consider this well. I have warned you beforehand. I shall keep strictly to my compact. Your wallet is old; don't overload it beyond its powers."

Our Beggar is almost too overjoyed to breathe. He scarcely feels the ground beneath his feet. He opens his wallet, and with generous hand a golden stream of ducats is poured into it. The wallet soon becomes rather heavy.

"Is that enough?"

"Not yet."

"Isn't it cracking?"

"Never fear."

"Consider, you're quite a Crœsus."

"Just a little more; just add a handful."

"There, it's full. Take care: the wallet is going to burst."

"Just a little bit more."

But at that moment the wallet split; the treasure fell through and turned to dust; and Fortune disappeared. The Beggar had nothing but his empty wallet, and remained as poor as before.

THE CUCKOO AND THE TURTLE-DOVE

A CUCKOO SAT ON A BOUGH, BITTERLY COMPLAINING.

"Why are you so sad, dear friend?" sympathisingly cooed the Turtle-dove to her, from a neighbouring twig. "Is it because spring has passed away from us, and love with it; that the sun has sunk lower, and that we are nearer to the winter?"

"How can I help grieving, unhappy one that I am?" replies the Cuckoo. "You yourself shall be the judge. This spring my love was a happy one, and, after a while, I became a mother. But my offspring utterly refuse even to recognise me. Was it such a return that I expected from them? And how can I help being envious when I see how ducklings crowd around their mother—

how chickens hasten to the hen when she calls to them? Just like an orphan I sit here, utterly alone, and know not what filial affection means."

"Poor thing!" says the Dove, "I pity you from my heart. As for me, though I know such things often occur, I should die outright if my dovelets did not love me. But tell me, have you already brought up your little ones? When did you find time to build a nest? I never saw you doing anything of the kind; you were always flying and fluttering about."

"Yes, indeed!" says the Cuckoo. "Pretty nonsense it would have been if I had spent such fine days in sitting on a nest! That would, indeed, have been the highest pitch of stupidity! I always laid my eggs in the nests of other birds."

"Then how can you expect your little ones to care for you?" says the Turtle-dove.

THE CANNON AND THE SAILS

A FIERCE QUARREL AROSE ON BOARD A SHIP BETWEEN ITS CANnon and its Sails. Poking their muzzles out of the port-holes, the Cannon thus murmured heavenward; "O ye gods! was ever such a thing seen, as that a set of trumpery linen fabrics should have the insolence to set up for being as useful as we are? In the whole course of our laborious voyage, what have they done? The moment a breeze begins to blow, they proudly swell out their breasts, carrying themselves above the waves as pompously as if they were really of great importance, but yet do nothing more than show off their airs. But, as for us, we thunder in battles. Is it not due to us that our ship rules the waves? Do not we carry with us everywhere terror and death? No; we do not wish to live any longer with the Sails. We can do everything for ourselves without them. Fly, then, to our aid, mighty Boreas, and quickly tear them into rags."

Boreas heard, and, flying thither, breathed on the sea. Immediately the waters were overcast and turned black, a heavy cloud covered the sky, and the waves ran mountain-high. Thunder deafened the ear; lightning blinded the eye. Boreas roared, and tore the sails into shreds. When nothing was left of them, the tempest ceased. But what followed? Deprived of its sails, the ship became a sport to the winds and waves, and drifted about at sea like a log. And in the first encounter with a hostile vessel, which thundered terrible broadsides along its whole length, our ship, now unable to move, was soon riddled like a sieve, and went down to the bottom like a stone—Cannon and all.

Every state is strong when its elements are wisely balanced. By its Cannon it is terrible to its foes; but its civil powers play the part of the Sails.

THE DIVERS

A CERTAIN KING COULD NOT MAKE UP HIS MIND AS TO WHETHER knowledge and science produce more good or harm. He consulted divers learned men on the subject, but they could not solve the problem to his satisfaction.

At last, one day, he met a venerable and remarkably intelligent hermit, to whom he confided his doubts, and who favoured him with the following apologue; "There was once a fisherman, in India, who lived on the sea-coast. After a long life of poverty and privation, he died, leaving three sons. They, seeing that their nets brought them in but a scanty livelihood, and detesting their father's vocation, determined to make the sea yield them a richer recompense—not fish, but pearls. So, as they knew how to swim and to dive, they gave themselves up to collecting that form of tribute from it. But the three brothers met with very different kinds of success.

"The first, the laziest of the family, spent his time in sauntering along the shore. He had an objection to wetting even so much as his feet, so he confined his expectations to picking up such pearls as the waves might wash ashore at his feet. But the result of this laziness of his was that he scarcely made enough to keep him alive. As to the second, he used to dive, and find rich pearls at the bottom of the sea, never sparing any pains, and knowing how to choose those depths only which it lay within his power to sound.

"But the third brother, troubled by a craving after vast treasures, reasoned with himself as follows; 'It is true that there are pearls which one can find near the shore; but what treasures, apparently, might I not expect if I could only succeed in reaching the lowest depths of the open sea! There, no doubt, lie heaps of countless riches—corals, pearls, and precious stones—all of which one might pick up and carry away at will.' Captivated by this idea, the foolish fellow straightway sought the open sea, chose the spot where the depths seemed blackest, and plunged into the abyss. But his recklessness cost him his life; for the deep swallowed him down, and he never returned to the light of day.

"O King," continued the hermit, "no doubt we recognise in knowledge the source of many benefits. But those who seek it in an irreverent spirit may find in it an abyss in which they may perish, like the diver, but with this difference, that they may too often involve others in their own ruin."

CANINE FRIENDSHIP

UNDER A KITCHEN WINDOW LAY BARBOS AND POLKAN, BASKING in the sunshine. It would have been more fitting in them to have been guarding the house at the gate in front of the courtyard. But they had eaten till they were full, and, besides, polite dogs do not bark at any one in the daytime. So they indulged in a discussion about all sorts of things—about their doggish service, about good and evil, and finally about friendship.

"What," says Polkan, "can be pleasanter than to live heart to heart with a friend?—in everything to offer mutual service; not to sleep or eat without one's friend, and to defend his body with all one's force; finally, for friends to look into one another's eyes, and each to think that only a fortunate hour in which he could please or amuse his friend, and to place all his own happiness in his friend's good fortune! Suppose, for instance, you and I were to contract such a friendship. I venture to say, we should not be able to tell how quickly time was flying."

"That is true. So be it," replies Barbos. "Long has it been grievous to me, my dear Polkan, that we, who are dogs of the same yard, cannot spend a single day without quarrelling: and why is it? Thanks to our master, we are neither closely pent nor

scantily fed. Besides, it really is scandalous. From the earliest times the dog has been the type of friendship; yet you scarcely ever see any more friendship among dogs than among men."

"Let us make manifest an instance of it to our own times," says Polkan.

"Your paw!"

"There it is."

Straightway the new friends begin to caress and fondle each other. They know not, in their raptures, to what to liken themselves.

"My Orestes!"

"My Pylades!"

"Away with all quarrels, all envy, all malice!"

Unluckily, at this moment the cook tosses a bone out of the kitchen. Our new friends fling themselves upon it furiously.

What has become of their harmonious alliance? Orestes and Pylades seize each other by the throat, so that their hair goes flying to the winds, and even torrents of water will scarcely separate them.

The world is full of such friendships.

THE PEASANT AND THE AXE

A MOUJIK, WHO WAS BUILDING A HUT, GOT VEXED WITH HIS Axe. The Axe became disagreeable to him; the Moujik waxed wroth. The fact was, he himself hewed abominably; but he laid all the blame on the Axe. Whatever happened, the Moujik found an excuse for scolding it.

"Good-for-nothing creature!" he cries, one day, "from this time forward I will never use you for anything but squaring stakes. Know that, with my cleverness and industry, and my dexterity to boot, I shall get on very well without you, and will cut with a common knife what another wouldn't be able to hew with an axe."

"It is my lot to work at whatever you lay before me," quietly replied the Axe to the angry rebuke, "and so your will, master, is sacred for me. I am ready to serve you in whatever way you please. Only reflect now, that you may not have to repent by-and-by. You may blunt me on useless labour, if you will; but you will certainly never be able to build huts with a knife."

THE LION

WHEN THE LION BECAME OLD AND WEAK, HIS HARD BED BEGAN to annoy him. It made his very bones ache; besides, it did not warm him. So he summons his nobles to his side, long-haired and shaggy wolves and bears, and says; "Friends, to old bones like mine, my bed has now become intolerably hard. So find out some way, without oppressing either the poor or the rich, to collect fleeces for me, that I may not have to sleep on the bare stones."

"Most illustrious Lion!" answer the grandees, "who would think of grudging you his skin, not to speak of his fleece? And are there but few shaggy beasts among us here? As to stags, hinds, chamois, and goats, they scarcely pay any tribute at all. We will take their fleeces from them at once. They will not be any the worse for that; on the contrary, indeed, they will be all the lighter for it."

This very wise advice was immediately carried out. The Lion could not sufficiently praise the zeal of his friends. But in what had they shown themselves zealous? Only in this, that they caught the poor creatures, and sent them away completely shorn. But they themselves, though they were twice as furry, did not contribute so much as a single hair of their own; on the contrary, each of them who happened to be on the spot turned that tribute to good account, and provided himself with a mattress for the winter.

THE EAGLE AND THE BEE

SEEING HOW A BEE WAS BUSYING ITSELF ABOUT A FLOWER, AN Eagle said to it, with disdain; "How I pity thee, poor thing, with all thy toil and skill! All through the summer, thousands of thy fellows are moulding honeycomb in the hive. But who will afterwards separate and distinguish the results of thy labour? I must confess, I do not understand what pleasure thou canst take in it. To labour all one's life, and to have in view—what? Why, to die without having achieved distinction, exactly like all the rest. What a difference there is between us! When I spread my sounding pinions, and am borne along near the clouds, I am everywhere a cause of alarm. The birds do not dare to rise from the ground; the shepherds fear to repose beside their well-fed flocks; and the swift does, having seen me, will not venture out into the plains."

But the Bee replies; "To thee be glory and honour! May Jupiter continue to pour on thee his bounteous gifts! I, however, born to work for the common good, do not seek to make my labour distinguished. But, when I look at our honeycombs, I am consoled by the thought that there are in them a few drops of my own honey."

Fortunate is he, the field of whose labour is conspicuous! He gains added strength from the knowledge that the whole world witnesses his exploits. But how deserving of respect is he who, in humble obscurity, hopes for neither fame nor honour in return for all his labour, for all his loss of rest—who is animated by this thought only, that he works for the common good!

THE SHEEP AND THE DOGS

IN A CERTAIN FLOCK OF SHEEP, IT WAS RESOLVED THAT THE number of dogs should be increased, in order that the wolves might worry the sheep no more. What was the result? Why, the number increased so greatly that at last, truly enough, the Sheep were no longer annoyed by the wolves. But dogs, too, must live. So, first, they deprived the Sheep of their fleeces, and then they tore their skins off them, choosing them by lot. At last, only five or six of the Sheep remained, and those also the dogs ate up.

THE ASS AND JUPITER

WHEN JUPITER STOCKED THE UNIVERSE WITH THE VARIOUS tribes of animals, the Ass, among others, came into the world. But, either purposely or from an accident owing to the press of work at such a busy time, the Cloud-compeller made a sad mistake, and the Ass came out of its mould no larger than a squirrel. Scarcely any one ever took any notice of the Ass, although the Ass yielded to no one in pride. The Ass was much inclined towards boasting. But what was it to boast of? With such a puny stature, it was ashamed to show itself in the world. So our conceited Ass went to Jupiter, and began to pray for a larger stature.

"Have pity on me!" it cried. "How can I bear this misery? Lions, panthers, elephants, all obtain honour everywhere, and, from the highest to the lowest, every one goes on talking about them only. Why have you treated Asses so unkindly that they never obtain any honour, and not a word is ever spoken about them by any one? But, if I were only as big as a calf, I would lower the pride of the lions and panthers, and all the world would be talking about me."

Every day our Ass continued to sing this same song to Jupiter, and bothered him so that at last he granted its request, and the Ass became a big beast. But, besides this, it acquired such a savage voice that our long-eared Hercules dismayed the whole forest. "Whatever is that brute? What family does it belong to? It has very long teeth, anyhow, hasn't it? and no end of horns!" At last, nothing else was talked about besides the Ass.

But how did it all end? Before the year was out, every one had discovered what the Ass really was. Our Ass became proverbial for stupidity, and, ever since that time, Asses have been beasts of burden.

Noble birth and high offices are excellent things; but how can they profit a man whose soul is ignoble?

FORTUNE'S VISIT

AT THE EXTREMITY OF A TOWN STOOD A WRETCHED OLD HOUSE. In it lived three brothers who could not get rich. Somehow, there was not a single thing that succeeded with them. Whatever any one of them took in hand was sure to prove unsuccessful. On all sides they met with hindrance and loss; and, according to them, it was all the fault of Fortune.

It happened that Fortune paid them a visit as she was passing by, and, touched by their great poverty, determined to do all she could to help them in everything they undertook, and to spend a whole summer with them. A whole summer!—a long time indeed. Well, the poor fellows soon find their affairs assuming a different aspect. One of them, although he was a poor hand at trading, gets a great profit now on everything he either buys or sells, utterly forgets that such a thing as loss exists, and rapidly becomes as rich as Crœsus. The second enters the public service. At another time he would have stuck fast among the copyists; but now he reaps successes on all sides. Every time he gives a dinner, or pays a visit of ceremony, he gets either rank conferred upon him or a place given him. See, he has an estate, a mansion in town, and a box in the country.

And now you will ask, what advantage did the third brother obtain? I suppose that Fortune really helped him also? Certainly; from his side she scarcely ever absented herself. The third brother chased flies all the summer, and that with the most wonderful success. I don't know whether he used to be clever at that sort of thing in former days, but during that summer his labour was never thrown away. In whatever manner he moved his hand (thanks to Fortune), he never once missed his shot.

But see! their guest, meanwhile, has brought her stay with the brothers to an end, and has set out on a long journey. Two of the brothers have gained greatly. One of them is rich; the other has got riches and rank besides. But the third brother curses his fate, inasmuch as malignant Fortune has left him nothing but a beggar's wallet.

THE WOLF AND THE CUCKOO

"FAREWELL, NEIGHBOUR!" SAID A WOLF TO A CUCKOO. "IN vain have I deluded myself with the idea of finding peace in this spot. Your people and your dogs are all alike here—one worse than the other; even if you were an angel, you couldn't help quarrelling with them."

"And is my neighbour going far? and where is that people so pious that you think you will be able to live in harmony with them?"

"Oh! I am going right away to the forest of the happy Arcadia. There, it is said, they don't know what war is. The men are as mild as lambs, and the rivers flow with nothing but milk. There, in a word, the Age of Gold is to be found. Every one treats his neighbour like a brother; and it is even said that the dogs never bark there, much less bite. Tell me, dear friend, would it not be charming to find oneself, even in a dream, in so peaceful a land as that? Farewell! Don't retain an unpleasant remembrance of me. There I shall really be able to live in harmony, in plenty, and in indulgence, and not, as here, have to be always on guard by day, and be deprived of one's quiet repose at night."

"A happy journey to you, dear neighbour," says the Cuckoo. "But, tell me, do you leave your teeth and your habits behind you, or do you take them with you?"

"How could I possibly leave them behind me? What nonsense are you talking?"

"Then, mark my words! your skin won't remain long on your back there."

THE EDUCATION OF THE LION

TO THE LION, THE KING OF THE FORESTS, HEAVEN GAVE A SON. You know how different from ours is the nature of beasts. Among us, a child a year old, if it belong to a royal family, is small and weak and stupid. But, by the time it has lived a twelvemonth, a lion-cub has long ago left off its baby-linen. So, at the end of a year, the Lion began seriously to consider that he must not allow his son to remain ignorant, not wishing that the royal dignity should be degraded in him, or that, when the son's turn should come to govern the kingdom, the nation should reproach the father on his account. But whom should he entreat, or compel, or induce by rewards to instruct the Czarevich how to become a Czar?

Should he hand him over to the Fox? The Fox is clever, but it is terribly addicted to telling lies; and a liar is perpetually getting into trouble. "No," thought the Lion; "the science of falsehood is not one which princes ought to study." Should he trust him to the Mole? Every one who speaks of that animal says that it is an extreme admirer of regularity in everything, and that it never takes a step without examining the ground before it, and that it cleans and shells with its own paws every grain of corn that comes to its table. In fact, the Mole has the reputation of being very great in small affairs. Unfortunately, however, though the Mole's eyes are keen for whatever is just under its nose, it cannot see anything at a distance. The Mole's love of order is an excellent thing for animals of its own kind; but the Lion's kingdom is considerably more extensive than a mole-run. Should he choose the Panther? The Panther is brave and strong, and, besides that, it is a great master of military tactics. But the Panther knows nothing about politics, and is absolutely ignorant of everything else that concerns civil affairs. Pretty lessons indeed it would give in ruling! A king must be a judge and a minister, as well as a warrior; but the Panther is good for nothing but fighting, so it, too, is unfit to educate royal children. To be brief, not a single beast, not even the Elephant himself, who was as much respected in the forest as Plato used to be in Greece, seemed wise enough or sufficiently well informed to satisfy the Lion.

By good fortune, or the opposite—we shall find out which before long,—another king, the king of birds, the Eagle, an old acquaintance and friend of the Lion, heard of that monarch's difficulty, and, wishing to do his friend a great kindness, offered to educate the young Lion himself. The Lion felt as if a weight were taken off his shoulders; and no wonder. What could be better, as it seemed, than to find a king as a prince's tutor? So the Lion-cub was got ready, and sent off to the Eagle's court, there to learn how to govern.

Two or three years go by; in the meantime, ask whom you will, you hear nothing but unanimous praise of the young Lion, and all the birds scatter through the forests wonderful stories about his merits. At last the appointed time comes, and the Lion sends for his son. The prince arrives, and the king gathers all his people together, summoning great and small alike. He embraces his son before them all, kisses him, and addresses him in these words; "My beloved son, you are my only heir. I am

now looking forward to the grave; but you are only just entering upon life, so I intend to make over my sceptre to you. Only
tell me first, in the presence of this assembly, what you have
been taught, how much you know, and in what manner you
propose to make your people happy."

"Papa," answered the prince, "I know what no one else here
knows. I can tell where each bird, from the Eagle to the Quail,
can most readily find water, on what each of them lives, and
how many eggs it lays; and I can count up all the wants of
every bird, without missing one. Here is the certificate my
tutor gave me. It was not for nothing that the birds used to
say that I could pick the stars out of the sky. And when you
have made up your mind to transfer your power to me, I will
immediately begin to teach the beasts how to make nests."

On this the king and all his beasts howled aloud. The members of the council hung their heads, and the old Lion perceived,
too late, that the young Lion had not learned what was wanted—
that he was acquainted with birds only, not knowing the nature
of beasts, although he was destined by birth to rule over beasts,
and that he was utterly ignorant of the knowledge which is
most requisite in kings—the knowledge of what are the wants
of their own people, and what are the interests of their own
country.

THE STRING OF CARTS

A NUMBER OF CARTS, LADEN WITH POTTERY, WERE GOING ALONG
in a string, and had to descend a steep hill. Having left the
others to wait a little on the top of the hill, the owner began very
cautiously to lead down the first cart. The good Horse which
drew it almost supported the weight on its croup, not allowing it
to roll down too fast. But a young Horse up on top took to
blaming the poor animal for every step it made; "Ah, praiseworthy animal! how wonderful! Just see, it crawls like a crab.
See there, it has almost stumbled over a stone! Look how awry,

how askew, are its movements! Ah! it's bolder now. There's a jostle again! Only here you ought to have gone a little more to the left. Oh, what a donkey! It would be all very well if this were night, or if it were going uphill. But now it is going downhill, and by daylight. One loses all patience while watching it. Really it's a water-carrier you ought to be, if you have no sense in you. But just look at us!—see how we will dash along. Never fear for us; we won't lose a moment: we shall not so much carry our loads as whirl them down."

With these words, straining its back and inflating its chest, the young Horse sets its load in motion. But no sooner does it commence the descent than the weight begins to press upon it heavily, the Cart to roll rapidly. The Horse, urged on from behind, and thrust from side to side, dashes on splendidly at a gallop. Over stones, across gullies, went the Cart amid shocks and boundings. More to the left—still to the left, till at last the Cart and its load goes headlong into the ditch with a crash! Farewell to the master's crockery.

THE INDUSTRIOUS BEAR

SEEING THAT A PEASANT, WHO EMPLOYED HIMSELF IN MAKING wooden arches for carriage shafts, disposed of them advantageously, a Bear determined to gain its living by the same business. The forest resounded with knocking and cracking, and the noise of the Bear's pranks could be heard a verst off.

It destroyed a prodigious number of elms, birches, and hazels; but its labours did not lead to a good result. (For arches are bent by dint of patience, and not in a moment.) So our Bear goes to the Peasant, and asks his advice, saying; "Neighbour, what is the reason of this? I can break trees; but I haven't been able to bend one into an arch. Tell me, in what does the real secret of success consist?"

"In that," answered the Peasant, "of which, my friend, you haven't a bit—in patience."

THE RAIN-CLOUD

A GREAT CLOUD PASSED RAPIDLY OVER A COUNTRY WHICH WAS parched by heat, but did not let fall a single drop to refresh it. Presently it poured a copious stream of rain into the sea, and then began boasting of its generosity in the hearing of a neighbouring Mountain.

But the Mountain replied; "What good have you done by such generosity? And how can one help being pained at seeing it? If you had poured your showers over the land, you would have saved a whole district from famine. But as to the sea, my friend, it has plenty of water already, without you adding to it."

THE EAGLE AND THE SPIDER

AN EAGLE HAD SOARED ABOVE THE CLOUDS TO THE LOFTIEST peak of the Caucasus. There, on an ancient cedar it settled, and admired the landscape visible at its feet. It seemed as if the borders of the world could be seen from thence. Here flowed rivers, winding across the plains; there stood woods and meadows, adorned with the full garb of spring; and beyond frowned the angry Caspian Sea, black as a raven's wing.

"Praise be to thee, O Jove, that, as ruler of the world, thou hast bestowed on me such powers of flight that I know of no heights to me inaccessible"—thus the Eagle addressed Jupiter—"insomuch that I now look upon the beauties of the world from a point whither no other being has ever flown."

"What a boaster you are!" replies a Spider to it from a twig. "As I sit here, am I lower than you, comrade?"

The Eagle looks up.   Truly enough, the Spider is busy spinning its web about a twig overhead, just as if it wanted to shut out the sunlight from the Eagle.

"How did you get up to this height?" asks the Eagle.   "Even among the strongest of wing there are some who would not dare to trust themselves here.   But you, weak and wingless, is it possible you can have crawled here?"

"No; I didn't use that means of rising aloft."

"Well, then, how did you get here?"

"Why, I just fastened myself on to you, and you brought me yourself from down below on your tail-feathers.   But I know how to maintain my position here without your help, so I beg you will not assume such airs in my presence; for know that I—"

At this moment a gust of wind comes suddenly flying by, and whirls the Spider again into the lowest depths.

THE OWL AND THE ASS

A BLIND ASS, WHICH HAD UNDERTAKEN A LONG JOURNEY, WANdered from the road into a forest.   As the night came on, our foolish fellow went so far into the thicket that it couldn't move either backwards or forwards; and even one who had eyes would have been unable to get out of that difficulty.   But an Owl, by good luck, happened to be in the neighbourhood, and offered to act as a guide to the Ass.

We all know how well Owls see at night.   Hills, hillocks, ditches, precipices—all these our Owl distinguished as if it had been daylight, and, by daybreak, it had made its way with the Ass to the level road. Now, how could any one part with such a guide? So the Ass entreated the Owl not to desert it, and determined to visit the whole world in the Owl's company. Our Owl seated itself like a lord on the back of the Ass, and the two friends began to continue their journey. But did it prosper? No. The sun had scarcely begun to glow in the morning sky, when a greater than nocturnal darkness hid everything from the Owl's eyes. But our Owl is obstinate; it directs the Ass at random.

"Take care!" it cries. "We shall tumble into a pool, if we go to the right."

There was really no pool on the right; but on the left there was even worse.

"Keep more to the left—another pace to the left!"

And,—the Owl and the Ass fell into the ravine together.

THE MISER

A CERTAIN GOBLIN USED TO KEEP WATCH OVER A RICH TREASURE buried underground. Suddenly, he was ordered by the ruler of the demons to fly away for many years to the other side of the world. His service was of such a nature, that he was obliged to do as he was bid, whether he liked it or not. Our Goblin fell into a terrible perplexity, wondering how he should preserve his treasure in his absence—who there was to take charge of it. To build a treasure-house, and hire a guardian—that would cost much money. To leave it to itself—that way it might be lost. Impossible to answer for it for a day. Some one might dig it up, and steal it: people are quick at scenting out money. He worried himself; he pondered over it; and at last an idea came into his head. The master of the house to which he was attached was a terrible Miser.

The Goblin, having dug up the treasure, appeared to the Miser, and said; "Dear master, they have ordered me to go away from your house to a distant land. But I have always been well disposed towards you, so don't refuse to accept this treasure of mine, as a parting token of affection. Eat, drink, and be merry, and spend it without fear; only, when you die, I am to be your sole heir. That is my single stipulation. As for the rest, may destiny grant you health and long life."

He spoke, and was off.

Ten—twenty years went by. Having completed his service, the Goblin flies home to his native land. What does he see? O rapturous sight! The Miser, dead from starvation, lies stretched on the strong box, its key in his hand; and the ducats are all there intact. So the Goblin gets his treasure back again, and rejoices greatly to think that it has had a guardian who did not cost him a single farthing.

When a miser has money, and yet grudges to pay for food and drink, is he not treasuring up his ducats for a goblin?

MIRON

THERE LIVED IN A CERTAIN CITY A RICH MAN, NAMED MIRON. Against this rich man arose complaints from his neighbours on all sides. And the neighbours were so far right that, although he had millions in his strong box, he never gave a penny to the poor.

But who is there who does not like to gain a good reputation? In order to give a different turn to the conversation about him, our Miron made it publicly known among the people, that in future he meant to give away food to the needy every Saturday. And, indeed, any one who passed his house, at the end of the week, could see that his gates were not closed.

"Poor fellow!" they think, "he will be utterly ruined." But of that there was no fear; for, every Saturday, he unchained a number of ferocious dogs, so that it was not a question with the poor who visited him of eating or of drinking, but simply of escaping, if Heaven willed it, with a whole skin.

In the meantime, Miron was looked upon as almost a saint.

Every one said; "One can't sufficiently admire Miron; only it's a pity that he keeps such savage dogs, and that it's so difficult to get to him; otherwise, he is ready to give away all he has, even to the uttermost penny."

It has often occurred to me to see how hard of access are the palaces of great people. But, of course, the fault is not due to the Mirons. It is always the dogs who are to blame.

THE MUSICIANS

A CERTAIN MAN INVITED A NEIGHBOUR TO DINNER, NOT WITH-out an ulterior purpose. He was fond of music, and he entrapped his neighbour into his house to listen to his choir. The honest fellows began to sing, each on his own account, and each with all his might. The guest's ears began to split, and his head to turn.

"Have a pity on me!" he exclaimed, in amazement. "What can any one like in all this? Why, your choristers bawl like madmen."

"It's quite true," replied the host, with feeling. "They do flay one's ears just a trifle. But, on the other hand, they are all of irreproachable behaviour, and they never touch a drop of intoxi-cating liquor."

THE COOK AND THE CAT

A CERTAIN COOK, RATHER MORE EDUCATED THAN HIS FELLOWS, went from his kitchen one day to a neighbouring tavern—he was of a serious turn of mind, and on that day he celebrated the anni-versary of a friend's death—leaving a Cat at home, to guard his viands from the mice. On his return, what does he see? The floor strewed with fragments of a pie, and Vaska the Cat crouch-ing in a corner behind a vinegar-barrel, purring with satisfaction, and busily engaged in disposing of a chicken.

"Ah, glutton! ah, evil-doer!" exclaims the reproachful Cook.

"Are you not ashamed of being seen by these walls, let alone living witnesses? What! be an honourable Cat up to this time—one who might be pointed out as a model of discretion! And now, ah me! how great a disgrace! Now all the neighbours will say, 'The cat Vaska is a rogue; the cat Vaska is a thief. Vaska must not be admitted into the kitchen, not even into the courtyard, any more than a ravenous wolf into the sheepfold. He is utterly corrupt; he is a pest, the plague of the neighbourhood.'"

Thus did our orator, letting loose the current of his words, lecture away without stopping. But what was the result? While he was delivering his discourse, Vaska the Cat ate up the whole of the chicken.

I would advise some cooks to inscribe these words on their walls; "Don't waste time in useless speech, when it is action that is needed."

THE WOLF AND ITS CUB

A WOLF, WHICH HAD BEGUN TO ACCUSTOM ITS CUB TO SUPPORT itself by its father's profession, sent it one day to prowl about the skirts of the wood. At the same time it ordered it to give all its attention to seeing whether it would not be possible, even at the cost of sinning a little, for them both to make their breakfast or dinner at the expense of some shepherd or other.

The pupil returns home, and says; "Come along, quick! Our dinner awaits us; nothing could possibly be safer. There are sheep feeding at the foot of yon hill, each one fatter than the other. We have only to choose which to carry off and eat; and the flock is so large that it would be difficult to count it over again."

"Wait a minute," says the Wolf. "First of all I must know what sort of a man the shepherd of this flock is."

"It is said that he is a good one—painstaking and intelligent. But I went round the flock on all sides, and examined the dogs; they are not at all fat, and seem to be spiritless and indolent."

"This description," says the old Wolf, "does not greatly attract me to the flock. For, decidedly, if the shepherd is good, he will not keep bad dogs about him. One might very soon get into trouble there. But come with me. I will take you to a flock where we shall be in less danger of losing our skins. Over that flock it is true that a great many dogs watch; but the shepherd is himself a fool. And where the shepherd is a fool, there the dogs too are of little worth."

THE PEASANT AND THE ROBBER

A PEASANT, WHO WAS BEGINNING TO STOCK HIS LITTLE FARM, had bought a cow and a milk-pail at a fair, and was going quietly homewards by a lonely path through the forest, when he suddenly fell into the hands of a Robber. The Robber stripped him as bare as a lime tree.

"Have mercy!" cried the Peasant. "I am utterly ruined. You have reduced me to beggary. For a whole year I have worked to buy this dear little cow. I could scarcely bear to wait for this day to arrive."

"Very good," replied the Robber, touched by compassion; "don't cry out against me. After all, I shall not want to milk your cow, so I'll give you back your milk-pail."

THE ELEPHANT AS GOVERNOR

AN ELEPHANT WAS ONCE APPOINTED RULER OF THE FOREST. Now, it is well known that the race of elephants is endowed with great intelligence; but every family has its unworthy scion. Our Governor was as stout as the rest of his race are, but as foolish as the rest of his race are not. As to his character, he would not intentionally hurt a fly. Well, the worthy Governor becomes aware of a petition laid before him by the Sheep, stating that their skins are entirely torn off their back by the Wolves.

"Oh, rogues!" cries the Elephant, "what a crime! Who gave you leave to plunder?"

But the Wolves say; "Allow us to explain, O father. Did not you give us leave to take from the Sheep a trifling contribution for our coats in winter? It is only because they are stupid sheep that they cry out. They have only a single fleece taken from each of them, but they grumble about giving even that!"

"Well, well," says the Elephant, "take care what you do. I will not permit any one to commit injustice. As it must be so, take a fleece from each of them. But do not take from them a single hair besides."

He who has rank and power, but wants sense, however good his heart may be, is sure to do harm.

THE BROOK

A SHEPHERD BY THE SIDE OF A BROOK COMPLAININGLY SANG, in his grief, of sad and irreparable loss. His pet lamb had lately been drowned in the neighbouring river.

Having heard the Shepherd, the Brook thus began to murmur indignantly; "Insatiable river! how would it be if thy depths, like mine, were clearly visible to all eyes, and every one could see, in thy most secret recesses, all the victims which thou hast so greedily swallowed up? I think that thou wouldst dive into the earth for shame, and hide thyself in its dark abysses. Methinks that, if Fate gave me such copious waters, I should become an ornament to Nature, and would never hurt even so much as a chicken. How cautiously should my waves roll past every bush, every cottage! My shores would only bless me, and I should bring fresh life to the adjacent valleys and meadows, without robbing them of so much as even a single leaflet. Then, in a word, I should perform my journey in a kindly spirit, nowhere causing misfortune or sorrow, and my waters should flow right down to the sea as pure as silver."

So spake the Brook, and so it really meant. But what happened? A week had not gone by before a heavy rain-cloud burst upon a neighbouring hill. In its affluence of waters the Brook suddenly rivalled the river. But, alas! what has become of the

Brook's tranquillity? The Brook overflows its banks with tur-
bid waters. It seethes; it roars; it flings about masses of soiled
foam. It overthrows ancestral oaks: their crashing may be
heard afar. And, at last, that very shepherd, on whose account
it lately upbraided the river with such a flow of eloquence,
perished in it with all his flock, and of his cottage not even a
trace was left behind.

How many brooks are there which flow along so smoothly,
so peacefully, and murmur so sweetly to the heart, only because
they have but very little water in them!

THE KITE

A KITE, WHICH HAD BEEN ALLOWED TO SOAR TO THE CLOUDS,
called out from on high to a Butterfly down below in the valley,

"I can assure you that I can scarcely make you out. Confess
now that you feel envious when you watch my so lofty flight."

"Envious? No, indeed! You have no business to think so
much of yourself. You fly high, it is true; but you are always
tied by a string. Such a life, my friend, is very far removed from
happiness. But I, though in truth but little exalted, fly wherever
I wish. I should not like all my life long to have to conduce to
some one else's foolish amusement."

THE IMPIOUS

IN THE DAYS OF OLD THERE WAS A PEOPLE, TO THE SHAME, BE IT
said, of the nations of the earth, which became so hardened in
heart, that it took up arms against the gods. Noisily, with
countless banners displayed, the insurgent crowds overrun the
plains, some armed with bows, others with slings. In order to
kindle more fury among the people, the ringleaders, in the insolence of their hearts, declare that the tribunal of Heaven is
harsh and foolish—that the gods either sleep or judge unreason-

ably—that the time has come to read them an unceremonious lesson—and that, as to the rest, it will not be difficult to hurl stones at the gods from the nearest hills, and to fill all Olympus with arrows.

Disquieted by the insolent blasphemies these fools uttered, all Olympus applied to Jupiter with the prayer that he would avert this evil. And even all the heavenly council was of opinion that, in order to confute the rebels, it would not be amiss to make manifest, at all events, a little miracle—a deluge or an earthquake, with thunder and lightning, or, perhaps, to crush them under a shower of stones.

"Let us wait a little," replied Jupiter; "for if they do not become quiet, but go on with their foolish violence, not fearing the immortals, they will be punished by their own deeds."

Then, with a roar, the banded rebels against the gods shot into the air a mass of arrows, a cloud of stones. But, laden with innumerable deaths, inevitable and terrible, their weapons fell back again upon their own heads.

THE PEASANT IN TROUBLE

A THIEF CREPT INTO A PEASANT'S HOUSE ONE AUTUMN NIGHT, and, betaking himself to the store-room, rummaged the walls, the shelves, and the ceiling, and stole, without remorse, all he could lay his hands on. So that our Moujik, poor fellow, who had lain down a rich man, woke up so bereft of everything, that a beggar's sack seemed the only resource left him in the world. Heaven grant that none of us may ever know a similar waking! The Peasant weeps and wails, and calls together his friends and relatives, his gossips, and all his neighbours.

"Can't you help me in my trouble?" he asks.

Then each begins to address the Peasant, and favours him with sage advice.

Says his gossip Karpich; "Ah, my light! you shouldn't have gone boasting to all the world that you were so rich."

Says his gossip Klimich, "In future, my dear gossip, you must take care to have the store-room close to the room you sleep in."

"Ah, brothers, you're all in the wrong," exclaims his neighbour Phocas. "The fault wasn't in the store-room being· at a distance. What you must do is to keep some fierce dogs in your yard. Take whichever you please of my Jouchka's puppies. I would far rather cordially make a present of them to a good neighbour than drown them."

And thus, as far as words went, his loving friends and relatives gave him a thousand excellent pieces of advice, each according to his power; but when it came to deeds, not one of them would help the poor fellow.

THE QUARTETTE

THE TRICKSY MONKEY, THE GOAT, THE ASS, AND BANDY-LEGGED Mishka the Bear, determined to play a quartette. They provide themselves with the necessary pieces of music—with two fiddles, and with an alto and a counter-bass. Then they sit down on a meadow under a lime-tree, prepared to enchant the world by their skill. They work away at their fiddlesticks with a will; and they make a noise, but there is no music in it.

"Stop, brothers, stop!" cries the Monkey, "wait a little! How can we get our music right? It's plain, you mustn't sit as you are. You, Mishka, with your counter-bass, face the alto. I will sit opposite the second fiddle. Then a different sort of music will begin: we shall set the very hills and forests dancing."

So they change places, and recommence; but the music is just as discordant as before.

"Stop a little," exclaims the Ass; "I have found out the secret. We shall be sure to play in tune if we sit in a row."

They follow its advice, and form in an orderly line. But the quartette is as unmusical as ever. Louder than before there arose among them squabbling and wrangling as to how they ought to be seated. It happened that a Nightingale came flying that way, attracted by their noise. At once they all entreat it to solve their difficulty.

"Be so kind," they say, "as to bear with us a little, in order that our quartette may come off properly. Music we have; instruments we have: tell us only how we ought to place ourselves."

But the Nightingale replies; "To be a musician, one must have a quicker intelligence and a finer ear than you possess. You, my friends, may place yourselves just as you like, but you will never become musicians."

THE LEAVES AND THE ROOTS

ON A BEAUTIFUL SUMMER DAY, THE LEAVES ON A TREE WHISpered softly to the zephyrs; and, as their shadow fell upon the valley, thus did they speak, vaunting their luxuriant verdure; "Is it not true that we are the pride of the whole valley? Is it not by us that this tree is rendered so bushy and wide-spreading, so stately and majestic? What would it be without us? Yes, indeed; we may praise ourselves without committing a sin! Do not we, by our cool shade, protect the shepherd and the traveller from the heat? Do not we, by our beauty, attract the shepherdess to dance here? From among us, in the morning and the evening twilight, the nightingale sings; and as to you, zephyrs, you scarcely ever desert us."

"You might add a word of thanks even to us," answered a feeble voice from underground.

"Who is it that dares thus audaciously to call us to account? Who are you who are talking there?" the Leaves began to lisp, noisily tossing on the tree.

"We are they," was the reply from down below, "who, burrowing in darkness here, provide you with nourishment. Is it possible that you do not recognize us? We are the roots of the tree on which you flourish. Go on rejoicing in your beauty: only remember there is this difference between us, that with the new spring a new foliage is born; but, if the roots perish, neither you nor the tree can survive."

THE WOLF AND THE FOX

A FOX, WHICH HAD FEASTED ON FOWLS UNTIL HE WAS FULL, AND had set aside a good store of spare food, lay down under a haycock, one evening, to sleep. Suddenly it looks up, and sees a hungry Wolf dragging itself along to pay it a visit.

"This is terrible, gossip!" says the Wolf. "I cannot anywhere find even the smallest of bones to pick, and I am actually dying of hunger. The dogs are malicious, the shepherd won't sleep, and I have nothing left but to hang myself."

"Really?"

"Really and truly."

"My poor old gossip! But won't you take a little hay? There is a whole haycock. I am delighted to oblige my friend."

But what its friend wanted was meat, not hay; and about its stock of provisions the Fox said never a word. So my grey-coated hero, though greatly caressed as to its ears by its gossip, had to go to bed supperless.

THE ASS AND THE NIGHTINGALE

AN ASS HAPPENED TO SEE A NIGHTINGALE, ONE DAY, AND SAID to it; "Listen, my dear. They say you have a great mastery over song. I have long wished very much to hear you sing, and to judge as to whether your talent is really so great."

On this the Nightingale began to make manifest its art—whistled in countless ways, sobbed, sustained notes, passed from one song to another; at one time let her voice die away, and echoed the distant murmur of the languishing reed; at another, poured through the wood a shower of tiny notes. Then all listened to the favourite singer of Aurora. The breezes died away; the feathered choir was hushed; the cattle lay down on the grass. Scarcely breathing, the shepherd revelled in it, and only now and then, as he listened to it, smiled on the shepherdess.

At length the singer ended. Then the Ass, bending its head towards the ground, observed; "It's tolerable. To speak the truth, one can listen to you without being bored. But it's a pity you don't know our Cock. You would sing a great deal better if you were to take a few lessons from him."

Having heard such a judgment, our poor Nightingale took to its wings and flew far away.

THE FOX AS ARCHITECT

A CERTAIN LION WAS EXCEEDINGLY FOND OF FOWLS, BUT THEY never throve with him. And that was no wonder. They lived utterly free from all restrictions; and so some of them were stolen, others disappeared of their own accord.

To remedy this unpleasantness and loss, the Lion determined to build a large poultry-yard, and so cunningly to design and arrange it, as entirely to keep out thieves, but to provide the fowls with plenty of space and all things needful.

Well, they inform the Lion that the Fox is a great hand at building, so the affair is entrusted to him. The building is begun and ended successfully, the Fox working at it with all conceivable industry and talent. The building is looked at and examined in detail. Truly, it is a work which cannot be too much admired. Everything is there which any one can possibly desire—

food close at hand, perches inserted everywhere, refuges from cold and heat, and retired little places for the sitting hens. All honour and glory to our good Fox! A liberal reward is bestowed on him, and an order is given to transfer the fowls, without loss of time, to their new abode.

But is the change of any use? Not at all. It is true that the building seems firm and massive, and the walls enclosing it lofty. But yet the fowls daily become fewer and fewer. No one can imagine whence this evil springs. But the Lion orders a watch to be set; and whom do they catch? Why, that villain, the Fox. It is true that he had constructed the building so that no one else could break in and steal; but he had taken care to leave a little hole by which he could get into it himself.

THE LION AND THE PANTHER

ONCE ON A TIME, IN ANCIENT DAYS, THE LION MAINTAINED A very long contest with the Panther about certain disputed forests, valleys, and caves. To go to law about their rights—this was not in accordance with their characters; for, in matters relating to law, the strong are often blind. For such affairs they have their own rule;—"Who conquers is right." But at last, that they might not eternally squabble, with claws ever becoming more blunt, our heroes determined to submit their dispute to law. Their intention was to put an end to their fighting, to settle all hostilities, and then, as is customary, to conclude a peace which should last uninterrupted—until the next quarrel.

"Let us each choose a secretary at once," proposes the Panther to the Lion, "and decide according as the two secretaries shall advise. I, for instance, will choose the Cat. It is not a very good-looking little animal; but, then, its conscience is clear. But do you, for your part, nominate the Ass, for it belongs to a distinguished order in the state; and, to tell the truth, you will have in it a very enviable beast. Trust me as a friend in this. All your court and council together are scarcely worth its hoof. Let us accept whatever arrangements it and my Cat may make."

And the Lion sanctioned the first part of the Panther's scheme without opposition; only he chose the Fox, instead of the Ass, to represent him in the discussion, saying to himself, after so doing,

"Truly, there is but little good to be gained from him whom an enemy recommends."

THE HOP-PLANT

A HOP-PLANT HAD MADE ITS WAY TO THE EDGE OF A GARDEN, and had begun to wind itself around a dry stake in the fence. Now, in the open field beyond stood an oak-sapling.

"What use is there in that stunted creature, or, indeed, in any of its kind?" Thus about the oak the Hop used to whisper to the stake. "How can it even be compared with you? You, simply by your erect carriage, look like a perfect lady in its presence. It is true that it is clothed with foliage; but how rough it is! what a colour it has! Why ever does the earth nourish it?"

Meanwhile, a week had scarcely passed, before the owner broke up that stake for firewood, and transplanted the young oak into his garden. His care resulted in full success, and the oak flourished, extending vigorous shoots. Observing this, our Hop-plant wound itself about it, and now its voice is entirely devoted to the oak's glory and honour.

THE SQUIRREL IN SERVICE

A SQUIRREL ONCE SERVED A LION: I KNOW NOT HOW, OR IN WHAT capacity. But this much is certain, that the Squirrel's service found favour in the Lion's eyes; and to satisfy the Lion is, certainly, no light affair. In return for this, it was promised a whole waggon-load of nuts. Promised—yes; but, meanwhile, time continues to fly by. Our Squirrel often suffers hunger, and has tears in its eyes while grinning in the Lion's presence. When it looks round in the forest, its former comrades show themselves here and there high up among the trees. It looks at them till its eyes begin to blink; but they keep on always cracking nuts. Our Squirrel takes a step towards the nut-bushes, looks at them—it can do no more. At one time it is called away, at another it is even dragged off, on the Lion's service.

But see! At last the Squirrel has grown old, and become tedious to the Lion. It is time for it to retire. They have granted the Squirrel its discharge, and they have actually given it the full load of nuts. Excellent nuts—such as the world has never seen before. All picked fruit—one as good as another; a perfect marvel; only one thing is unlucky—the Squirrel has long ago lost all its teeth.

THE FOX AND THE MARMOT

"WHERE ARE YOU RUNNING SO FAST, GOSSIP, WITHOUT EVER looking back?" a Marmot asked a Fox.

"Oh, my friend, my dear gossip, I have had a calumnious accusation brought against me, and I have been dismissed as an extortioner. You know, I was the judge of the poultry-yard. In that position I lost my health and my peace of mind. From the press of business, I never had time to get a comfortable meal, and at nights I could not sleep soundly. And now, in return for this, I have incurred the wrath of my employers, and all on account of a calumny. Only just think! Who in the world shall be without reproach, if calumnies are listened to? I an extortioner! Do they suppose I've gone out of my mind? Now, I appeal to you, have you ever seen that I took part in that wickedness? Think the matter over; reflect on it well."

"No, gossip, no; but I have often remarked that there were some feathers on your muzzle."

Many an official complains that he is forced to spend every rouble he has; and all the town knows that, originally, he had nothing, and that he got nothing with his wife. But see! little by little he builds a house; he buys an estate. Now, in what manner can you reconcile his salary with his expenditure? Although you can prove nothing against him legally, yet you will not be committing a sin if you say, "That fellow has feathers on his muzzle."

THE WHISK

GREAT HONOURS WERE SUDDENLY CONFERRED UPON A DIRTY Whisk. It will not now any longer sweep the floors of kitchens; for the master's caftans are handed over to it, the servants having, probably, got drunk. Well, our Whisk set to work vigorously. It was never tired of belabouring the master's clothes, and it thrashed the caftans like so much rye. Undoubtedly its industry was great; only the misfortune was, that it was itself so dirty. Of what use, then, was all its toil? The more it tried to clean anything, the dirtier did it make it.

Just as much harm is done when a fool interferes in what is out of his own line, and undertakes to correct the work of a man of learning.

THE GRANDEE

ONCE, IN THE DAYS OF OLD, A CERTAIN GRANDEE PASSED FROM his rich soft bed into the realm which Pluto sways. To speak more simply, he died. And so, as was anciently the custom, he appeared before the justice-seat of Hades. Straightway he was asked; "Where were you born? What have you been?"

"I was born in Persia, and my rank was that of a Satrap. But, as my health was feeble during my lifetime, I never exercised any personal control in my province, but left everything to be done by my secretary."

"But you—what did you do?"

"I ate, drank, and slept; and I signed everything he set before me."

"Enter, then, at once into Paradise!"

"How now! Where is the justice of this?" thereupon exclaimed Mercury, forgetting all politeness.

"Ah, brother," answered Eacus, "you know nothing about it. But don't you see this? The dead man was a fool. What would have happened if he, who had such power in his hands, had unfortunately interfered in business? Why, he would have ruined the whole province. The tears which would have flowed then would have been beyond all calculation. Therefore it is that he has gone into Paradise, because he did not interfere with business."

I was in court yesterday, and I saw a judge there. There can be no doubt that he will go into Paradise.

THE PIKE

AN APPEAL TO JUSTICE WAS MADE AGAINST THE PIKE, ON THE ground that it had rendered the pond uninhabitable. A whole cart-load of proofs were tendered as evidence; and the culprit, as was beseeming, was brought into court in a large tub. The judges were assembled not far off, having been set to graze in a neighbouring field. Their names are still preserved in the archives. There were two Donkeys, a couple of old Horses, and two or three Goats. The Fox also was added to their number, as assessor, in order that the business might be carried on under competent supervision.

Now, popular report said that the Pike used to supply the table of the Fox with fish. However this might be, there was no partiality among the judges; and it must also be stated that it was impossible to conceal the Pike's roguery in the affair in question. So there was no help for it. Sentence was passed, condemning the Pike to an ignominious punishment. In order to frighten others, it was to be hung from a tree.

"Respected judges," thus did the Fox begin to speak, "hanging is a trifle. I should have liked to have sentenced the culprit to such a punishment as has never been seen here among us. In order that rogues may in future live in fear, and run a terrible risk, I would drown it in the river."

"Excellent!" cry the judges, and unanimously accept the proposition.

So the Pike was flung—into the river.

TRISHKA'S CAFTAN

TRISHKA'S CAFTAN WAS OUT AT THE ELBOWS. WHY SHOULD he ponder long over it? He took to his needle, cut a quarter off each sleeve; so mended the elbows. The caftan was all right again, only his arms were bare for a quarter of their length. That is no great matter; but every one is always laughing at Trishka. So Trishka says; "As I'm no fool, I'll set this affair straight also. I'll make the sleeves longer than they were before. Oh! Trishka is no common-place fellow."

So he cut off the skirts of his caftan, and used them to lengthen his sleeves. Then Trishka was happy, though he had a caftan which was as short as a waistcoat.

In a similar way have I sometimes seen other embarrassed people set their affairs straight. Take a look at them as they dash away. They have all got on Trishka's caftan.

THE PEASANT AND THE HORSE

A PEASANT WAS SOWING OATS ONE DAY. SEEING THAT, A YOUNG Horse began to reason about it, grumbling to itself.

"A pretty piece of work this, for which he brings such a lot of oats here! And yet they say men are wiser than we are. Can anything possibly be more foolish or ridiculous than to plough up a whole field like this, in order to scatter one's oats over it afterwards to no purpose? Had he given them to me, or to the bay here, or had he even thought fit to fling them to the fowls, it would have all been more like business. Or even if he had hoarded them up, I should have recognized avarice in that. But to fling them uselessly away! No; that is sheer stupidity."

Meanwhile time passed; and in the autumn the oats were garnered, and the Peasant fed this very Horse on them.

Reader, there can be no doubt that you do not approve of the Horse's opinions. But, from the oldest times to our own days, has not man been equally audacious in criticising the designs of Providence, although, in his blind folly, he sees nothing of its means or ends?

THE ELEPHANT AND THE PUG-DOG

AN ELEPHANT WAS BEING TAKEN THROUGH THE STREETS, PROBably for show. It is well known that Elephants are a wonder among us; so crowds of gaping idlers followed the Elephant. From some corner or other, a Pug-dog comes to meet him. It

looks at the Elephant, and then begins to run at it, to bark, to squeal, to try to get at it, just as if it wanted to fight it.

"Neighbour, cease to bring shame on yourself," says Shafka, a long-haired dog. "Are you capable of fighting an Elephant? Just see now, you are already hoarse; but it keeps straight on, and does not pay you the slightest attention."

"Aye, aye!" replies the Pug-dog, "that's just what gives me courage. In this way, you see, without fighting at all, I may get reckoned among the greatest bullies. Just let the dogs say; 'Ah, look at Puggy! He must be strong, indeed, that's clear, or he would never bark at an Elephant.'"

THE WOLF IN THE KENNEL

A WOLF, ONE NIGHT, THINKING TO CLIMB INTO A SHEEPFOLD, fell into a kennel. Immediately the whole kennel was up in arms. The dogs, scenting the grisly disturber so near at hand, began to bark in their quarters, and to tear out to the fight.

"Hallo, lads, a thief!" cried the keepers; and immediately the gates were shut. In a moment the kennel became a hell. Men come running, one armed with a club, another with a gun. "Lights!" they cry; "bring lights!" The lights being brought, our Wolf is seen sitting squeezed up in the furthest corner, gnashing its teeth, its hide bristling, and its eyes looking as if it would fain eat up the whole party.

Seeing, however, that it is not now in the presence of the flock, and that it is now called upon to pay the penalty for the sheep it has killed, my trickster resorts to negotiation, beginning thus; "Friends, what is all this fuss about? I am your ancient gossip and comrade; and I have come here to contract an alliance with you—not with the slightest intention of quarrelling. Let us forget the past, and declare in favour of mutual harmony. Not only will I for the future avoid touching the flocks belonging to this spot, but I will gladly fight in their behalf against others; and I swear on the word of a Wolf that I—"

"Listen, neighbour," here interrupts the huntsman. "You

are grey-coated; but I, friend, am grey-headed, and I have long known what your wolfish natures are like, and therefore it is my custom never to make peace with wolves until I have torn their skin from off their backs."

With that he let go the pack of hounds on the Wolf.

THE ORACLE

IN A CERTAIN TEMPLE THERE WAS A WOODEN IDOL WHICH BEGAN to utter prophetic answers, and to give wise counsels. Accordingly, it rejoiced in a very rich attire, being covered from top to toe with gold and silver; and was gorged with sacrifices, deafened by prayers, and choked with incense. Every one believed blindly in the Oracle.

All of a sudden—wonderful to relate!—the Oracle began to talk nonsense—took to answering incoherently and absurdly, so that, if any one consulted it about anything, whatever our Oracle said was a lie; so that every one wondered what had become of its prophetic faculty. The fact was, that the idol was hollow, and the priests used to sit in it in order to reply to the laity; and so, as long as the priest was discreet, the idol did not talk nonsense; but when a fool took to sitting in it, the idol became a mere dummy.

I have heard—can it be true?—that in days gone by there used to be judges who were renowned for ability—so long as they kept an able secretary.

THE LION, THE CHAMOIS, AND THE FOX

A LION WAS CHASING A CHAMOIS ALONG A VALLEY. HE HAD ALL but caught it, and with longing eyes was anticipating a certain and a satisfying repast. It seemed as if it were utterly impossible for the victim to escape; for a deep ravine appeared to bar the way for both the hunter and the hunted. But the nimble

Chamois, gathering together all its strength, shot like an arrow from a bow across the chasm, and stood still on the rocky cliff on the other side. Our Lion pulled up short. But at that moment a friend of his happened to be near at hand. That friend was the Fox.

"What!" said he, "with your strength and agility, is it possible that you will yield to a feeble Chamois? You have only to will, and you will be able to work wonders. Though the abyss be deep, yet, if you are only in earnest, I am certain you will clear it. Surely you can confide in my disinterested friendship. I would not expose your life to danger if I were not so well aware of your strength and dexterity."

The Lion's blood waxed hot, and began to boil in his veins. He flung himself with all his might into space. But he could not clear the chasm; so down he tumbled headlong, and was killed by the fall. Then what did his dear friend do? He cautiously made his way down to the bottom of the ravine, and there, out in the open space and the free air, seeing that the Lion wanted neither flattery nor obedience now, he set to work to pay the last sad rites to his dead friend, and in a month picked his bones clean.

THE DANCING FISH

HAVING WATERS AS WELL AS WOODS IN HIS DOMINIONS, THE Lion called the beasts together to a council, to consider who should be appointed governor of the Fish. They gave their votes in the usual manner, and the Fox was chosen. Well, the Fox sat in the governor's seat, and visibly waxed fat. He had a Moujik as friend, kinsman, and gossip, and the two used to lay their heads together. The Fox conducted business and pronounced legal decisions on the shore; and meantime his gossip angled after the Fish, and, like a trusty comrade, shared what he caught with his friend.

But rogues do not always succeed. The Lion somehow grew suspicious, from rumours it heard, that the scales had been falsified in its law courts; so, having found a leisure time, it determined to investigate the state of its dominions.

Having gone to the shore, it found that the good gossip had caught some fish, and had kindled a fire by the riverside, intending to feast on them with his comrade. The poor fish were bounding into the air to get away from the heat, each one to the best of its power; each one, seeing its end close at hand, flung itself about, gaping at the Moujik.

"Who are you, and what are you doing?" angrily asked the Lion.

"Great king!" answers the chief rogue—the Fox always has a trick in reserve—"great king! this is my chief secretary here, who is esteemed for his probity by all the nation; and these are carp, all inhabitants of the waters. We have all come here to congratulate you, our good king, on your arrival."

"Well, how is justice dispensed here? Is your district content?"

"Great king! here they do not merely live; they are in Paradise. If only your royal life may be prolonged!" (All this time the fish were leaping about in the pan.)

"But tell me," said the Lion, "why do they fling themselves about topsy-turvy in this manner?"

"O wise Lion," replied the Fox, "they are dancing for joy at seeing you." Then the Lion, tapping the Starost kindly on the breast, proceeded on his journey.

THE WOLVES AND THE SHEEP

THE SHEEP COULD NOT LIVE IN PEACE ON ACCOUNT OF THE Wolves, and the evil increased to such a pitch, that at last the rulers of the beasts had to take vigorous steps towards interfering and saving the victims. With that intent a council was summoned. The majority of its members, it is true, were Wolves; but then all Wolves are not badly spoken of. There have been Wolves known, and that often (such instances are never forgotten), to have walked past a flock quite peacefully—when completely gorged. So why should not Wolves have seats in the council? Although it was necessary to protect the Sheep, yet there was no reason for utterly suppressing the Wolves.

Well, the meeting took place in the thick wood. They pondered, considered, harangued, and at last framed a decree. Here you have it, word for word; "As soon as a Wolf shall have disturbed a flock, and shall have begun to worry a Sheep, then the Sheep shall be allowed, without respect to persons, to seize it by the scruff of the neck, to carry it into the nearest thicket or wood, and there to bring it before the court."

This law is everything that can be desired. Only, I have remarked, up to the present day, that although the Wolves are not to be allowed to worry with impunity, yet in all cases, whether the Sheep be plaintiff or defendant, the Wolf is always sure, in spite of all opposition, to carry off the Sheep into the forest.

THE SWORD-BLADE

THE KEEN BLADE OF A SWORD, MADE OF DAMASCUS STEEL, WHICH had been thrown aside on a heap of old iron, was sent to market with the other pieces of metal, and sold for a trifle to a Moujik. Now, a Moujik's ideas move in a narrow circle. He immediately set to work to turn the blade to account. Our Moujik fitted a handle to the blade, and began to strip lime trees with it in the forest. The bark he wanted for shoes, while at home he unceremoniously splintered fir chips with it. Sometimes, also, he would lop off twigs with it, or small branches for mending his wattled fences, or would shape stakes with it for his garden paling.

The result was that, before the year was out, our blade was notched and rusted from one end to the other, and the children used to ride astride of it. So one day a Hedgehog, which was lying under a bench in the cottage, close by the spot where the blade had been flung, said to it; "Tell me, what do you think of this life of yours? If there is any truth in all the fine things that are said about Damascus steel, you surely must be ashamed of having to splinter fir chips, and square stakes, and of being turned, at last, into a plaything for children."

But the Sword-blade replied; "In the hands of a warrior, I should have been a terror to the foe; but here my special faculties are of no avail. So in this house I am turned to base uses only. But am I free to choose my employment? No! Not I, but he, ought to be ashamed, who could not see for what I was fit to be employed."

THE PEASANT AND THE SHEEP

A PEASANT SUMMONED A SHEEP INTO COURT, CHARGING THE poor thing with a criminal offence. The judge was—the Fox. The case got into full swing immediately. Plaintiff and defend-ant were equally adjured to state, point by point, and without both speaking at once, how the affair took place, and in what their proofs consisted.

Says the Peasant; "On such and such a day, I missed two of my fowls early in the morning. Nothing was left of them but bones and feathers. And no one had been in the yard but the Sheep." Then the Sheep depones that it was fast asleep all the night in question; and it calls all its neighbours to testify that they had never known it guilty either of theft or of any roguery; and, be-sides this, it states that it never touches flesh-meat.

Here is the Fox's decision, word for word; "The explanation of the Sheep cannot under any circumstances be accepted. For all rogues are notoriously clever at concealing their real designs; and it appears manifest, on due inquiry, that on the aforesaid night the Sheep was not separated from the fowls; and fowls are ex-ceedingly savoury, and opportunity favoured it. Therefore I decide, according to my conscience, that it is impossible that the Sheep could have forborne to eat the fowls; and accordingly the Sheep shall be put to death, and its carcase shall be given to the court, and its fleece shall be taken by the plaintiff."

THE GEESE

A PEASANT, WITH A LONG ROD IN HIS HAND, WAS DRIVING SOME Geese to a town where they were to be sold; and, to tell the truth, he did not treat them over-politely. In hopes of making a good bargain, he was hastening on so as not to lose the market-day (and when gain is concerned, geese and men alike are apt to suffer). I do not blame the peasant; but the Geese talked about him in a different spirit, and, whenever they met any passers-by, abused him to them in such terms as these; "Is it possible to find any Geese more unfortunate than we are? This Moujik harasses us so terribly, and chases us about just as if we were common Geese. The ignoramus does not know that he ought to pay us reverence, seeing that we are the noble descendants of those geese to whom Rome was once indebted for her salvation, and in whose honour even feast-days were specially appointed there."

"And do you want to have honour paid you on that account?" a passer-by asked them.

"Why, our ancestors—"

"I know that—I have read all about it; but I want to know this—of what use have you been yourselves?"

"Why, our ancestors saved Rome!"

"Quite so; but what have you done?"

"We? Nothing."

"Then what merit is there in you? Let your ancestors rest in peace—they justly received honourable reward; but you, my friends, are only fit to be roasted!"

It would be easy to make this fable still more intelligible; but I am afraid of irritating the Geese.

THE CUCKOO AND THE EAGLE

THE EAGLE PROMOTED A CUCKOO TO THE RANK OF A NIGHTIN-gale. The Cuckoo, proud of its new position, seated itself proudly on an aspen, and began to exhibit its musical talents. After a time, it looks round. All the birds are flying away, some laughing at it, others abusing it. Our Cuckoo grows angry, and hastens to the Eagle with a complaint against the birds.

"Have pity on me!" it says. "According to your command, I have been appointed Nightingale to these woods, and yet the birds dare to laugh at my singing."

"My friend," answers the Eagle, "I am a king, but I am not God. It is impossible for me to remedy the cause of your complaint. I can order a Cuckoo to be styled a Nightingale; but to make a Nightingale out of a Cuckoo—that I cannot do."

THE PIKE AND THE CAT

A CONCEITED PIKE TOOK IT INTO ITS HEAD TO EXERCISE THE functions of a cat. I do not know whether the Evil One had plagued it with envy, or whether, perhaps, it had grown tired of fishy fare; but, at all events, it thought fit to ask the Cat to take it out of the chase, with the intention of catching a few mice in the warehouse. "But, my dear friend," Vaska says to the Pike, "do you understand that kind of work? Take care, gossip, that you don't incur disgrace. It isn't without reason that they say, 'The work ought to be in the master's power.' "

"Why really, gossip, what a tremendous affair it is! Mice, indeed! Why, I have been in the habit of catching perches!"

"Oh, very well. Come along!"

They went; they lay each in ambush. The Cat thoroughly enjoyed itself; made a hearty meal; then went to look after its comrade. Alas! the Pike, almost destitute of life, lay there gasping, its tail nibbled away by the mice. So the Cat, seeing that its comrade had undertaken a task quite beyond its strength, dragged it back, half dead, to its pond.

THE FOX IN THE ICE

VERY EARLY ONE WINTER MORNING, DURING A HARD FROST, A Fox was drinking at an ice-hole, not far from the haunts of men. Meanwhile, whether by pure accident or from negligence doesn't much matter, the end of its tail got wet, and froze to the ice. No great harm was done; the Fox could easily remedy it. It had only to give a tolerably hard pull, and leave about a score of its hairs behind; then it could run away home quickly, before any one came. But how could it make up its mind to spoil its tail? Such a bushy tail as it was, so ample and golden! No; better wait a little. Surely, men are sleeping still. It's even possible that a thaw may, meanwhile, set in. In that case, it will be able to withdraw its tail easily from the ice-hole.

So it waits: it goes on waiting, but its tail only freezes all the more. It looks round; the day is already beginning to dawn. People are stirring; voices are to be heard. Our poor Fox begins to rush about wildly—now this way, now that. But still it cannot free itself from the hole. Luckily, a Wolf comes running that way.

"Dear friend, gossip, father!" cries the Fox, "do save me!   I am all but lost!"

So the Wolf stopped, and set to work to rescue the Fox.   Its method was a very simple one: it bit the tail of the Fox clean off. So our foolish friend went home tailless, but rejoicing that its skin was still on its back.

THE AUTHOR AND THE ROBBER

IN THE GLOOMY REALM OF SHADOWS, TWO SINNERS APPEARED before the judges for sentence at the very same time. The one was a Robber, who used to extract tribute on the highway, and who had at last come to the gallows; the other an Author, covered with glory, who had infused a subtle poison into his works, had promoted atheism, and had preached immorality, being, like the Siren, sweet-voiced, and, like the Siren, dangerous.

In Hades judicial ceremonies are brief; there are no useless delays. Sentence was pronounced immediately. Two huge iron cauldrons were suspended in the air by two tremendous iron chains; in each of these one of the sinners was placed. Under the Robber a great pile of wood was heaped up, and then one of the Furies herself set it on fire, kindling such a terrible flame, that the very stone in the roof of the infernal halls began to crack. The Author's sentence did not seem to be a severe one. Under him, at first, a little fire scarcely glowed; but, the longer it burned, the larger it became.

Centuries have now gone by, but the fire has not gone out. Beneath the Robber the flame has long ago been extinguished; beneath the Author it grows hourly worse and worse. Seeing that there is no mitigation of his torments, the writer at last cries out amidst them that there is no justice among the gods; that he had filled the world with his renown; and that, if he had written a little too freely, he had been punished too much for it; and that he did not think he had sinned more than the Robber. Then before him, in all her ornaments with snakes hissing amid her hair, and with bloody scourges in her hands, appeared one of the three Infernal Sisters.

"Wretch!" she exclaims, "dost thou upbraid Providence? Dost thou compare thyself with this robber? His crime is as nothing compared with thine. Only as long as he lived did his cruelty and lawlessness render him hurtful. But thou—long ago have thy bones turned to dust, yet the sun never rises without bringing to light fresh evils of which thou art the cause. The poison of thy writings not only does not weaken, but, spreading abroad, it becomes more malignant as years roll by. Look there!" and for a moment she enables him to look upon the world; "behold the crimes, the misery, of which thou art the cause. Look at those children who have brought shame upon their families, who have reduced their parents to despair. By whom were their heads and hearts corrupted? By thee. Who strove to rend asunder the bonds of society, ridiculing as childish follies all ideas of the sanctity of marriage and the right of authority and law, and rendering them responsible for all human misfortunes? Thou art the man! Didst thou not dignify unbelief with the name of enlightenment? Didst thou not place vice and passion in the most charming and alluring of lights? And now look!—a whole country, perverted by thy teaching, is full of murder and robbery, of strife and rebellion, and is being led onwards by thee to ruin. For every drop of that country's tears and blood thou art to blame. And now dost thou dare to hurl thy blasphemies against the gods? How much evil have thy books yet to bring upon the world? Continue, then, to suffer; for here the measure of thy punishment shall be according to thy deserts." Thus spoke the angry Fury, and slammed down the cover on the cauldron.

THE STONE AND THE WORM

"WHAT A FUSS EVERY ONE IS MAKING! HOW WANTING IN MANners!" observed, with respect to a shower, a Stone which lay in a field. "Have the kindness to look. Every one is delighted with it. They have longed for it as if it were the best of guests; but what is it that it has done? It has come for a couple of hours or so—no more. But they should make a few inquiries about me. Why, I have lain here for centuries. Modest and unassuming, I lie quietly where I am thrown. And yet I have never heard from a single person so much as a 'Thank you!' It is not without reason that the world gets reviled. I cannot see a grain of justice anywhere in it."

"Hold your tongue!" exclaimed a Worm. "This shower, brief as it has been, has abundantly watered the fields, which were being rendered sterile by the drought, and has revived the hopes of the farmer. But you contribute nothing to the ground but a useless weight."

Thus many a man will boast of having served the state for forty years; but as for being useful, he has never been a bit more so than the Stone.

THE ASS

A PEASANT HAD AN ASS WHICH SEEMED TO BEHAVE ITSELF SO discreetly that he could not praise it too highly. But, in order that it might not get lost in the forest, our peasant tied a bell round its neck. On this our Ass, who had evidently heard a great deal of talk about decorations, became puffed up, began to grow proud and conceited, and looked upon itself as a very important gentleman.

But its new rank proved ruinous to the Ass, poor thing!—a fact which may serve as a lesson for others besides asses. I ought to tell you beforehand that the Ass was never over-honest; but until it got its bell everything went smoothly with it. If it made its way into a field of rye or oats, or into a garden, it ate what it wanted, and then got out again quietly. But now it is a very different story with him.

Whenever our illustrious gentleman trespasses, the bell which now adorns his neck goes with him, and rings an incessant peal.

Every one looks out to see what it is. Here, one man, seizing a bludgeon, drives our poor beast out of his rye-field or his garden; and there, another, who owns a field of oats, no sooner hears the sound of the bell, than he catches up a stake, and begins thrashing the unfortunate animal's flanks. So that by the autumn our poor grandee is half dead: the Ass has nothing but skin and bone.

In the same way among men, also, rank proves injurious to rogues. As long as a rogue's position is humble, he is not re-marked. But a lofty rank is, to a rogue, as it were a bell round his neck. Its noise is loud, and may be heard afar off.

THE POOR MAN ENRICHED

"IS IT WORTH WHILE BEING RICH, IF ONE IS NEVER TO EAT OR drink delicately, and to do nothing but heap up money? And to what end? We die, and then leave all behind. We only torment ourselves, and get a bad name. No; if riches had fallen to my share, not only roubles, but even thousands of them wouldn't have been grudged by me, so long as I could live sumptuously and luxuriously; and my feasts should have been talked about far and wide. Besides, I should have done good to others. To rich misers, their life is a kind of torment."

So reasoned a Poor Man with himself, lying on the bare boards in a wretched hovel. Suddenly, gliding to his side through a chink, there appeared—some say a wizard, others say the Evil One—most likely the latter, as the end of the story will show— and began to speak thus; "You wish to be rich; I have heard you say why. I am glad to help a friend, so here is a purse for you; there is a ducat in it—no more. But, as soon as you have taken one coin out of it, you will find another in it all ready for you. So now, my friend, your growing rich depends entirely upon your own wishes. Take the purse, and freely supply yourself from it until your craving is satisfied. Only bear this in mind,—until you shall have flung the purse into the river, you are forbidden to spend a single ducat."

He spoke, and left the purse with the Poor Man. The Poor Man was almost beside himself for joy. But, as soon as he returned to his senses, he began to handle the purse; and with what results? Scarcely could he believe it was not a dream. He had hardly taken one ducat out, before another was already stirring in the purse. Our needy friend says to himself,

"I will shake out a heap of ducats. Then, to-morrow I shall be rich, and I will begin to live like a Sybarite."

But the next morning he had changed his mind.

"It's true," he says, "I am rich now. But who isn't glad to get hold of a good thing? and why shouldn't I become twice as rich? It surely wouldn't be laziness in me to spend another day over the purse. Here I have money for a mansion, an equipage, a country house. But if I might buy estates too, wouldn't it be stupid in me to lose such an opportunity? Yes, I will keep the wonderful purse. So be it: I will fast one day more. As to that, I shall always have time enough for luxurious living."

But what happens? A day goes by, and then a week, a month, a year. Our Poor Man has long ago lost all count of the ducats. Meanwhile, he eats scantily, and drinks scantily. Scarcely has the day begun to break before he is back at the old work. The day comes to an end; but, according to his calculations, something or other is still sure to be wanting. Sometimes he makes up his mind to throw away the purse. But then his heart grows faint within him. He reaches the bank of the river, and—then turns back again.

"How can I possibly part with the purse," he says, "while it yields a stream of gold of its own accord?"

By this time our poor friend has grown grey, and thin, and as yellow as his own gold. He no more so much as thinks about luxury now. He has become faint and feeble; health and rest have utterly deserted him. But still with trembling hand he goes on taking ducats out of the purse. He takes, and takes; and how does it all end? On the bench on which he used to sit gloating over his wealth—on that very bench he dies, in the act of counting the last coins of his ninth million.

THE HIND AND THE DERVISH

A YOUNG HIND, BEREFT OF HER MUCH-LOVED FAWNS, AND STILL having her udders full of milk, found two young wolves deserted in a forest, and immediately began to fulfil the sacred duty of a mother towards them, feeding them with her milk. A Dervish, who inhabited the same forest, astonished at this proceeding of hers, cried out; "Imprudent creature that thou art! On what kind of animal art thou conferring thy milk? On what art thou wasting thy affections? Is it possible that thou canst expect gratitude from such as they are? Or is it that thou dost not know their evil nature? Some day, perhaps, it will be thy blood that they will drink."

"It may be so, indeed," replied the Hind; "but I did not think, nor do I wish to think, of that. It is only as a mother that I care to feel just now; and my milk would have been a burden to me if I had not given suck to these little ones."

Thus genuine charity does good without thinking of recompense. To the really benevolent, their abundance would be burdensome if they could not share it with those who are in want.

THE PEASANTS AND THE RIVER

SOME PEASANTS, WHO HAD BEEN DRIVEN OUT OF ALL PATIENCE by the ruin which the brooks and rivulets had brought upon them by their overflowing, set out to seek redress from the River into which those streams fell. And, indeed, there was much reason for denouncing them. They had torn away the seed from the newly-sown fields, they had overthrown and washed away mills, and it was impossible to count the cattle they had drowned. But the River flows so gently, though indeed proudly: on its banks great cities stand, and no one ever hears such tricks laid to its charge. So, doubtless, it will put a check upon these streams.

Thus did the Peasants reason among themselves. But what happened? When they had drawn near to the banks of the

River, and looked out upon its surface, they saw that its stream was bearing along half of their missing property. The Peasants, without beginning a fruitless complaint, only gazed on the waters for a while. Then, after looking in each other's faces, and shaking their heads, they returned home; and as they went, they said,

"Why should we waste our time? You'll never get any redress for what the children have stolen, so long as their parents go halves with them in the spoil."

THE MAN AND HIS SHADOW

THERE WAS A CERTAIN ORIGINAL MAN WHO DESIRED TO CATCH his own Shadow. He makes a step or two towards it, but it moves away from him. He quickens his pace; it does the same. At last he takes to running; but the quicker he goes, the quicker runs the Shadow also, utterly refusing to give itself up, just as if it had been a treasure. But see! our eccentric friend suddenly turns round, and walks away from it. And presently he looks behind him; the Shadow runs after him now.

Ladies fair, I have often observed—what do you suppose?—no, no; I assure you I am not going to speak about you—that Fortune treats us in a similar way. One man tries with all his might to seize the goddess, and only loses his time and his trouble. Another seems, to all appearance, to be running out of her sight; but, no: she herself takes a pleasure in pursuing him.

DEMIAN'S FISH SOUP

"NEIGHBOUR, LIGHT OF MY EYES! DO EAT A LITTLE MORE."

"Dear neighbour, I am full to the throat."

"No matter; just a little plateful. Believe me, the soup is cooked gloriously."

"But I've had three platefuls already."

"Well, what does that matter? If you like it and it does you good, why not eat it all up? What a soup it is! How rich! It looks as if it had been sprinkled over with amber. Here is bream; there is a lump of sterlet. Take a little more, dear, kind friend. Just another spoonful! Wife, come and entreat him."

Thus does Demian feast his neighbour Phocas, not giving him a moment's breathing-time. Phocas feels the moisture trickling down his forehead; still he takes one more plateful, attacks it with all the strength he has left, and somehow manages to swallow the whole of it.

"That's the sort of friend I like!" cries Demian. "I can't bear people who require pressing. But now, dear friend, take just one little plateful more!"

But, on hearing this, our poor Phocas, much as he liked fish soup, catching hold of his cap and sash, runs away home without looking behind him. Nor from that day to this has he crossed Demian's threshold.

THE PEBBLE AND THE DIAMOND

A DIAMOND, WHICH SOME ONE HAD LOST, LAY FOR SOME TIME on the high road. At last it happened that a merchant picked it up. By him it was offered to the king, who bought it, had it set in gold, and made it one of the ornaments of the royal crown.

Having heard of this, a Pebble began to make a fuss. The brilliant fate of the Diamond fascinated it; and, one day, seeing a Moujik passing, it besought him thus; "Do me a kindness, fellow-countryman, and take me with you to the capital. Why should I go on suffering here in rain and mud, while our Diamond is, men say, in honour there? I don't understand why it has been treated with such respect. Side by side with me here it lay so many years; it is just such a stone as I am—my close companion. Do take me! How can one tell? If I am seen there, I too, perhaps, may be found worthy of being turned to account."

The Moujik took the stone into his lumbering cart, and conveyed it to the city. Our stone tumbled into the cart, thinking that it would soon be sitting by the side of the Diamond. But a quite different fate befell it. It really was turned to account, but only to mend a hole in the road.

THE PIG

A PIG ONCE MADE ITS WAY INTO THE COURTYARD OF A LORDLY mansion, sauntered at its will around the stables and the kitchen, wallowed in filth, bathed in slops, and then returned home from its visit a thorough pig.

"Well, Kavronya, what have you seen?" says the Swineherd to the Pig. "They do say that there is nothing but pearls and diamonds in rich people's houses, and that there each thing is richer than the rest."

"I assure you they talk nonsense," grunted Kavronya. "I saw no riches at all—nothing but dirt and offal; and yet you may suppose I didn't spare my snout, for I dug up the whole of the back yard."

God forbid I should hurt any one by my comparison; but how can one help calling those critics Kavronyas who, in whatever they have to discuss, have the faculty of seeing only that which is bad?

THE DIVISION

CERTAIN HONEST MERCHANTS, WHO HAD THEIR DWELLING AND their counting-house in common, made a heap of money. Having wound up their business, they wish to divide their gains. But how can a division take place without squabbling? They have begun to quarrel about the money and the stock, when suddenly there is a cry that the house is on fire.

"Quick, quick, save the goods and the house!" shouts one of them. "Come along; we will settle our accounts afterwards!"

"Give me another thousand first!" screams a second, "or I will not stir from the spot."

"You have given me two thousand too little!" exclaims a third; "but here are my accounts, all perfectly straight."

"No, no; we protest against such an idea. How, for what, and why, do you claim that?"

Forgetting that the house was on fire, these strange fellows went on squabbling where they were, till they were suffocated by the smoke, and they and their goods were all burnt up together.

THE BAG

AN EMPTY BAG LONG LAY NEGLECTED ON THE GROUND, IN THE corner of an antechamber, the lowest menials of the house often using it as a mat to rub their shoes upon. But suddenly our Bag was turned to honourable account, and filled full of ducats. In an iron-bound coffer it now lies in security. Its master caresses it with his own hand, and takes such care of it that not a breath of wind is able to ruffle it; no fly dares to light upon it. Besides this, the whole town becomes well acquainted with the Bag. If a friend comes to visit its master, he willingly begins to say pleasant things about the Bag. Whenever it is opened, every one smiles sweetly upon it; and whoever sits down by its side is sure to pat it or stroke it affectionately, seeing that it is universally respected.

The Bag begins to be puffed up, to make much of itself, to air its cleverness. It begins to chatter and to give utterance to nonsense, discussing and criticising everything; "This is not so," and "That man is a fool," or "That affair will turn out badly."

Every one gives it his entire attention, listening with open mouth, although it talks nonsense enough to make their ears tingle. But, unfortunately, men have this weakness, that they are sure to admire whatever a Bag says, so long as it is full of ducats.

But did the Bag long enjoy honour?—did its reputation for cleverness last, and was it long the object of endearment? Only until its last ducat had been taken out of it; then it was flung out of doors, and nothing more was ever heard of it.

THE INQUISITIVE MAN

"GOOD DAY, DEAR FRIEND; WHERE DO YOU COME FROM?"

"From the Museum, where I have spent three hours. I saw everything they have there, and examined it carefully. So much have I seen to astonish me, that, if you will believe me, I am neither strong enough nor clever enough to give you a full description of it. Upon my word it is a palace of wonders. How rich Nature is in invention! What birds and beasts haven't I seen there! What flies, butterflies, cockroaches, little bits of beetles! —some like emeralds, others like coral. And what tiny cochineal insects! Why, really, some of them are smaller than a pin's head."

"But did you see the elephant? What did you think it looked like? I'll be bound you felt as if you were looking at a mountain."

"Are you quite sure it's there?"

"Quite sure."

"Well, brother, you mustn't be too hard upon me; but, to tell the truth, I didn't notice the elephant."

THE WOLF AND THE MOUSE

A GRISLY WOLF CARRIED OFF A SHEEP FROM THE FOLD INTO A retired nook in the forest—not from hospitality, one may well suppose. The glutton tore the skin off the poor sheep, and began devouring it so greedily that the bones cracked under its teeth. But, in spite of its rapacity, it could not eat it all up; so it set aside what remained over for supper, and then, lying down close by it, cuddled itself together at its ease, after the succulent repast.

But, see, the smell of the banquet has attracted its near neighbour, a young Mouse. Between the mossy tufts and hillocks it has crept, has seized a morsel of meat, and has run off quickly to its home in a hollow tree. Perceiving the theft, our Wolf begins to howl through the forest, crying; "Police! Robbery! Stop thief! I'm ruined! I've been robbed of everything I possessed!"

Just such an occurrence did I witness in the town. A thief stole a watch from Clement, the judge; and the judge shouted after the thief, "Police, police!"

THE ELEPHANT IN FAVOUR

ONCE UPON A TIME, THE ELEPHANT STOOD HIGH IN THE GOOD graces of the Lion. The forest immediately began to talk about the matter, and, as usual, many guesses were made as to the means by which the Elephant had gained such favour.

"It is no beauty," say the beasts to each other, "and it is not amusing. And what habits it has! what manners!"

Says the Fox, whisking about his brush; "If it had possessed such a bushy tail as mine, I should not have wondered."

"Or, sister," says the Bear, "if it had got into favour on account of claws, no one would have found the matter at all extraordinary; but it has no claws at all, as we all know well."

"Its tusks must have brought it into favour?" thus the Ox broke in upon their conversation. "Haven't they, perhaps, been mistaken for horns?"

"Is it possible," said the Ass, shaking its ears, "that you don't know how it has succeeded in making itself liked, and in becoming distinguished? Why, I have guessed the reason. If it hadn't been distinguished for its long ears, it never would have got into favour."

THE BEAR AMONG THE BEES

THE BEASTS ELECTED THE BEAR, ONE SPRING, INSPECTOR OF THE Beehives. They might, it is true, have chosen a more trustworthy animal, seeing that the bear is passionately fond of honey. The matter was one to be regretted; but who can expect wisdom from beasts? Every other solicitor for the post of Hive Inspector they sent away with a refusal, and finally, as if by way of pleasantry, the Bear made his appearance in that capacity. But harm soon came of the appointment for our Bear carried off all the honey into his den. The theft was found out, an alarm was sounded, and legal proceedings were taken in due form. Eventually, the Bear was dismissed from his office, and the old rogue was sentenced to lie in his den all the winter.

The Court decided, ratified, and countersigned; but, in spite of all this, it did not return the honey. As for Mishka, he didn't pay the slightest attention to the affair. Bidding the world farewell for a season, he betook himself to his warm den. There he sucks his honeyed paw, and waits till fair weather invites him to a fresh cruise.

THE CROW AND THE HEN

WHEN THE PRINCE OF SMOLENSK, USING SKILL AS A WEAPON against insolence, laid a snare for the modern Vandals, and left them Moscow for their ruin, then all its inhabitants, old and young, assembled together without loss of time, and departed from the city, like a swarm of bees leaving their hive. On all the disquiet which then took place a Crow looked down tranquilly from a housetop, whetting its beak the while.

"What! are not you ready to start, gossip?" cried a Hen to it from a passing cart. "Why, they say the enemy is at our very gates."

"What is that to me?" replied the bird of omen. "I shall remain here quietly. You and your sisters can do as you please. But people don't boil crows, or roast them either; so I shall have no difficulty in living on good terms with the new-comers. It may even happen, perhaps, that I may get some cheese from them, or a stray bone, or something or other. Farewell, my fowl! a happy journey to you."

The Crow really did stay; but, instead of its gaining anything by doing so, when the time came in which the Prince of Smolensk began to starve his guests, it was itself seized by them, and turned into soup.

THE SLANDERER AND THE SNAKE

ON THE OCCASION OF SOME TRIUMPHAL PROCESSION IN THE realms below, the Snake and the Slanderer refused to yield each other precedence, and began a noisy quarrel as to which of the two had the best right to go first.

Now, in the infernal regions, as is well known, he takes precedence who has done most harm to his fellow-creatures. So in this hot and serious dispute, the Slanderer showed his tongue to the Snake; and the Snake boastingly talked to the Slanderer about its sting, hissed out that it was unable to put up with an affront, and strove hard to crawl past him. The Slanderer actually found himself being left behind. But Beelzebub could not allow this;

he himself took the Slanderer's part, and drove the Snake back, saying,

"Although I recognise your merit, yet I justly assign precedence to him. You are excessively venomous, and dangerous in the extreme to everything which is near you; your sting is fatal, and you sting—which is no small merit—without provocation. But can you wound from afar, like the deadly tongue of the Slanderer, from whom there is no escape, even though mountains or oceans intervene? It is clear, then, that he is more deadly than you; so give place to him, and in future behave more quietly."

Since that time, Slanderers have been honoured more than Snakes in hell.

THE MILLER

THE WATER BEGAN TO DRIBBLE AWAY THROUGH A MILLER'S DAM. At first there would have been no great harm done, if he had taken the matter in hand. But why should he? Our Miller does not think of troubling himself. The leak becomes worse every day, and the water pours out as if from a tap.

"Hallo, Miller! don't stand gaping there! It's time you should set your wits to work."

But the Miller says; "Harm's a long way off. I don't require an ocean of water, and my mill is rich enough in it for all time."

He sleeps; but meantime the water goes on running in torrents. And see! harm is here now in full force. The millstone stands still; the mill will not work. Our Miller bestirs himself, groans, troubles himself, and thinks how he can keep the waters back. While he is here on the dam, examining the leak, he observes his fowls coming to drink at the river.

"You stupid, good-for-nothing birds!" he cries. "I don't know where I'm to get water, even when you are out of the question; and here you come and drink the little that remains."

So he begins pelting them with faggots. What good did he do by this? Without a fowl left, or a drop of water, he went back home.

THE ASS AND THE PEASANT

A PEASANT, WHO HAD HIRED AN ASS FOR HIS GARDEN DURING THE summer, set it to drive away the impudent race of crows and of sparrows. The Ass was one of a most honest character, utterly unacquainted with either rapacity or theft. It never profited by a single leaf belonging to its master, and it would indeed be a sin to say that it connived at the proceedings of the birds. Still the Peasant got but little good out of his garden. The Ass, as it chased the birds with all its might, galloped across all the beds, backwards and forwards, in such a manner that it trod underfoot and trampled in pieces everything that grew in the garden.

Seeing then that all his pains were thrown away, the Peasant took a cudgel and revenged himself for his loss on the back of the Ass. "No wonder!" says every one; "serve the beast right! Was it for a creature of its parts to undertake such a business?"

But I say—though not with the intention of defending the Ass; it was certainly in fault, and it has already paid the penalty—surely he also was to blame who set the Ass to guard his garden.

THE COMB

A LOVING MOTHER BOUGHT A GOOD STRONG COMB TO KEEP HER boy's hair in order. The child never let his new present go out of his hands. Whether playing or learning his alphabet, he was always lovingly passing his Comb through the twining curls of his waving golden hair, soft as fine flax. And what a Comb it was! Not only did it not pull out his hair, but it never even got caught in it; so smoothly and easily did it glide through his locks. It was a priceless Comb in the eyes of the child. But at last it happened, one day, that the Comb was mislaid. Our boy went playing and romping about, until he got his hair into a regular tangle. Scarcely had the nurse touched it, when he began to howl,

"Where is my Comb?"

At last it was found; but when they tried to pass it through his locks, it could not be moved either backwards or forwards: all it did was to pull his hairs out by the roots, so as to bring the tears into his eyes.

"How wicked you are, you bad Comb!" cries the boy.

But the Comb replies; "My dear, I am what I always was; only your hair has become tangled."

Whereupon our young friend, giving way to rage and vexation, flings his Comb into the river. And now the Naiads comb their hair with it.

THE LANDLORD AND THE MICE

A CERTAIN MERCHANT BUILT A WARE-HOUSE, IN WHICH HE stored away his stock of edibles; and, in order that the mice should not damage them, he instituted a police of cats. And now the Merchant lives in peace. His stores are patrolled day and night, and all goes well. Unfortunately, an unexpected contingency occurs. One of the guardians proves himself a thief. Among cats, as with us (who knows it not?), the police are not faultless. But then, instead of detecting and punishing the thief, and sparing the honest servant, our landlord orders all his cats to be whipped.

As soon as they hear this ingenious sentence, honest and guilty alike, they all run out of the house as quickly as possible; our landlord remains catless. This is just what the mice have been hoping and longing for. They enter the stores as soon as the cats have left, and in two or three weeks they contrive to eat up the whole of their contents.

THE CUCKOO AND THE COCK

"HOW PROUDLY AND SONOROUSLY YOU SING, MY DEAR COCK!"

"But you, dear Cuckoo, my light, how smoothly flows your long-drawn-out note! There is no such singer in all the rest of our forest."

·"To you, my dear gossip, I could listen for ever."

"And as for you, my beauty, I swear that, when you are silent, I scarcely know how to wait till you begin again. Where do you get such a voice from?—so clear, so soft, and so high! But no doubt you were always like that; not very large in stature, but in song—a regular nightingale."

"Thanks, gossip. As for you, I declare, on my conscience, you sing better than the birds in the garden of Eden. For a proof of this, I appeal to public opinion."

At this moment a Sparrow, which had overheard their conversation, said to them,

"You may go on praising one another till you are hoarse, my friends; but your music is utterly worthless."

Why was it that, not being afraid to sin, the Cuckoo praised the Cock? Simply because the Cock praised the Cuckoo.

THE MERCHANT

"COME HERE, ANDREW, MY BROTHER! WHERE HAVE YOU GOT to? Come here, quickly, and admire your uncle's doings. Deal as I do, and you'll never suffer loss." Thus in his shop spoke a Merchant to his nephew. "You know that remnant of Polish cloth—the one we have had on our hands so long, because it was old, and damp, and rotten? Well, I've just passed it off for English. Here is a hundred-rouble note I have just this instant got for it. Heaven must have sent a fool this way."

"Just so, uncle, just so," replied the nephew. "Only, I'm not quite so sure as to which was the fool. Just look here; you'll see you've taken a forged note."

To cheat!—the Merchant cheated: there's nothing wonderful in that. But if one looks around in the world a little higher than where the shops are, one sees that even there people go on in the self-same manner. Almost all of them are occupied in everything by the same calculation; and that is; "How can one man best succeed in cheating another?"

THE PEASANT AND THE LABOURER

AN OLD PEASANT AND A LABOURER WERE GOING HOME THROUGH the forest to the village one evening, in the time of the hay-harvest, when they suddenly found themselves face to face with a bear. Scarcely had the Peasant time to utter a cry when the bear was upon him; it threw him down, rolled him over, made his bones crack again, and began looking about for a soft spot at which to commence its meal. Death draws near to the old man.

"Stefan, my kinsman, my dear friend, do not desert me!" he cries, from under the bear, to the Labourer.

Then Stefan, putting forth all his strength like a new Hercules, splits the bear's head in two with his axe, and drives his pitchfork into its bowels. The bear howls, and falls dying. Our bear expires.

The danger having vanished, the Peasant gets up, and soundly scolds the Labourer. Our poor Stefan is astounded.

"Pardon me, what have I done?"

"What have you done, you blockhead? I'd like to know what you are so absurdly pleased about; why, you've gone and stuck the bear in such a manner that you've utterly ruined his fur!"

THE MONKEY AND THE SPECTACLES

A MONKEY BECAME WEAK-SIGHTED IN OLD AGE. NOW IT HAD heard men say that this misfortune was one of no great importance; only one must provide oneself with glasses. So it gets half-a-dozen pairs of spectacles, turns them now this way and now that, puts them on the top of its head, applies them to its tail, smells them, licks them; still the spectacles have no effect at all on its sight.

"Good lack!" it cries, "what fools they be who listen to all the nonsense men utter! They've told me nothing but lies about the spectacles. There isn't an atom of good in them."

Here the Monkey, in its vexation and annoyance, flung them

down on a stone so violently that they were utterly broken to bits.

Unfortunately, men behave in the same way. However useful a thing may be, an ignorant man, who knows nothing about its value, is sure to speak ill of it, and, if he possesses any influence, he persecutes it too.

JONATHAN

BIRCH

England 1783 -- 1847

THE TWO FLIES

"MOTHER," SAID A YOUNG FLY IN GREAT AGITATION, "YOU CER-tainly are in error about the *beauty* of these persons who are so affronted with us whenever we touch them. I but just now set-tled on the cheek of a lady of high fashion which appeared to be smooth and natural: but Lord! dear Mother, I thought I should never get back to you again, for I stuck in this filthy red mud; and, with the greatest difficulty I got away: only look at my feet and legs! If they thought themselves so handsome as you say they do, I'm sure they would never cover their faces with such stuff as this!"

THE LADY AND THE MONKEY

A LITTLE MONKEY, THE FAVOURITE OF AN ANTIQUATED LADY, had often watched the process of the toilet-table, and heard with surprise the self-gratulations of his mistress when "made up" for the drawing-room. One evening, knowing that his patroness was invited to a large party, he determined to be more than usually at-tentive to her proceedings: when, her ladyship having, in her own opinion, been quite killingly successful in blending the lily and the rose, she thus rapturously soliloquized; "In truth I was never more captivating in my life!   Surely I shall make an impression on the young warrior to-night."   Then, giving her eyebrows a final touch: "He *must* surrender."   "No, he won't," said Pug. "What means the saucebox?" said the angered fair.   "Why, my dear mistress," replied he, "when you read or write, you put on spectacles to assist your eyes; and when you scrutinize the labours of your milliner you use them: but I have remarked that you never require their help when you look in the 'mirror.'   Put them on *now*, and you will at once perceive what the young warrior *has long since discovered*."

Poor Pug had the fan broken about his unlucky head, and was disposed of to the first showman that passed by.

THE HOG AND THE GOAT

"GOOD MORNING TO YE!" SAID A GOAT SARCASTICALLY TO AN enormous hog destined by the farmer to obtain the "prize," and whom he had known when only a curly-tailed grunter.

"Methinks, our master is killing you with kindness; surely you cannot feel comfortable under so great a load of flesh and fat: are you not dreadfully troubled with dyspepsia?"

"I am," replied he.

"If so," said the goat, "then tell me, thou beautiful piece of rotundity, what, being so circumstanced, can induce you to go on thus gluttonizing!"

"Am I not admired, you fool?" grunted the hog.

THE BEE, THE SPIDER, AND THE TOMTIT

A TOMTIT, WHO HAD LISTENED FOR SOME CONSIDERABLE TIME to a conversation between a Spider and a Bee, relative to the skill and mathematical knowledge displayed in the construction of their web and comb, fancied he could take a part, in equally erudite terms: so down he flew, thinking to silence and astonish them by discussing the superior merits of his nest. "I have overheard you," said he, "disputing a length of time about the lines and proportions of your worthless webs and combs, without so much as once mentioning my inimitable habitation. What are *they* when compared with the delicate skill, just assortment of material, and glowing warmth displayed in the fabrication of *my* nest? There you have *Mathematics,* if you please!"

The Spider and Bee stared with astonishment, and at length burst very unceremoniously into a laugh, which so nettled the Tomtit that he quickly took to his tree again.

THE THISTLE AND THE WHEAT

"WHAT AN UNARMED, PUSILLANIMOUS, HUMBLE BEING ART thou!"—said a Thistle to a blade of Wheat—"without a weapon to repulse an enemy, and contented to keep the benefit of thy acquirements within a circumscribed space. Why dost thou not make a bustle in the world, as I do, keeping every one at bay, and when I choose disseminating my opinions East, West, North, and South?"

"I am not," replied the Wheat, "aware of having any enemies, and therefore need no weapon of defence. If I possess cultivated abilities, I am satisfied to comfort and instruct my immediate neighbourhood therewith, and my instructions are received cordially. *Thou* needest not to pride thyself on spreading afar thy opinions, since thy neighbours wish not for them; and, for my own part, I am inclined to believe that, wherever thy wild doctrines take root, they invariably prove a curse!"

THE LADY AND THE VIOLET

A LADY WAS PROMENADING IN HER GARDEN ON A FINE SPRING day, and just as she passed a Sweetbriar which had not yet put forth its perfumed leaves, she unexpectedly inhaled a fragrance for which she could not account: astonished and delighted, she searched, but searched in vain for the cause; at last, addressing the Briar, "Tell me," said she, "from whence proceeds this fragrance, so far surpassing that of the exotic inmates of my greenhouse, in order that I may select and cherish the plant in a manner commensurate with its worth!"

"Madam," replied the Briar, "the source of your pleasurable surprise is the insignificant-looking plant that but yesterday unsuccessfully solicited your protection. It, like myself, is a humble native of your own country. Alas! fair Lady, your notice and your kind intentions come too late! you have slighted it, because of its rusticity, and have placed your foot on the unassuming plant: you have crushed its sweet flower and destroyed it for ever!"

THE MONKEY AND THE WASP

A MONKEY, WHILST MUNCHING A RIPE PEAR, WAS PESTERED BY the bare-faced importunities of a Wasp, who, *nolens volens,* would have a part. After threatening the Monkey with his anger if he further hesitated to submit to his demand, he settled on the fruit; but was as soon knocked off by the Monkey.

The irritable Wasp now had recourse to invective,—and, after using the most insulting language, which the other calmly listened to, he so worked himself up into violent passion that, losing all consideration of the penalty, he flew to the face of the Monkey, and stung him with such rage that he was unable to extricate his weapon, and was compelled to tear himself away, leaving it in the wound—thus entailing on himself a lingering death, accompanied by pains much greater than those he had inflicted.

RALPH WALDO

EMERSON

America 1803 -- 1882

FABLE

THE MOUNTAIN AND THE SQUIRREL
Had a quarrel,
And the former called the latter "Little Prig";
Bun replied,
"You are doubtless very big;
But all sorts of things and weather
Must be taken in together,
To make up a year
And a sphere.
And I think it no disgrace
To occupy my place.
If I'm not so large as you,
You are not so small as I,
And not half so spry.
I'll not deny you make
A very pretty squirrel track;
Talents differ; all is well and wisely put;
If I cannot carry forests on my back,
Neither can you crack a nut."

LEO NIKOLAIEVICH

TOLSTOI

Russia 1828 -- 1910

THE FOOL AND HIS KNIFE

A FOOL HAD AN EXCELLENT KNIFE. WITH THIS KNIFE THE fool tried to cut a nail. The knife would not cut the nail.

Then the fool said; "My knife is mean," and he tried to cut some soft jelly with his knife. Wherever the knife went through the jelly the liquid closed together again.

The fool said, "Miserable knife! it won't cut jelly either," and he threw away his good knife.

THE TSAR AND THE FALCON

A TSAR, WHILE OUT HUNTING, UNLEASED HIS FAVORITE FALCON at a hare, and galloped after it.

The Falcon caught the hare. The Tsar took away the hare, and started to seek for some water to quench his thirst. The Tsar found the water on a hillside. But it trickled out, a drop at a time. So the Tsar drew his cup from the holster, and placed it under the water. The water trickled into the cup, and when the cup was full, the Tsar put it to his mouth, and was about to drink. Suddenly the Falcon fluttered down upon the Tsar's hand, flapped his wings, and spilled the water.

Again the Tsar placed the cup under the spring. He waited long, until it was filled brimming full, and again, when he lifted it to his lips, the Falcon flew upon his wrist and spilled the water.

When for the third time the Tsar managed to get his cup filled, and was lifting it to his lips, the Falcon again spilled it.

The Tsar grew wroth, and struck the Falcon with all his might with a stone, and killed him.

Then came the Tsar's servants, and one of them ran up to the head of the spring in order to find a more plentiful supply of water and came back quickly with a full cup.

But the servant brought no water back; he returned with an empty cup, and said; "The water is not fit to drink; there is a serpent in the spring, and it has poisoned all the water. It is a good thing that the Falcon spilt it. If you had drunk of the water, you would have perished."

The Tsar said; "Foully have I recompensed the Falcon; he saved my life, and I killed him for it."

THE HERON, THE FISHES, AND THE CRAB

A HERON LIVED BY A POND, AND WAS BEGINNING TO GROW OLD. She was no longer strong enough to catch fish. So she began to plan how she might contrive to get a living. And she said to the Fishes; "Fishes, you have not the least idea what misfortune is threatening you. I have heard some men say that they are going to drain the pond, and catch all of you. I happen to know that beyond this mountain is a nice little pond. I would help you to get there; but I am now in years; it is hard for me to fly."

The Fishes began to beseech the Heron to help them. The Heron replied; "I will do my best for you, I will carry you over; but I cannot do it all at once, only one at a time."

And so the Fishes were delighted; they all said; "Carry me! carry me!"

And the Heron began to carry them; she would take up one

at a time, carry him off to a field, and feast on him. In this way she ate up many fishes. Now there lived in the pond an aged Crab. When the Heron began to carry off the Fishes, he suspected the true state of affairs; and he said; "Well, now, Heron, take me also to your new settlement."

The Heron seized the Crab, and flew off with him. As soon as she reached the field, she was going to drop the Crab. But the Crab, seeing the bones of the Fishes on the field, clasped his claws around the Heron's neck, and strangled her; and then he crawled back to the pond and told the Fishes.

THE VERY BEST PEARS

A GENTLEMAN SENT HIS SERVANT TO BUY THE VERY BEST PEARS. The servant went to the shop, and asked for pears.

The merchant gave them to him; but the servant said; "No; give me your very best pears."

The merchant said; "Taste one; you will find that they are delicious."

"How can I know," exclaimed the servant, "that they are all delicious, if I taste only one?"

So he bit a little bit of each pear, and took them to his master. Then his master dismissed him.

THE QUAIL AND HIS MATE

A QUAIL HAD BEEN LATE IN BUILDING HIS NEST IN A MEADOW; and when haying-time came, his Mate was still sitting on her eggs.

Early in the morning the peasants came to the meadow, took off their caftans, whetted their scythes, and went, one after the other, cutting the grass and laying it in windrows.

The Quail flew up to see what the mowers were doing. When

he saw that one peasant was swinging his scythe and had just cut a snake in two, he was rejoiced, flew back to his Mate, and said; "Don't be afraid of the peasants; they have come out to kill our snakes; for a long time there has been no living on account of them."

But his Mate said; "The peasants are cutting grass; and with the grass they cut everything that comes in their way,—either a snake or a quail's nest. I am sick at heart, for I cannot either carry away my eggs, or leave my nest lest they get cold."

When the mowers reached the quail's nest, one peasant swung his scythe and cut off the mother-bird's head; but he put the eggs in his pocket, and gave them to his children to play with.

THE LOAD

AFTER THE FRENCH HAD LEFT MOSCOW, TWO PEASANTS WENT out to search for treasures. One was wise, the other stupid. They went together to the burnt part of the city, and found some scorched wool. They said, "That will be useful at home."

They gathered up as much as they could carry, and started home with it. On the way they saw lying in the street a lot of cloth. The wise peasant threw down the wool, seized as much of the cloth as he could carry, and put it on his shoulders. The stupid one said; "Why throw away the wool? It is nicely tied up, and nicely fastened on." And so he did not take any of the cloth.

They went farther, and saw lying in the street some ready-made clothes that had been thrown away. The wise peasant unloaded the cloth, picked up the clothes, and put them on his shoulders. The stupid one said; "Why should I throw away the wool? It is nicely tied up and securely fastened on my back."

They went on their way, and saw silver plate scattered about. The wise peasant threw down the clothes, and gathered up as much of the silver as he could, and started off with it; but the stupid one did not give up his wool, because it was nicely tied up and securely tied on.

Going still farther, they saw gold lying on the road. The wise peasant threw down his silver and picked up the gold; but the stupid one said; "What is the good of taking off the wool? It is nicely tied up and securely fastened to my back."

And they went home. On the way a rain set in, and the wool became water-soaked, so that the stupid man had to throw it away, and thus reached home empty-handed; but the wise peasant kept his gold and became rich.

THE JACKALS AND THE ELEPHANT

THE JACKALS HAD EATEN ALL THE DEAD BEASTS IN THE FOREST, and there was nothing left for them to devour. Now there was an aged Jackal, and he devised a plan to get food. He went to the Elephant, and said; "We used to have a tsar, but he became spoiled; he would lay such tasks on us that it was impossible to do them; we wish to elect another tsar; and my people have sent me to beg you to become our tsar. We live well; whatever you wish, that we will do, and we will honor you in all respects. Come, let us go to our empire."

The Elephant consented, and followed the Jackal. The Jackal led him into a bog. When the Elephant began to sink, the Jackal said; "Now order whatever you desire, and we will do it."

The Elephant said; "I command you to pull me out of here."

The Jackal laughed, and said; "Seize my tail with your trunk, and I will instantly pull you out."

The Elephant replied; "Can you pull me out with your tail?"

But the Jackal demanded; "Why, then, did you order anything that was impossible to do? We drove away our first tsar for the very reason that he laid impossible commands on us!"

When the Elephant had perished in the swamp, the Jackals came and ate him up.

THE BIG OVEN

ONCE UPON A TIME A MAN HAD A BIG HOUSE, AND IN THE house there was a big oven; but this man's family was small—only himself and his wife.

When winter came, the man tried to keep his oven going; and in one month he burnt up all his firewood. He had nothing to feed the fire, and it was cold.

Then the man began to break up his fences, and use the boards for fuel. When he had burnt up all of his fences, the house, now without any protection against the wind, was colder than ever, and still they had no firewood.

Then the man began to tear down the ceiling of his house, and burn that in the oven. A neighbor noticed that he was tearing down his ceiling, and said to him; "Why, neighbor, have you lost your mind?—pulling down your ceiling in winter! You and your wife will freeze to death!"

But the man said; "No, brother; you see I am pulling down my ceiling so as to have something to heat my oven with. We have such a curious one; the more I heat it up, the colder we are!"

The neighbor laughed, and said; "Well, then, after you have burnt up your ceiling, then you will be tearing down your house. You won't have anywhere to live; only the oven will be left, and even that will be cold!"

"Well, that is my misfortune," said the man. "All my neighbors have firewood enough for all winter; but I have already burnt up my fences and the ceiling of my house, and have nothing left."

The neighbor replied; "All you need is to have your oven rebuilt."

But the man said; "I know well that you are jealous of my house and my oven because they are larger than yours, and so you advise me to rebuild it."

And he turned a deaf ear to his neighbor's advice, and burnt up his ceiling, and burnt up his whole house, and in the end had to go and live with strangers.

THE ASS AND THE LION

ONCE UPON A TIME A LION WENT OUT TO HUNT, AND HE TOOK with him an Ass. And he said to him; "Ass, now you go into the woods, and roar as loud as you can; you have a capacious throat. The prey that run away from your roaring will fall into my clutches."

And so he did. The Ass brayed, and the timid creatures of the wood fled in all directions, and the Lion caught them.

After the hunting was over, the Lion said to the Ass; "Now I will praise you. You roared splendidly."

And since that time the Ass is always braying, and always expects to be praised.

THE FOX'S BRUSH

A MAN MET A FOX, AND ASKED HER; "WHO TAUGHT YOU FOXES to deceive dogs with your tails?"

The Fox asked; "How do you mean *deceive?* We do not deceive the dogs, but merely run from them with all our might."

The man said; "No; you deceive them with your brushes.

When the dogs chase you, and are about to seize you, you throw your brushes to one side; the dog makes a sharp turn after it, and then you dash off in another direction."

The Fox laughed, and said; "We do this, not to deceive the dogs, but we only do it so as to dodge; when the dogs chase us, and we see that we cannot run straight, we dodge to one side; and in order that we may dodge to that side, we have to fling our brushes to the other, just as you do the same thing with your hands when you try to turn round when you are running. This is not reason on our part. God Himself thought it out when He made us—for this reason, that the dogs might not catch all the foxes."

TWO PEASANTS

ONCE UPON A TIME TWO PEASANTS ATTEMPTED TO PASS EACH other, and their sledges became entangled. One cried; "Give me room; I must get to town as quickly as possible"; and the other said; "You give me room; I must get home as quickly as possible."

Thus for a long time they disputed. A third peasant saw it, and said; "If you are in such a hurry, then each of you give way a little."

THE OAK AND THE HAZEL BUSH

AN ANCIENT OAK LET DROP AN ACORN ON A HAZEL BUSH. THE Hazel Bush said to the Oak; "Have you, then, so little room under your branches? You might drop your acorns on a clear space. Here I myself have scarcely room for my branches; I don't throw my nuts away, though, but I give them to men."

"I live two hundred years," replied the Oak; "and the little oak that will come up from the acorn will live as many more."

Then the Hazel Bush grew angry, and said; "Then I will choke off your little oak, and it will not live three days."

The Oak made no reply to this, but told his little son to come forth from the acorn.

The acorn grew moist, burst open, and the rootlet caught hold of the earth with its little hooks, and another sprout was sent up above.

The Hazel Bush tried to choke it, and would not give it the sun. But the little Oak stretched up into the air, and waxed strong in the Hazel Bush's shadow.

A hundred years passed away. The Hazel Bush had long ago died away; and the Oak had grown from the acorn as high as heaven, and spread its tent on every side.

THE MOUSE AND THE FROG

A MOUSE WENT TO VISIT A FROG. THE FROG MET THE MOUSE on the bank, and urged him to visit his chamber under the water. The Mouse climbed down to the water's edge, took a taste of it, and then climbed back again.

"Never," said he, "will I make visits to people of alien race."

THE AX AND THE SAW

TWO PEASANTS WERE GOING TO THE FOREST AFTER WOOD. ONE had an ax and the other had a saw. After they had selected a tree they began to dispute.

One said it was better to chop down the tree, and the other said it ought to be sawed.

A third peasant said; "I will settle the question for you in a moment: if the ax is sharp, then it is better to chop; but if the saw is sharper, then it is better to saw."

He took the ax and began to chop the tree. But the ax was

dull, so that it was impossible for him to cut.   He took the saw;
the saw was wretched, and would not cut at all.   Then he said;
"Don't be in haste to quarrel; the ax does not chop, and the saw
does not cut.   Sharpen your ax and file your saw, and then quarrel
as much as you wish."

The two peasants, however, became even more angry with
each other than before, because the one had a blunted ax, the
other had an ill-set saw; and they fell to blows.

THE MOUSE UNDER THE GRANARY

A MOUSE LIVED UNDER A GRANARY.   IN THE GRANARY FLOOR
was a little hole and the grain slipped down through the hole.
The Mouse's life was happy, but the desire came over her to make
a show of her life.   She gnawed a larger hole, and invited other
Mice.

"Come," said she, "and have a feast; there will be food enough
for all."

But after she had brought the Mice, she discovered that there
was no hole at all.   The farmer had noticed the big hole in the
floor, and closed it up.

THE TWO HORSES

TWO HORSES WERE CARRYING TWO LOADS.   THE FRONT HORSE
went well, but the rear Horse was lazy.   The men began to pile
the rear Horse's load on the front Horse; when they had transferred it all, the rear Horse found it easy going, and he said to the
front Horse; "Toil and sweat!   The more you try, the more
you have to suffer."

When they reached the tavern, the owner said; "Why should
I fodder two horses when I carry all on one?   I had better give
the one all the food it wants, and cut the throat of the other; at
least I shall have the hide."   And so he did.

THE MONKEY

A MAN WENT INTO THE WOODS. HE FELLED A TREE, AND BE-
gan to cut it in pieces. He lifted the end of the tree on the
stump, sat astride upon it, and began to saw. Then he drove a
wedge into the cleft, and began to saw farther along; then he removed the wedge, and put it in the new place.

A Monkey was sitting on a tree, watching him.

When the man lay down to sleep, the Monkey got astride of
the tree and began to saw; but when he took out the wedge, the
tree closed together again, and nipped his tail. He began to
struggle and squeal.

The man awoke, knocked the Monkey down, and tied him
with a rope.

THE TSAR AND THE ELEPHANTS

AN INDIAN TSAR COMMANDED TO GATHER TOGETHER ALL THE
blind men, and when they were collected, he commanded to
show them his Elephants. The blind men went to the stables,
and began to feel of the Elephants.

One felt of the leg; another, of the tail; a third, of the rump; a
fourth, of the belly; a fifth, of the back; a sixth, of the ears; a
seventh, of the tusks; an eighth, of the trunk.

The Tsar called the blind men to him, and asked them; "What are my Elephants like?"

And one blind man said; "Thy Elephants are like pillars." This blind man had felt of the legs.

The second blind man said; "They are like brooms." This one had felt of the tail.

The third said; "They are like wood." This one had felt of the rump.

The one who had felt of the belly said; "Elephants are like lumps of earth."

The one who had felt of the side said; "They are a wall."

The one who had felt of the back said; "They are like a hill."

The one who had felt of the ears said; "They are like a handkerchief."

The one who had felt of the head said; "They are like a mortar."

The one who had felt of the tusks said; "They are like horns."

The one who had felt of the trunk said; "They are like a stout rope."

And all the blind men began to dispute and quarrel.

THE MONKEY AND THE PEAS

A MONKEY WAS CARRYING TWO HANDFULS OF PEAS. ONE LITTLE pea dropped out. He tried to pick it up, and spilt twenty. He tried to pick up the twenty, and spilt them all. Then he lost his temper, scattered the peas in all directions, and ran away.

THE SETTING HEN AND THE CHICKENS

A BROOD HEN HATCHED OUT SOME CHICKENS, AND DID NOT know how to take care of them. And so she said to them; "Creep into the shell again; when you are in the shell, I will sit on you, as I used to sit on you, and I will take care of you."

The Chickens obeyed their mother, tried to creep into the shell; but they found it perfectly impossible to get into it again, and they only broke their wings.

Then one of the Chickens said to his mother; "If we were to remain always in the shell, it would have been better if you had not let us out of it."

THE DOGS AND THE COOK

A COOK WAS PREPARING DINNER; SOME DOGS WERE LYING AT THE kitchen door. The cook killed a calf, and threw the insides into the yard.

The dogs seized them, ate them up, and said; "The cook is good; he knows how to cook well."

After a little the cook began to clean turnips and onions, and he threw away the outsides. The dogs ran up to them, turned up their noses, and said; "Our cook is spoiled; he used to make good things, but now he is worthless."

But the cook did not hear the dogs, and cooked the dinner in his usual way. The people of the house, however, ate up the dinner and praised it, if the dogs did not.

THE WOLF AND THE BOW

A HUNTSMAN WITH HIS BOW AND ARROWS WENT OUT TO HUNT; he killed a goat, flung it over his shoulders, and was carrying it home. On the way he saw a wild boar. The Huntsman dropped the goat, shot the boar, and wounded him. The boar rushed upon the Huntsman, gored him to death with his tusks, and then himself died.

A Wolf smelled the blood, and came to the place where were lying the goat, the boar, the man and his bow. The Wolf was overjoyed, and said to himself, "Now I shall have enough to eat for a long time; but I am not going to eat it all up at once; I will eat a little at a time, so that none of it may be wasted. First I will eat the hardest part, and then I will feast on the softest and daintiest."

The Wolf sniffed the goat, the boar, and the man, and he said; "This food is soft, I will eat this afterward; but first of all I will eat the tendon on this bow."

And he began to gnaw at the tendon on the bow. When he had bitten through the bowstring, the bow sprang and hit the Wolf in the belly. And the Wolf also perished, and the other wolves came and ate up the man, and the goat, and the boar, and the Wolf.

LIFE DULL WITHOUT SONG

IN THE UPPER PART OF A HOUSE LIVED A RICH BARON, AND ON the floor below lived a poor tailor. The tailor was always singing songs at his work, and prevented the baron from sleeping.

The baron gave the tailor a purse full of money not to sing. The tailor became rich, and took good care of his money, and refrained from singing.

But it grew tiresome to him; he took the money and returned it to the baron, saying; "Take back your money and let me sing my songs again, or I shall die of melancholy."

THE WOLF IN THE DUST

A WOLF WAS ANXIOUS TO STEAL A SHEEP FROM THE FLOCK AND went to the leeward, so that the dust from the flock might cover him. The Shepherd Dog saw him and said; "It's no use, Wolf, for you to go in the dust; it will spoil your eyes."

But the Wolf replied: "It is very unfortunate, Doggy, my eyes were spoiled long ago, but they say that the dust from a flock of sheep is an excellent remedy for the eyes."

THE PEASANT AND THE HORSE

A PEASANT WENT TO TOWN TO GET OATS FOR HIS HORSE. AS soon as he got out of the village, the Horse wanted to return home. The Peasant lashed the Horse with his whip.

The horse started up, but in regard to the Peasant it thought; "The fool! Where is he driving me? We should be better off at home."

Before they reached the city the Peasant noticed that the mud made the going hard for the Horse, so he turned him upon the wood-block pavement; but the Horse refused to go upon the pavement.

The Peasant lashed the Horse again, and twitched at the reins. The animal turned off upon the pavement, and said to himself; "Why did he turn me off upon the pavement; it only breaks my hoofs. It is hard here under my feet."

The Peasant drove up to the shop, bought his oats, and went home. When he reached home he gave the Horse the oats. The Horse began to eat, and said to himself; "What stupid things men are! They only love to show their mastery over us, but their intelligence is less than ours. Why did he take so much trouble to-day? Where did he go and drive me? We had no sooner got there than we returned home. It would have been better for both of us if we had stayed at home in the first place. He would have sat by the oven, and I should have been eating oats."

THE MILCH COW

A MAN HAD A COW; EVERY DAY SHE GAVE A PAIL OF MILK. THE man invited some guests. In order to get more milk he did not milk the Cow for ten days.

He thought that on the tenth day the Cow would give him ten pails of milk. But the Cow's milk had dried up, and she gave less milk than ever before.

UNCLE MITYA'S HORSE

UNCLE MITYA HAD A VERY FINE BAY HORSE. SOME THIEVES heard about the bay horse, and laid their plans to steal it. They came after it was dark, and crept into the yard.

Now it happened that a peasant who had a bear with him came to spend the night at Uncle Mitya's. Uncle Mitya took the peasant into the cottage, let out the bay horse into the yard, and put the bear into the inclosure where the bay horse was.

The thieves came in the dark into the inclosure, and began to grope around. The bear got on his hind legs, and seized one of the thieves, who was so frightened that he bawled with all his might.

Uncle Mitya came out and caught the thieves.

THE BIRDS IN THE SNARE

A HUNTSMAN SET A SNARE BY A LAKE. MANY BIRDS WERE caught in it. The birds were large; they seized the snare, and flew off with it.

The Huntsman began to run after the birds. A peasant saw him running after them, and he said; "Where are you going? Can you catch birds on foot?"

The Huntsman replied; "If there were only one bird, I should not catch him; but as it is, I shall bag my game."

And so it proved. When evening came, the birds each tried to fly off in his own direction; one to the forest, another to the swamp, a third to the field, and all fell with the net to the ground, and the Huntsman captured them.

THE WATER-SPRITE AND THE PEARL

A MAN WAS SAILING IN A BOAT, AND DROPPED A PRECIOUS PEARL into the sea. The man returned to land, and took a pail, and began to scoop up the water and pour it on the shore. For three days unweariedly he scooped and poured.

On the fourth day a Water-sprite came up out of the water, and asked; "Why are you scooping?"

The man replied; "I am scooping because I have lost a pearl."

The Water-sprite asked; "Are you going to stop before long?"

The man replied; "When I have scooped the sea dry, then I shall stop."

Then the Water-sprite returned into the depths, and brought up the very same pearl, and gave it to the man.

THE VAINGLORIOUS COCKEREL

TWO COCKERELS FOUGHT ON A DUNGHEAP. ONE COCKEREL was the stronger: he vanquished the other and drove him from the dungheap.

All the Hens gathered around the Cockerel, and began to laud him. The Cockerel wanted his strength and glory to be known in the next yard. He flew on top of the barn, flapped his wings, and crowed in a loud voice; "Look at me, all of you. I am a victorious Cockerel. No other Cockerel in the world has such strength as I."

The Cockerel had not finished, when an Eagle killed him, seized him in his claws, and carried him to his nest.

THE HARE AND THE HOUND

A HARE ONCE ASKED A HOUND; "WHY DO YOU BARK WHEN YOU chase us? You would be much more likely to catch us, if you ran without barking. But when you bark, you only drive us into the huntsman's hands; he hears where we are running, and he hastens up, shoots us with his gun, kills us, and does not give you anything."

The Dog replied; "That is not the reason that I bark; I bark simply because I get scent of you; I become excited, or else glad because I am going to catch you immediately; and I myself know not why, but I cannot help barking."

THE EAGLE AND THE SOW

AN EAGLE BUILT A NEST ON A TREE, AND HATCHED OUT SOME eaglets. And a wild Sow brought her litter under the tree. The Eagle used to fly off after her prey, and bring it back to her young. And the Sow rooted around the tree and hunted in the woods, and when night came she would bring her young something to eat.

And the Eagle and the Sow lived in neighborly fashion. And a Grimalkin laid his plans to destroy the eaglets and the little sucking pigs. He went to the Eagle, and said; "Eagle, you had better not fly very far away. Beware of the Sow; she is planning an evil design. She is going to undermine the roots of the tree. You see she is rooting all the time."

Then the Grimalkin went to the Sow and said; "Sow, you have not a good neighbor. Last evening I heard the Eagle saying to her eaglets; 'My dear little eaglets, I am going to treat you to a nice little pig. Just as soon as the Sow is gone, I will bring you a little young sucking pig.'"

From that time the Eagle ceased to fly out after prey, and the Sow did not go any more into the forest. The eaglets and the young pigs perished of starvation, and Grimalkin feasted on them.

THE DIVISION OF THE INHERITANCE

A FATHER HAD TWO SONS. HE SAID TO THEM; "I AM DYING; divide everything equally."

When the father was dead, the sons could not make the division without quarreling. They went to a neighbor to help them decide. And the neighbor asked them what their father had commanded them to do.

They replied; "He commanded us to make equal shares of everything."

Then said the neighbor; "Tear all the raiment in two; break all the utensils in two; cut all the live stock in two."

The brothers took the neighbor's advice, and at the end neither had anything.

THE BLIND MAN AND THE MILK

ONE BLIND FROM BIRTH ASKED A MAN WHO COULD SEE; "WHAT color is milk?"

The man who could see replied; "The color of milk is like white paper."

The blind man asked; "This color, then, rustles in the hands like paper?"

The man who could see replied; "No; it is white, like white flour."

The blind man asked; "Then it is soft and dry like flour, is it?"

The man who could see replied; "No; it is simply white, like a rabbit."

The blind man asked; "Then it is downy and soft like a rabbit, is it?"

The man who could see replied; "No; white is a color exactly like snow."

The blind man asked; "Then it is cold like snow, is it?"

And in spite of all the comparisons which the man who could see made, still the blind man was wholly unable to comprehend what the color of milk really was.

THE BOY DRIVER

A PEASANT WAS RETURNING FROM MARKET WITH HIS SON Vanka. The peasant went to sleep in his cart, and Vanka held the reins and cracked the whip. They happened to meet another team. Vanka shouted; "Turn out to the right! I shall run over you!"

And the peasant with the team said; "It is not a big cricket, but it chirps so as to be heard!"

FINE THREADS

A MAN BADE A SPINNER SPIN FINE THREADS. THE SPINNER spun fine threads; but the man declared that the threads were not good, and that he wished the *very finest* of fine threads.

The spinner said; "If these are not fine enough for you, then here are some others that will suit you."

And she pointed to a bare spot. The man declared that he could not see them.

The spinner replied; "The fact that you cannot see them proves that they are very fine; I can't see them myself."

The fool was rejoiced, and ordered some more of the same thread, and paid down the money for it.

THE FARMER'S WIFE AND THE CAT

A FARMER'S WIFE WAS ANNOYED BY MICE EATING UP THE TALlow in her cellar.   She shut the cat into the cellar, so that the cat might catch the mice.

But the cat ate up, not only the tallow, but the milk and the meat also.

THE FALCON AND THE COCK

A FALCON BECAME TAME, AND WOULD FLY TO HIS MASTER'S HAND whenever he called.   The Cock was afraid of the master, and screamed when he came near him.

And the Falcon said to the Cock; "You Cocks have no sense of gratitude!   What a race of slaves you are!   As soon as you are hungry, you go to your master.   It is a very different thing with us wild birds; we are strong and we can fly faster than all others, and we are not afraid of men; but we go of our own accord and perch on their hands when they call us.   We remember that they have given us food."

And the Cock said; "You do not run away from men, because you never saw a Falcon roasted; but many a time have we seen Cocks roasted!"

THE HEAD AND TAIL OF THE SERPENT

THE SERPENT'S TAIL WAS DISPUTING WITH THE SERPENT'S HEAD as to which should go first.

The Head said: "You cannot go first; you have no eyes or ears."

The Tail replied: "But at all events I have the strength to make you go. If I wanted, I could twine around a tree, and you could not stir."

The Head said: "Let us part company."

And the Tail tore itself free from the Head, and crawled away in its own direction.

But as soon as it had left the Head, it came upon a cranny and fell stupidly into it.

WHY THERE IS EVIL IN THE WORLD

A HERMIT LIVED IN THE FOREST, AND THE ANIMALS WERE NOT afraid of him. He and the wild animals used to talk together, and they understood one another.

Once the Hermit lay down under a tree, and a Raven, a Dove, a Stag, and a Snake came to the same place to sleep. The animals began to reason why evil should exist in the world.

The Raven said; "It is all owing to hunger that there is evil in the world. When we have as much as we wish to eat, we sit by ourselves on the bough and caw, and everything is good and gay, and we are in every respect well off; but some other day we are famished, and everything is quite the opposite, so that we can see no brightness in God's world, and we feel full of unrest; we fly about from place to place, and there is no rest for us. And even if we see some meat afar off, then it becomes still worse; for if we fly down to get it, either sticks and stones are thrown at us, or wolves and dogs chase us, and we are absolutely destroyed. How much trouble comes upon us from hunger! All evil is caused by it."

The Dove said; "In my opinion, evil does not arise from hunger, but it all comes from love. If we only lived alone, we should have little trouble. Wretchedness shared makes one doubly wretched. And so we always live in pairs. And if we love our mates there is no peace for us at all. We are always thinking, 'Has she had enough to eat? is she warm?' And when our mate is away from us anywhere, then we are wholly lost; we cannot help worrying all the time, 'If only the hawk does not carry her off, or men make away with her'; and we ourselves fly off in pursuit of her, and perhaps find the poor thing either in the hawk's claws or in the snare. And if our mate is lost, then there is no more comfort for us. We cannot eat, we cannot drink; we can only fly about and mourn. How many of us have perished in this way! No; evil comes not from hunger, but from love."

The Snake said; "No; evil arises neither from hunger nor from love, but from ill-temper. If we lived peacefully, we should not do so much harm; everything would be delightful for us. But now if anything is done to us, we fall into a rage, and then there is nothing gentle about us; we only think how we can avenge the wrong on some one. We lose control of ourselves and hiss, and try to bite some one. We would not have pity on any one, we would bite our own father and mother! It seems as if we could eat our own selves. The moment we begin to lose our temper we are undone. All the evil in the world arises from ill-temper."

The Stag said; "No; not from ill-temper, and not from love, and not from hunger arises all the evil that is in the world, but evil arises from fear. If it were possible for us to live without fear, all would be well with us. We are swift-footed, and have great strength. With our antlers we can defend ourselves from little animals; and we can run from the large ones. But it is impossible to escape fear. If it is only the twigs creaking in the forest, or the leaves rustling, we are all of a tremble with fear, our heart beats, we instinctively start to run, and fly with all our might. Another time a hare runs by or a bird flutters, or a dry twig crackles, and we think it is a wild beast, and in running away we really run into danger. And again we are running from a dog, and we come upon a man. Oftentimes we are frightened and start to flee, we don't know whither, and we roll over a precipice and perish. And we have to sleep with one eye open, with one ear alert, and we are always in alarm. There is no peace. All evil comes from fear."

Then the Hermit said; "Not from hunger, nor from love, nor from ill-temper, nor from fear come all our troubles; but all the evil that is in the world is due to our different natures. Hence come hunger and love, ill-temper and fear."

THE WOLF AND THE FOX

A WOLF WAS RUNNING FROM THE DOGS, AND WANTED TO HIDE in a cleft. But a Fox was lying in the cleft; she showed her teeth at the Wolf, and said; "You cannot come in here; this is my place."

The Wolf did not stop to dispute the matter, but merely said; "If the dogs were not so near, I would teach you whose place it is; but now the right is on your side."

THE WOLF AND THE HUNTSMEN

A WOLF WAS EATING UP A SHEEP. THE HUNTSMEN DISCOVERED him, and began to beat him.

The Wolf said; "It is not right for you to beat me. It is not my fault that I am grey; God made me so."

But the Huntsmen replied; "We do not beat wolves because they are grey, but because they eat the sheep."

THE DUCK AND THE MOON

A DUCK WAS FLOATING DOWN THE RIVER; SHE HAD BEEN HUNT-ing for a fish, and all day long she had not found one. When night came, she saw the Moon in the water, and thought that it was a fish, and she dived down to catch the Moon.

The other ducks saw this, and began to make sport of her. From that time forth the Duck began to be ashamed and lose courage, so that whenever she saw a fish under the water she would not seize it, and so she died of starvation.

THE COW AND THE GOAT

AN OLD WOMAN HAD A COW AND A GOAT. THE COW AND THE Goat went to pasture together. The Cow always turned around when they came after her. The old woman brought bread and salt, gave it to the Cow, and said; "Now stand still, little mother, na, na, I will bring you some more; only stand still."

On the next evening the Goat returned from the pasture before the Cow, spread his legs, and stood before the old woman. The old woman waved her handkerchief at him, but the Goat stood without moving. He thought that the old woman gave bread to the Cow because she stood still. The old woman perceived that the Goat did not move away; she took her stick and beat him. When the Goat went away, the old woman began to feed the Cow again with grain, and to coax her.

"There is no justice in men," thought the Goat; "I stood stiller than the Cow does, but she beat me."

He ran to one side, hurried back, kicked over the milk-pail, spilled the milk, and knocked over the old woman.

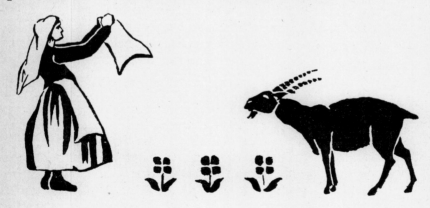

THE SQUIRREL AND THE WOLF

A SQUIRREL WAS LEAPING FROM LIMB TO LIMB, AND FELL DIrectly upon a sleeping Wolf. The Wolf jumped up, and was going to devour him. But the Squirrel begged the Wolf to let him go.

The Wolf said; "All right; I will let you go on condition that you tell me why it is that you squirrels are always so happy. I am always melancholy; but I see you playing and leaping all the time in the trees."

The Squirrel said; "Let me go first, and then I will tell you; but now I am afraid of you."

The Wolf let him go, and the Squirrel leaped up into a tree, and from there it said; "You are melancholy because you are bad. Wickedness consumes your heart. But we are happy because we are good, and do no one any harm."

THE BOOK

TWO MEN TOGETHER FOUND A BOOK IN THE STREET, AND BEGAN to dispute as to the ownership of it.

A third happened along, and asked; "Which of you can read?"

"Neither of us."

"Then why do you want the book? Your quarrel reminds me of two bald men who fought for possession of a comb, when neither had any hair on his head."

AMBROSE
BIERCE

America 1842 -- 19 -- ?

MAN AND BIRD

A MAN WITH A SHOTGUN SAID TO A BIRD; "IT IS ALL NONSENSE, you know, about shooting being a cruel sport. I put my skill against your cunning—that is all there is to it. It is a fair game."

"True," said the Bird, "but I don't wish to play."

"Why not?" inquired the Man with a Shotgun.

"The game," the Bird replied, "is fair as you say; the chances are about even; but consider the stake. I am in it for you, but what is there in it for me?"

Not being prepared with an answer to the question, the Man with a Shotgun sagaciously removed the propounder.

THE MIRROR

A SILKEN-EARED SPANIEL WHO TRACED HIS DESCENT FROM KING Charles the Second chanced to look into a mirror that was leaning against the wainscoting of a roof on the ground floor of his mistress' house. Seeing his reflection, he supposed it to be another dog, outside, and said; "I can chew up any such milksoppy pup as that, and I will."

So he ran out-of-doors and around to the side of the house where he fancied the enemy was. It so happened that at that moment a Bulldog sat there sunning his teeth. The Spaniel stopped short in dire consternation and after regarding the Bulldog a moment from a safe distance said; "I don't know whether you cultivate the arts of peace or your flag is flung to the battle and the breeze and your voice is for war.   If you are a civilian the windows of this house flatter you worse than a newspaper, but if you're a soldier they do you a grave injustice."

This speech being unintelligible to the Bulldog he only civilly smiled, which so terrified the Spaniel that he dropped dead in his tracks.

AN OPTIMIST

TWO FROGS IN THE BELLY OF A SNAKE WERE CONSIDERING THEIR altered circumstances.

"This is pretty hard luck," said one.

"Don't jump to conclusions," the other said; "we are out of the wet and provided with board and lodging."

"With lodging, certainly," said the First Frog; "but I don't see the board."

"You are a croaker," the other explained.   "We are the board."

FORTUNE AND FABULIST

A WRITER OF FABLES WAS PASSING THROUGH A LONELY FOREST, when he met a Fortune.   Greatly alarmed, he tried to climb a tree, but the Fortune pulled him down and bestowed itself upon him with cruel persistence.

"Why did you try to run away?" said the Fortune, when his struggles had ceased and his screams were stilled.   "Why do you glare at me so inhospitably?"

"I don't know what you are," replied the Writer of Fables, deeply disturbed.

"I am wealth; I am respectability," the Fortune explained; "I am elegant houses, a yacht and a clean shirt every day. I am leisure, I am travel, wine, a shiny hat and an unshiny coat. I am enough to eat."

"All right," said the Writer of Fables, in a whisper; "but for goodness' sake speak lower!"

"Why so?" the Fortune asked, in surprise.

"So as not to wake me," replied the Writer of Fables, a holy calm brooding upon his beautiful face.

WOLF AND TORTOISE

A WOLF MEETING A TORTOISE SAID; "MY FRIEND, YOU ARE THE slowest thing out of doors. I do not see how you manage to escape from your enemies."

"As I lack the power to run away," replied the Tortoise, "Providence has thoughtfully supplied me with an impenetrable shell."

The Wolf reflected for a long time, then he said; "It seems to me that it would have been just as easy to give you long legs."

THE SAGACIOUS RAT

A RAT THAT WAS ABOUT TO EMERGE FROM HIS HOLE CAUGHT A glimpse of a Cat waiting for him, and descending to the colony at the bottom of the hole invited a Friend to join him in a visit to a neighboring corn-bin. "I would have gone alone," he said, "but could not deny myself the pleasure of such distinguished company."

"Very well," said the Friend, "I will go with you. Lead on."

"Lead?" exclaimed the other. "What! I precede so great and illustrious a rat as you? No, indeed—after you, sir, after you."

Pleased with this great show of deference, the Friend went ahead, and, leaving the hole first, was caught by the Cat, who trotted away with him. The other then went out unmolested.

THE ASS AND THE MOON

AN ASS WANDERING NEAR A VILLAGE IN THE EVENING SAW THE light of the rising moon beyond a hill.

"Ho-ho, Master Redface," said he, "you are going to point out my long ears to the villagers, are you? I'll meet you at the crest and set my heels into you!"

So he scrambled painfully up to the crest and stood outlined against the broad disc of the unconscious luminary, a more conspicuous ass than ever before.

SHEEP AND LION

"YOU ARE A BEAST OF WAR," SAID THE SHEEP TO THE LION, "YET men go gunning for you. Me, a believer in non-resistance, they do not hunt."

"They do not need to," replied the son of the desert; "they can breed you."

THE TAIL OF THE SPHINX

A DOG OF A TACITURN DISPOSITION SAID TO HIS TAIL; "WHEN-ever I am angry you rise and bristle; when I am pleased you wag;

when I am alarmed you tuck yourself in out of danger. You are too mercurial—you disclose all my emotions. My notion is that tails are given to conceal thought. It is my dearest ambition to be as impassive as the Sphinx."

"My friend, you must recognize the laws and limitations of your being," replied the Tail, with flexions appropriate to the sentiments uttered, "and try to be great some other way. The Sphinx has one hundred and fifty qualifications for impassiveness which you lack."

"What are they?" the Dog asked.

"One hundred and forty-nine tons of sand on its tail."

"And—?"

"A stone tail."

PHILOSOPHERS THREE

A BEAR, A FOX, AND AN OPOSSUM WERE ATTACKED BY AN IN-undation.

"Death loves a coward," said the Bear, and went forward to fight the flood.

"What a fool!" said the Fox. "I know a trick worth two of that." And he slipped into a hollow stump.

"There are malevolent forces," said the Opossum, "which the wise will neither confront nor avoid. The thing is to know the nature of your antagonist."

So saying the Opossum lay down and pretended to be dead.

THE FOX, THE DUCK, AND THE LION

A FOX AND A DUCK HAVING QUARRELED ABOUT THE OWNERSHIP of a frog, referred the matter to a Lion. After hearing a deal of argument the Lion opened his mouth to deliver judgment.

"I know what your decision is," said the Duck, interrupting.

"It is that by our own showing the frog belongs to neither of us, and you will eat him yourself. Permit me to say that this is unjust, as I shall prove."

"To me," said the Fox, "it is clear that you will give the frog to the Duck and the Duck to me and take me yourself. I am not without experience of the law."

"I was about to explain," said the Lion, yawning, "that during the arguments in this case the property in dispute has hopped away. Perhaps you can procure another frog."

A NIGGARDLY OFFER

TWO SOLDIERS LAY DEAD UPON THE FIELD OF HONOR.

"What would you give to be alive again?" one asked the other.

"To the enemy, victory," was the reply, "to my country, a long life of disinterested service as a civilian. What would you give?"

"The plaudits of my countrymen."

"You are a pretty tight-fisted bargainer," said the other.

THE DISINTERESTED ARBITER

TWO DOGS WHO HAD BEEN FIGHTING FOR A BONE, WITHOUT advantage to either, referred their dispute to a Sheep. The Sheep patiently heard their statements, then flung the bone into a pond.

"Why did you do that?" said the Dogs.

"Because," replied the Sheep, "I am a vegetarian."

THE OPOSSUM OF THE FUTURE

ONE DAY AN OPOSSUM WHO HAD GONE TO SLEEP HANGING FROM the highest branch of a tree by the tail, awoke and saw a large Snake wound about the limb, between him and the trunk of the tree.

"If I hold on," he said to himself, "I shall be swallowed; if I let go I shall break my neck."

But suddenly he bethought himself to dissemble.

"My perfect friend," he said, "my parental instinct recognizes in you a noble evidence and illustration of the theory of development. You are the Opossum of the Future, the ultimate Fittest Survivor of our species, the ripe result of progressive prehensility —all tail!"

But the Snake, proud of his ancient eminence in Scriptural history, was strictly orthodox and did not accept the scientific view.

THE MAN PLUCKING THE GOOSE

A MAN WAS PLUCKING A LIVE GOOSE, WHEN THE BIRD ADDRESSED him thus; "Suppose that you were a goose; do you think that you would relish this sort of thing?"

"Suppose that I were," said the Man; "do you think that you would like to pluck me?"

"Indeed I should!" was the natural, emphatic, but injudicious reply.

"Just so," concluded her tormentor, pulling out another handful of feathers; "that is the way that *I* feel about it."

THE TYRANT FROG

A SNAKE SWALLOWING A FROG HEAD-FIRST WAS APPROACHED BY a Naturalist with a stick.

"Ah, my deliverer," said the Snake as well as he could, "you have arrived just in time; this reptile, you see, is pitching into me without provocation."

"Sir," replied the Naturalist, "I need a snakeskin for my collection, but if you had not explained I should not have molested you, for I thought you were at dinner."

THE ALL-DOG

A LION SEEING A POODLE FELL INTO LAUGHTER AT THE RIDICU-lous spectacle.

"Who ever saw so small a beast?" he said.

"It is very true," said the Poodle, with austere dignity, "that I am small; but, sir, I beg you to observe that I am all dog."

THE INEFFECTIVE ROOTER

A DRUNKEN MAN WAS LYING IN THE ROAD WITH A BLEEDING nose, upon which he had fallen, when a Pig passed that way.

"You wallow fairly well," said the Pig, "but, my fine fellow, you have much to learn about rooting."

THE PIG TRANSFORMED TO A MAN

A CERTAIN MAGICIAN HAD A LEARNED PIG WHO HAD LIVED A cleanly, gentlemanly life, achieving a wide renown and winning the hearts of the people, attending his elevating performances. But perceiving that the creature was unhappy, the Magician transformed him to a man.

Straightway the man abandoned his cards, his timepiece, his musical instruments and the other devices of his profession, and betook himself to a pool of mud, wherein he inhumed himself to the tips of his nose, grunting with sodden satisfaction.

THE EARTHQUAKE

A JACKAL IN PURSUIT OF A DEER WAS ABOUT TO SEIZE IT, WHEN an earthquake opened a broad and deep chasm between him and his prey.

"This," he said, "is a pernicious interference with the laws of Nature.   I refuse to recognize any such irregularity."

So he resumed the chase, endeavoring to cross the abyss by two leaps.

THE TORTOISE AND THE ARMADILLO

A TORTOISE AND AN ARMADILLO, HAVING QUARRELED, REPAIRED to a secluded spot to vindicate their honor by an appeal to arms.

"Now, then," shouted the Tortoise shrinking into the innermost recesses of his shell, "come on!"

"Very well," assented the Armadillo, coiling up tightly in his coat of mail, "I am ready for you!"

An historian of the period obscurely alludes to the incident as foreshadowing the naval engagement of the future.

TWO HORSES

A WILD HORSE MEETING A DOMESTIC ONE, TAUNTED HIM WITH his condition of servitude. The tame animal swore that he was as free as the wind.

"If that is so," said the other, "pray what is the office of that bit in your mouth."

"That," was the answer, "is iron, one of the best tonics known."

"But what is the meaning of the rein attached to it?"

"That keeps it from falling from my mouth when I am too indolent to hold it."

"How about the saddle?"

"It spares me fatigue: when I am tired I mount and ride."

REVELATION

A LION WAS ATTACKED BY A PACK OF FAMISHED WOLVES, WHO circled about him, howling as loud as they could, though none dared approach him.

"These are very useful creatures," said the Lion, as he lay down for his afternoon nap—"they apprise me of my virtues. I never before knew that I was good to eat."

THE LION AND THE LAMB

"THE MILLENNIUM IS COME," SAID A LION TO A LAMB INSIDE the fold. "Come out and let us lie down together, as it has been foretold that we shall."

"Have you brought along the little child that is to lead us?" the Lamb asked.

"No; I thought that perhaps a child of the shepherd would serve."

"I distrust a Millennium that requires the shepherd to supply both the feast and the leader of the revel. My notion of that happy time is that it is to be a period in which mutton is unfit to eat and a lion the product of the sculptor's art."

Finding no profit in dissimulation, the Lion walked thoughtfully away and candidly dined on the village priest.

THE REBELLIOUS ANT

LADEN WITH A GRAIN OF WHEAT WHICH HE HAD ACQUIRED WITH infinite toil, an Ant was breasting a current of his fellows, each of whom, as is their etiquette, insisted on stopping him, feeling him all over and shaking hands. It occurred to him that excess of ceremony is abuse of courtesy; so he laid down his burden, sat upon it, folded all his legs and smiled a smile of great grimness.

"Hello!" said his Fellow Ants, "what is the matter with you?"

"Sick of the hollow conventionalities of an effete civilization," was the rasping reply—"returned to the simplicity of primitive life."

"Ah! then we must trouble you for that grain. In the primitive life there are no rights of property."

A great white light fell upon the understanding of that rebellious insect. He rose and grappling the grain of wheat trotted away with alacrity. It was observed that he submitted with a wealth of patience to manipulation of his friends and neighbors and went long distances out of his way to shake hands with strangers on competing lines of traffic.

THE NEGRO AND THE OSTRICH

A NEGRO SEEING AN OSTRICH BEGAN PELTING HIM WITH STONES. When a considerable number had been flung the Ostrich turned to and ate them.

"Pray tell me," he said, "to what virtue I am indebted for this excellent meal."

"To generosity," the Negro answered, now eager to conciliate one whom he thought miraculously gifted; "if it had not been for a charitable impulse I should have eaten those stones myself."

"My good fellow," said the Ostrich, "it seems that some of the lesser human virtues are not readily distinguishable from an imperfect digestion."

THE PARROT THAT CHATTERED IN GREEK

HAVING BEEN TAUGHT GREEK, A PARROT WAS PUFFED UP WITH conceit.

"Observe," said he, "the advantages of a classical education! I can chatter nonsense in the tongue of Plato."

"I should advise you," said his Master, quietly, "to let it be nonsense of a character somewhat different from that of some of Plato's most admired compatriots if you value the privilege of hanging at that open window.   Commit no mythology, please."

THE WITCH'S STEED

A BROOMSTICK THAT HAD LONG SERVED A WITCH AS A STEED complained of the nature of its employment, which it thought degrading.

"Very well," said the Witch, "I will give you work in which you will be associated with intellect—you will come in contact with brains. I shall present you to a housewife."

"What!" said the Broomstick, "do you consider the hands of a housewife intellectual?"

"I referred," said the Witch, "to the head of her good man."

DOG AND DOCTOR

A DOG THAT HAD SEEN A DOCTOR ATTENDING THE BURIAL OF A wealthy patient, said; "When do you expect to dig it up?"

"Why should I dig it up?" the Doctor asked.

"When I bury a bone," said the Dog, "it is with an intention to uncover it later and pick it."

"The bones that I bury," said the Doctor, "are those that I can no longer pick."

LION AND RATTLESNAKE

A MAN HAVING FOUND A LION IN HIS PATH UNDERTOOK TO subdue him by the power of the human eye; and near by was a Rattlesnake engaged in fascinating a small bird.

"How are you getting on, brother?" the Man called out to the other reptile, without removing his eyes from those of the Lion.

"Admirably," replied the serpent. "My success is assured; my victim draws nearer and nearer in spite of her efforts."

"And mine," said the Man, "draws nearer and nearer in spite of mine. Are you sure it is all right?"

"If you don't think so," the reptile replied as well as he then could, with his mouth full of bird, "you'd better give it up."

A half-hour later the Lion, thoughtfully picking his teeth with his claws, told the Rattlesnake that he had never in all his varied experience in being subdued, seen a subduer try so earnestly to give it up. "But," he added, with a wide, significant smile, "I looked him into countenance."

CAT AND KING

A CAT WAS LOOKING AT A KING, AS PERMITTED BY THE PROVERB.

"Well," said the monarch, observing her inspection of the royal person, "how do you like me?"

"I can imagine a King," said the Cat, "whom I should like better."

"For example?"

"The King of Mice."

The sovereign was so pleased with the wit of the reply that he gave her permission to scratch his Prime Minister's eyes out.

THE SHEEP AND THE SHEPHERD

A SHEEP MAKING A LONG JOURNEY FOUND THE HEAT OF HER fleece insupportable, and seeing a flock of others in a fold, evidently in expectation, leaped in and joined them in the hope of being shorn. Perceiving the Shepherd approaching, and the other sheep huddling into a remote corner of the fold, she shouldered her way forward and said; "Your flock is insubordinate; it is fortunate that I came along to set them an example of docility. Seeing me operated on, they will be encouraged to offer themselves."

"Thank you," said the Shepherd, "but I never kill more than one at a time. Mutton does not keep well in warm weather."

ANATOLE

FRANCE

France 1844 -- 1924

THE MEDITATIONS OF RIQUET

I

MEN, BEASTS AND STONES GROW GREAT AS THEY COME NEAR AND loom enormous when they are upon me.   It is not so with me.   I remain equally great wheresoever I am.

II

When my master places for me beneath the table the food which he was about to put into his own mouth, it is in order that he may tempt me and that he may punish me if I yield to temptation.   For I cannot believe that he would deny himself for my sake.

III

The smell of dogs is sweet in the nostrils.

IV

My master keeps me warm when I lie behind him in his chair. It is because he is good.   In front of the fire-place is a hot stone. That stone is divine.

V

I speak when I please.   From my master's mouth proceed likewise sounds which make sense. But his meaning is not so clear as that expressed by the sounds of my voice. Every sound that I utter has a meaning. From my master's lips come forth many idle noises. It is difficult but necessary to divine the thoughts of the master.

VI

To eat is good. To have eaten is better. For the enemy who lieth in wait to take your food is quick and crafty.

VII

All is flux and reflux. I alone remain.

VIII

I am in the centre of all things; men, beasts and things, friendly and adverse, are ranged about me.

IX

In sleep one beholdeth men, dogs, horses, trees, forms pleasant and unpleasant. When one awaketh these forms have vanished.

X

Reflection. I love my master, Bergeret, because he is powerful and terrible.

XI

An action for which one has been beaten is a bad action. An action for which one has received caresses or food is a good action.

XII

At nightfall evil powers prowl round the house. I bark in order that my master may be warned and drive them away.

XIII

Prayer. O my master, Bergeret, god of courage, I adore thee. When thou art terrible, be thou praised. When thou art kind be thou praised. I crouch at thy feet: I lick thy hands. When, seated before thy table spread, thou devourest meats in abundance, thou art very great and very beautiful. Very great art thou and very beautiful when, striking fire out of a thin splint of wood, thou changest night into day. Keep me in thine house and keep out every other dog. And thou, Angélique, the cook, divinity good and great, I fear thee and I venerate thee in order that thou mayest give me much to eat.

XIV

A dog who lacketh piety towards men and who scorneth the fetishes assembled in his master's house liveth a miserable and a wandering life.

XV

One day, from a broken pitcher, filled with water which was being carried across the parlour, water ran on to the polished floor. A thrashing must have been the punishment of that dirty pitcher.

XVI

Men possess the divine power of opening all doors. I by myself am only able to open a few. Doors are great fetishes which do not readily obey dogs.

XVII

The life of a dog is full of danger. If he would escape suffering he must be ever on the watch, during meals and even during sleep.

XVIII

It is impossible to know whether one has acted well towards

men.   One must worship them without seeking to understand them.   Their wisdom is mysterious.

XIX

Invocation.   O Fear, Fear, august and maternal, Fear sacred and salutary, possess me, in danger fill me, in order that I may avoid that which is harmful, lest, casting myself upon the enemy, I suffer for my imprudence.

XX

Vehicles there are which horses pull through the street.   They are terrible.   Other vehicles there are which move of themselves breathing loudly.   These are also fearful.   Men in rags are detestable, likewise such as carry baskets on their heads or roll casks. I do not love children who utter loud cries and flee from and pursue each other swiftly in the streets.   The world is full of hostile and dreadful things.

HURRAH FOR THE PENGUINS

(*from Penguin Island*)

THE PENGUINS REMAINED WARLIKE FOR A LENGTHY PERIOD. One of them, Jacquot, the Philosopher, has painted their character in a little moral picture that I reproduce here, and that, doubtless, will not be read without pleasure:—

The Philosopher, Gratien, travelled through Penguinia in the time of the later Draconides.   One day as he passed through a pleasant valley where the cow-bells tinkled in the pure air, he seated himself on a bench at the foot of an oak, close beside a cottage.   At the threshold a woman was nursing her child; a little boy was playing with a big dog; a blind old man, seated in the sun with his lips half-opened, drank in the light of day.

The master of the house, a young and sturdy man, offered some bread and milk to Gratien.

The Porpoise philosopher having taken this rural repast:

"Delightful inhabitants of a delightful country, I give you

thanks," said he. "Everything here breathes forth joy, concord, and peace."

As he said this a shepherd passed by playing a march upon his pipe.

"What is that lively air?" asked Gratien.

"It is the war-hymn against the Porpoises," answered the peasant. "Everybody here sings it. Little children know it before they can speak. We are all good Penguins."

"You don't like the Porpoises then?"

"We hate them."

"For what reason do you hate them?"

"Need you ask? Are not the Porpoises neighbours of the Penguins!"

"Of course."

"Well, that is why the Penguins hate the Porpoises."

"Is that a reason?"

"Certainly. He who says neighbours says enemies. Look at the field that borders mine. It belongs to the man I hate most in the world. After him my worst enemies are the people of the village on the other slope of the valley at the foot of that birchwood. In this narrow valley formed of two parts there are but that village and mine: they are enemies. Every time that our lads meet the others, insults and blows pass between them. And you want the Penguins not to be the enemies of the Porpoises! Don't you know what patriotism is? For my part there are two cries that rise to my lips: 'Hurrah for the Penguins! Death to the Porpoises!'"

ROBERT LOUIS
STEVENSON

England 1850 -- 1894

THE CITIZEN AND THE TRAVELLER

"LOOK AROUND YOU," SAID THE CITIZEN. "THIS IS THE LARGEST market in the world."

"Oh, surely not," said the traveller.

"Well, perhaps not the largest," said the citizen, "but much the best."

"You are certainly wrong there," said the traveller. "I can tell you . . ."

They buried the stranger in the dusk.

THE DEVIL AND THE INNKEEPER

ONCE UPON A TIME THE DEVIL STAYED AT AN INN, WHERE NO one knew him, for they were people whose education had been neglected. He was bent on mischief, and for a time kept everybody by the ears. But at last the innkeeper set a watch upon the devil and took him in the fact.

The innkeeper got a rope's end.

"Now I am going to thrash you," said the innkeeper.

"You have no right to be angry with me," said the devil. "I am only the devil, and it is my nature to do wrong."

"Is that so?" asked the innkeeper.

"Fact, I assure you," said the devil.

"You really cannot help doing ill?" asked the innkeeper.

"Not in the smallest," said the devil; "it would be useless cruelty to thrash a thing like me."

"It would indeed," said the innkeeper.

And he made a noose and hanged the devil.

"There," said the innkeeper.

THE PENITENT

A MAN MET A LAD WEEPING. "WHAT DO YOU WEEP FOR?" HE asked.

"I am weeping for my sins," said the lad.

"You must have little to do," said the man.

The next day they met again. Once more the lad was weeping. "Why do you weep now?" asked the man.

"I am weeping because I have nothing to eat," said the lad.

"I thought it would come to that," said the man.

THE SICK MAN AND THE FIREMAN

THERE WAS ONCE A SICK MAN IN A BURNING HOUSE, TO WHOM there entered a fireman.

"Do not save me," said the sick man. "Save those who are strong."

"Will you kindly tell me why?" inquired the fireman, for he was a civil fellow.

"Nothing could possibly be fairer," said the sick man. "The strong should be preferred in all cases, because they are of more service in the world."

The fireman pondered a while, for he was a man of some philosophy. "Granted," said he at last, as part of the roof fell in;

"but for the sake of conversation what would you lay down as the proper service of the strong?"

"Nothing can possibly be easier," returned the sick man: "the proper service of the strong is to help the weak."

Again the fireman reflected, for there was nothing hasty about this excellent creature. "I could forgive your being sick," he said at last, as a portion of the wall fell out, "but I cannot bear your being such a fool." And with that he heaved up his fireman's axe, for he was eminently just, and clove the sick man to the bed.

THE READER

"I NEVER READ SUCH AN IMPIOUS BOOK," SAID THE READER, throwing it on the floor.

"You need not hurt me," said the book; "you will only get less for me second hand, and I did not write myself."

"That is true," said the reader. "My quarrel is with your author."

"Ah, well," said the book, "you need not buy his rant."

"That is true," said the reader. "But I thought him such a cheerful writer."

"I find him so," said the book.

"You must be differently made from me," said the reader.

"Let me tell you a fable," said the book. "There were two men wrecked upon a desert island; one of them made believe he was at home, the other admitted—"

"Oh, I know your kind of fable," said the reader. "They both died."

"And so they did," said the book. "No doubt of that. And everybody else."

"That is true," said the reader. "Push it a little further for this once. And when they were all dead?"

"They were in God's hands the same as before," said the book.

"Not much to boast of, by your account," cried the reader.

"Who is impious now?" said the book.

And the reader put him on the fire.

> *The coward crouches from the rod,*
> *And loathes the iron face of God.*

THE TWO MATCHES

ONE DAY THERE WAS A TRAVELLER IN THE WOODS IN CALIFORnia, in the dry season, when the Trades were blowing strong. He had ridden a long way, and he was tired and hungry, and dismounted from his horse to smoke a pipe. But when he felt in his pocket, he found but two matches. He struck the first, and it would not light.

"Here is a pretty state of things," said the traveller. "Dying for a smoke; only one match left; and that certain to miss fire! Was there ever a creature so unfortunate? And yet," thought the traveller, "suppose I light this match, and smoke my pipe, and shake out the dottle here in the grass—the grass might catch on fire, for it is dry like tinder; and while I snatch out the flames in front, they might evade and run behind me, and seize upon yon bush of poison oak; before I could reach it, that would have blazed up; over the bush I see a pine tree hung with moss; that too would fly in fire upon the instant to its topmost bough; and the flame of that long torch—how would the trade wind take and brandish that through the inflammable forest! I hear this dell roar in a moment with the joint voice of wind and fire, I see myself gallop for my soul, and the flying conflagration chase and outflank me through the hills; I see this pleasant forest burn for days, and the cattle roasted, and the springs dried up, and the farmer ruined, and his children cast upon the world. What a world hangs upon this moment!"

With that he struck the match, and it missed fire.

"Thank God," said the traveller, and put his pipe in his pocket.

THE TADPOLE AND THE FROG

"BE ASHAMED OF YOURSELF," SAID THE FROG.

"When I was a tadpole, I had no tail."

"Just what I thought!" said the tadpole. "You never were a tadpole."

THE CARTHORSES AND THE SADDLEHORSE

TWO CARTHORSES, A GELDING AND A MARE, WERE BROUGHT TO Samoa, and put in the same field with a saddlehorse to run free on the island. They were rather afraid to go near him, for they saw he was a saddlehorse, and supposed he would not speak to them. Now the saddlehorse had never seen creatures so big. "These must be great chiefs," thought he, and he approached them civilly. "Lady and gentleman," said he, "I understand you are from the colonies. I offer you my affectionate compli-ments, and make you heartily welcome to the island."

The colonials looked at him askance, and consulted with each other.

"Who can he be?" said the gelding.

"He seems suspiciously civil," said the mare.

"I do not think he can be much account," said the gelding.

"Depend upon it he is only a Kanaka," said the mare.

Then they turned to him.

"Go to the devil!" said the gelding.

"I wonder at your impudence, speaking to persons of our quality!" cried the mare.

The saddlehorse went away by himself. "I was right," said he, "they are great chiefs."

DEMYAN

BEDNEY

(Yefim Pridvorov)

Russia 1883 --

PEDIGREE

A LADY ONCE HAD A DOG OF STRANGE PEDIGREE.   AND BESIDES
the dog had a strange foreign name.   But he was as dear to the
lady as if he were her own son.   Every day she petted him, washed
him with her own hands in rose-water, powdered him and sprayed
him with perfume.   A peasant by the name of Akim was ordered to look after the little dog with the pedigree.   It was his
duty to wait upon the dog and take care of all its wants.   But
after some time Akim grew weary of his task and this is what
happened:

"Hm," said Akim.   "I will go and serve some other master.
I would bear hard labor without complaint.   I would serve anybody, yes, even the devil himself.   But I will not serve a dog."

Thus he made a firm resolution and as he did so he found himself alone with the dog.   Akim said; "Tell me, you goggie-muggie,
why do you hold your nose up so proudly?   And I cannot understand also why I am ordered to serve a dog.   After all you are
nothing but a little monstrosity.   Why do you demand such respect?"

"Why!" answered the Dog in a rage.   "Why?   Because you
are a low peasant and being a low peasant you must respect my
high pedigree."

But Akim, like most common people, forgot all about birth

and station and soon put the little dog in his place. Akim is not unlike the average person—and if I have here offended some dog, —then please forgive me, your highness.

THE CLARINET AND THE HORN

A SHEPHERD'S HORN ONCE MET WITH A CLARINET ON THE sunny soft banks of a river beyond the village. "How do you do!" squeaked the Clarinet.

"How do you do, brother," answered the Horn; "how do you do! I see you are from the city, but I cannot make out your rank or station. Are you from the gentry or what?"

"This is something new," replied the Clarinet somewhat offended. "Instead of asking me awkward questions you might first rub your eyes and have a good look at me. I am a clarinet and a well known musician besides. Of course it is true that my voice somewhat resembles yours but my talent,—what wonderful places my talent brings me to! Merely telling you about them would make you tremble. But I cannot keep it secret and must tell you all. Princes and Dukes often dance to my music. How could you compare your playing to mine! When you play only steers and cows swish their tails."

"That may be so," said the Horn. "Princes are not related to us but remember, some day they too will dance to my music."

BIRDS

WHILE THE GREAT FALCON WITH ALL HIS COURT WAS SOARING in the blue skies some enemy raided his nest and devoured all the small falcon chicks, leaving behind only the bones. When the Falcon returned to his nest his eyes grew dim. "Deliver to me this hawk!" he cried. "He is my enemy and he has done this deed with his claws. He, and he alone, is the cause of my misfortune." Thus the Falcon decided to clear the skies of his enemy the Hawk.

But as soon as the Eagle heard of this threat he decided to make war on his relative the Falcon. With a great deal of noise he made his decision known to all the birds of the sky and this caused a great commotion. "Your majesty!" pleaded the learned Parrot. "Don't go to war. All you have to do is to scare them." The Parrot was a famous jurist and acted as minister of state to the Eagle. "Is it proper for you to enter into this quarrel? The Hawk really did commit an out-and-out act of terror, and this kind of act—"

"That's enough, my little Parrot," interrupted the Eagle. "You are funny even if you are a jurist. Where did you learn that I myself do not commit these acts of terror?"

THE CANNON AND THE PLOW

ON SEEING A PLOW THE CANNON SAID; "LISTEN HERE, OLD woman—are you deaf? Here I am thundering away all day long and you do not even hear me. What are you doing here anyway? Really I must laugh—ha-ha!"

"Plowing," said the Plow. "Just plowing."

"Plowing? Now don't make me laugh. Who can you be working for? In the village that I have destroyed not a living soul will be found. Now the only thing left for you to do is to rest."

"To rest? No!" said the Plow. "The time is now to plow."

The Plow cut through the stony and thorny furrows of the abandoned field. From morning until night, while the Cannon roared its battle boom, the Plow plowed on, so that the soldiers fighting for humanity could some day reap the seed of peaceful and patient labor.

OSCAR

WILDE

England 1856 -- 1900

THE ARTIST

ONE EVENING THERE CAME INTO HIS SOUL THE DESIRE TO FASHion an image of "The Pleasure that Abideth for a Moment." And he went forth into the world to look for bronze. For he could only think in bronze.

But all the bronze of the whole world had disappeared; nor anywhere in the whole world was there any bronze to be found, save only the bronze of the image of "The Sorrow that Endureth for Ever."

Now this image he had himself, and with his own hands, fashioned, and had set on the tomb of the one thing he had loved in life. On the tomb of the dead thing he had most loved had he set this image of his own fashioning, that it might serve as a sign of the love of a man that dieth not, and a symbol of the sorrow of man that endureth for ever. And in the whole world there was no other bronze save the bronze of this image.

And he took the image he had fashioned, and set it in a great furnace, and gave it to the fire.

And out of the bronze of the image of "The Sorrow that Endureth for Ever" he fashioned an image of "The Pleasure that Abideth for a Moment."

THE DISCIPLE

WHEN NARCISSUS DIED, THE POOL OF HIS PLEASURE CHANGED from a cup of sweet waters into a cup of salt tears, and the Oreads came weeping through the woodland that they might sing to the pool and give it comfort.

And when they saw that the pool had changed from a cup of sweet waters into a cup of salt tears, they loosened the green tresses of their hair, and cried to the pool, and said: "We do not wonder that you should mourn in this manner for Narcissus, so beautiful was he."

"But was Narcissus beautiful?" said the pool.

"Who should know better than you?" answered the Oreads. "Us did he ever pass by, but you he sought for, and would lie on your banks and look down at you, and in the mirror of your waters he would mirror his own beauty."

And the pool answered: "But I loved Narcissus because, as he lay on my banks and looked down at me, in the mirror of his eyes I saw my own beauty mirrored."

THE END

CUPID AND THE LION

THE LION ONCE CAME TO CUPID AND SAID: "I COME TO YOU BECAUSE you alone would have a fair judgment."

"And why do you compliment me so highly?" asked Cupid.

"You see," said the Lion. "I have just finished reading over seven-hundred fables and you are the only person I know who is not mentioned in any of these little stories of wisdom. Therefore you could judge me fairly."

"But why should you, the king of all beasts, come to me for judgment?"

The Lion shed a few tears. "In all the fables that I have just read not one tells the truth about me. Either I am made to appear ridiculous and a little mouse must save me or I am shown to be ungrateful, as when I failed to reward the Crane, who with his long bill drew the bone from my throat. And besides all this I am also pictured as a bad beast. Now you know, little Cupid, that this is most unfair. I am not as evil as I am painted. The Ass and the Ox, and even the Crow and the Snake, have all been given good characters; and you know as well as I do that even the Trees in my forests are more upright than they. Why don't you go and tell them that at heart I am really a good old Lion? Why don't you make them love me?"

"Poor Lion. Poor mistreated Lion. Now don't cry. I would gladly make all the beasts of the forests love one another but I cannot fly as fast as the Eagle nor can I run as fast as the Fox. If you had my politeness and I had only half your strength, all would be well."

"Little Cupid," asked the Lion, "if all the beasts loved one another would they love me also?"

"Yes. They would love you too. But you must go before them and be polite. You must bow to them, and if you bow at all, bow low. It is easier to capture a whole herd of Elephants than to conquer the heart of an Ox."

And so the Cupid and the Lion agreed upon a plan of action. The strong Lion was to carry the little Cupid on his back while Cupid was to shoot his arrows of love at all the beasts of the forest.

"Remember to bow low," said Cupid.

"And you remember also," replied the Lion, "that I am after all a Lion and that he who rides a Lion cannot dismount."